LOGIC, ALGEBRA AND DATABASES

ELLIS HORWOOD SERIES IN COMPUTERS AND THEIR APPLICATIONS

Series Editor: Brian Meek, Director of the Computer Unit, Queen Elizabeth College, University of London

ELLIS HORWOOD BOOKS IN COMPUTING

LOGIC, ALGEBRA AND DATABASES

PETER M. D. GRAY, MA, D. Phil, MBCS
Senior Lecturer
Department of Computing Science, King's College
University of Aberdeen, Scotland

ELLIS HORWOOD LIMITED
Publishers · Chichester

Halsted Press: a division of
JOHN WILEY & SONS
New York · Chichester · Brisbane · Toronto

First published in 1984
and Reprinted in 1985 by
ELLIS HORWOOD LIMITED
Market Cross House, Cooper Street, Chichester, West Sussex, PO19 1EB, England

*The publisher's colophon is reproduced from James Gillison's drawing of the
ancient Market Cross, Chichester.*

Distributors:

Australia, New Zealand, South-east Asia:
Jacaranda-Wiley Ltd., Jacaranda Press,
JOHN WILEY & SONS INC.,
GPO Box 859, Brisbane, Queensland 4001, Australia

Canada:
JOHN WILEY & SONS CANADA LIMITED
22 Worcester Road, Rexdale, Ontario, Canada.

Europe, Africa:
JOHN WILEY & SONS LIMITED
Baffins Lane, Chichester, West Sussex, England.

North and South America and the rest of the world:
Halsted Press: a division of
JOHN WILEY & SONS
605 Third Avenue, New York, NY 10158, USA

© 1984 P.M.D. Gray/Ellis Horwood Limited

British Library Cataloguing in Publication Data
Gray, Peter M.D.
Logic, algebra and databases. —
(Ellis Horwood series in computers and their applications)
1. Data base management 2. Logic, symbolic and mathematical
I. Title
001.64'42   QA76.9.D3

Library of Congress Card No. 84-12854

ISBN 0-85312-709-3 (Ellis Horwood Limited — Library Edn.)
ISBN 0-85312-803-0 (Ellis Horwood Limited — Student Edn.)
ISBN 0-470-20103-7 (Halsted Press — Library Edn.)
ISBN 0-470-20259-9 (Halsted Press — Student Edn.)

Typeset by Ellis Horwood Limited
Printed in Great Britain by R.J. Acford, Chichester

Table of Contents

Author's Preface

This book is primarily aimed at students, postgraduates, and programmers who have some knowledge of a programming language which can manipulate records, such as Pascal, Algol 68 or PL/I, and who wish to find out both about database query languages and the newer languages used in functional and logic programming, and to understand the relationship between them. We start by exploring the ideas behind languages such as Prolog, KRC, FQL and HOPE, in the early part, and illustrate these ideas in detail by exploring the *database* languages QUEL, SQL, QBE, ASTRID R.A. and DAPLEX in the later part. All of these languages are based either on *Logic* using the Predicate Calculus, or on *Algebra* and Function Composition, using the Lambda Calculus. Thus Chapters 1 and 2 give an introduction to the Predicate Calculus, whilst Chapter 3 gives an introduction to the lambda Calculus, which lays a foundation for subsequent chapters. Chapters 4 and 5 consider particular examples of Logic and Functional programming languages, which use these principles.

Books on Logic tend to be very formal and theoretical, but since this book is intended for a wider audience, it takes a more informal approach, illustrated throughout with examples from programming languages. The emphasis is on the use of Predicate Calculus and its notation rather than on formal theorems, for which reference is made to other works. Those who are already familiar with logic, and wish to learn of its applications to databases, should read the chapters on the relational model of databases, and on the relational calculus and its transformation into a functional equivalent (Chapters 6 to 9). Likewise those already familiar with databases, who wish to understand the Prolog language, and its applications to lists and sets of data, and to databases, should read Chapters 1 to 4 before reading Chapters 7 to 9. No previous knowledge of Prolog (or any of the other languages) is assumed.

The reason for introducing material on applicative and functional languages, in Chapters 3 and 5, is to lead up to the Functional Data Model in Chapter 10, through which we get a deeper understanding of the CODASYL model. CODASYL databases are in widespread use, but they seem very different from relational databases, and rather complicated. Chapter 11 explains the basic ideas of a CODASYL database, without going too deeply into the complications. Chapter 12 explains how to transform and execute queries on a CODASYL database, by viewing it first in terms of the Functional Data Model, and then in terms of the relational model, using a query language based on function composition. In discussing the three data models (Relational, Functional, CODASYL), we use examples from the same specimen database, on World Cup soccer games, given in Appendix I. Thus the same queries are formulated in each query language, which helps to show the distinctions between them. The database is chosen because its meaning is obvious, and we hope, interesting.

Finally, Chapters 9 and 12 pull together the various themes of the book. In Chapter 9 we explore algorithms for translating queries from calculus to algebraic form, and vice versa, together with important optimisations. In Chapter 12 we consider how to answer queries in calculus and algebraic languages on a CODASYL database, and thus obtain a deeper insight into these two apparently dissimilar formalisms, which are crucial to computation. Chapter 12 finishes by looking to future research problems which are opening up, for example, the use of Prolog with large 'knowledge bases'.

Acknowledgements

I am grateful to many friends and colleagues who have looked over the manuscript and offered suggestions, particularly Malcolm Atkinson, Ben du Boulay, David Lindsey, Graham Storrs and David Turner. I am especially grateful to Brian Meek, the Series Editor, who read every page with great care. I am very grateful to Alison Smith, who typed most of the manuscript, and to Nan Keith and Allan Gray, who also helped. I also owe a great deal to my very understanding wife, who provided support in many ways while I was working on the book.

Many of the ideas in Chapters 8, 9 and 12 come from the ASTRID project, and I am particularly grateful to Robert Bell who pioneered it, and to Peter Esslemont, Alison Smith, Tim Scott and David Moffat who did most of the coding. This book is, in part, a tribute to their hard work. The project was supported throughout the period 1976–84 by grants from the Science Research Council, without which it would not have happened.

I would like to thank Cambridge University Press for permission to use extracts from my articles in *Databases: Role & Structure,* edited by P. M. Stocker, in Chapters 10 and 12. The description and examples of the languages SQL and QBE are my own, but both of them are available as commercial products from IBM Corporation.

To
EWE, JMF
and RB

For inspiration
and companionship

The Propositional Calculus

1.1 INTRODUCTION

The word 'Logic' refers to a systematic method of reasoning, and we shall be looking at two particular systems: a basic method (Propositional Calculus) and a more advanced one (Predicate Calculus). A 'Calculus' is just a set of rules for calculating with symbols. The most well-known calculus is the Differential Calculus, which has rules for calculating slopes of curves by manipulating algebraic expressions. The Propositional Calculus also has a set of rules, but they are very different, since they are used to determine the truth or falsehood of combinations of propositions. The advantage of a calculus is that it saves you guessing, and enables you to work out the answer in a systematic way. The propositions we shall be looking at are ones used in everyday speech, and with the aid of the calculus we shall be able to do basic reasoning.

The exciting part about using a calculus for reasoning is that we can program it into a computer, which can thus be given the ability to reason, in an elementary fashion. In later chapters we shall be looking at a more powerful set of rules, the Predicate Calculus, and in particular at the Resolution Method, which enables one to do very general reasoning. This method is the basis of many computer programs which reason, and also of a Logic Programming Language 'Prolog'. Because it is very general, it can also be applied to the Propositional Calculus.

This chapter starts by explaining how to form logical propositions, using the connectives 'and' and 'or'. It goes on to explain how to evaluate or rewrite such propositions by using Boolean Algebra, in much the same way that numerical expressions can be rewritten and simplified in ordinary arithmetic. It then explains the classic methods of inference which are used to deduce propositions from others (rather like the methods of Sherlock Holmes, or of Euclid). It then explains how to prove that a given proposition follows from another set of propositions (the premises), by various methods. It concludes by explaining the Resolution proof method.

1.2 TRUTH AND FALSEHOOD OF PROPOSITIONS – TWO-VALUED LOGIC

A proposition is just a statement, which may be true or false. For example 'My car is red', 'It is sunny', 'M8085 chips have 40 pins', are all propositions. In fact they are *atomic* propositions, since they have no components. Later we shall be concerned with *compound* propositions such as 'my car is red and it has four road wheels'; this contains two separate atomic propositions, each of which may be true or false. For example, if the car is actually blue then the proposition 'my car is red' is false. However, if it is the usual type of car, then the proposition 'my car has four road wheels' is true. The compound proposition using 'and' is true only when both its atomic components are true; thus the proposition as a whole is false. Such a proposition is called a *formula* of logic. Its truth can be determined from the truth values of its components.

The Propositional Calculus does not deal with statements which have values other than 'true' and 'false'. For example it does not deal with numerical values like 'The balance in my account' or 'The distance from Aberdeen to Edinburgh'. We must wait for the Predicate Calculus in order to symbolise such values. Nor does it deal with three-valued logic, e.g. 'Yes', 'No' and 'Don't know'. It is a two-valued logic. Thus any answer which is not 'yes' must be 'no'. The ancient philosophers called this the 'Law of the Excluded Middle'. Other logics are of course possible, but they have different rules from the propositional calculus. One such is 'Fuzzy Logic' which deals with statements like 'it is 90% probable that A is bigger than 100'. Fuzzy Logic has rules for combining these probabilities. This can be useful in systems for medical diagnosis like MYCIN (Shortliffe 1976), whereas Propositional Logic would assume that a particular combination of symptoms led to an infallible diagnosis of a disease.

1.3 COMPOUND PROPOSITIONS

There are two basic connectives used in everyday speech for making compound propositions: 'and' and 'or'. The same connectives are present in the Propositional Calculus. In the case of 'and' the meaning is the same: the 'and' of two propositions is true only if they are both true. In the case of 'or' we have the dual form: the 'or' of two propositions is false only if they are both false. By induction, if the second proposition is itself an 'or', then we have that:

The *'or'* of many propositions is *false* only if they are *all false.*

For example consider the statement 'Your subscription is reduced if you are a student or you are under 21 or you are unemployed'; thus you pay an unreduced subscription only if all three cases for exemption are false. A similar generalisation holds for 'and':

The *'and'* of many propositions is *true* only if they are *all true.*

For example consider 'To pass the exam, you must arrive on time and have a class certificate and answer most of the questions correctly'; all three conditions must be true in order to pass the exam. We speak about a sequence of 'and's joining propositions as a *conjunction* of propositions, and a sequence of 'or's as a *disjunction*.

Unfortunately, in everyday speech we often use 'A or B' to mean 'either A is true or B is true, but not both', e.g. 'He is at the football match or he is swimming'; 'We will beat them or perish in the attempt'. This is called the *exclusive or* ('xor'). In logic we use the *inclusive or* whose definition was given above. This uses 'A or B' to mean 'A is true, or B is true, or both are true'.

1.4 TRUTH TABLES FOR BASIC OPERATIONS

We can see this more clearly if we use a *truth table* to tabulate the truth values of a formula in terms of the truth of its components. In Table 1.1 the truth values of proposition A and proposition B are shown in the first two columns, using T for true and F for false. There is one row for each of the four possible combinations. The truth values of 'and', 'or' and 'exclusive or' ('xor') are shown in the last three columns, for each combination. We observe that 'and' is true for only one combination, and that 'or' is false for only one combination, as defined above. However, 'xor', is false when both components are true as well as when they are both false.

Table 1.1
Truth table for 'and', 'or' 'xor'

A	B	A and B	A or B	A xor B
T	T	T	T	F
T	F	F	T	T
F	T	F	T	T
F	F	F	F	F

Besides 'and' and 'or' there is a modifier 'not' which negates the truth value of a statement. That is, it reverses it so that

not(True) = False   not(False) = True

This is the meaning of 'not' in everyday speech. In logic the double negative 'not(not(A))' has the same truth value as the original proposition A, after two reversals, just as '$-(-A) = A$' in arithmetic. However, in ungrammatical speech an extra negative may be used to reinforce the original one as in 'He never never did that burglary'! Double negatives are confusing in ordinary speech and we try to avoid them.

Because there are only four different combinations of truth values (TT,TF, FT,FF), and only two different possible results for each one, then there are only

16 (=2x2x2x2) different possible columns in the truth table. Formally speaking we say that there are only 16 different boolean functions of two arguments, where a boolean function produces only true or false as its result. It turns out that all 16 functions can be represented in terms of 'and', 'or', 'not' and the constants True and False. Thus we do not need extra operations though, as we shall see later, some extra ones may be convenient. In particular we can express the exclusive or ('xor') in terms of 'and', 'or' and 'not' as:

A xor B = (A and not B) or (not A and B)

We can verify this in the truth table (Table 1.2) where the last column is is the 'or' of the two previous columns.

Table 1.2

A	B	not A	not B	A and not B	not A and B	A xor B
T	T	F	F	F	F	F
T	F	F	T	T	F	T
F	T	T	F	F	T	T
F	F	T	T	F	F	F

1.5 THEOREMS FROM BOOLEAN ALGEBRA

The mathematician George Boole (1815–1864) established an algebra based on the operators 'and', 'or' and 'not' (symbolised as . + ~), and *boolean variables* which only took two values. The values could for example be 0 and 1, representing the presence of current in a circuit, or 'on' and 'off' representing the states of a switch. Thus Boolean Algebra has been used for designing basic computer circuits, and for analysing their properties, even though it does not model the effects of time delays or pulse distortion. The basic laws of Boolean Algebra are given below.

The first five laws of Boolean Algebra

Commutative Law	:	A and B = B and A
		A or B = B or A
Associative Law	:	A and (B and C) = (A and B) and C
		A or (B or C) = (A or B) or C
Properties of And, Or	:	A and true = A : A and false = false
		A or false = A : A or true = true
Property of Negation	:	A and not A = false
		A or not A = true
Distribution	:	A and (B or C) = (A and B) or (A and C)
		A or (B and C) = (A or B) and (A or C)

The Commutative Law says that we can re-order the operands. Thus 'The car is red and the weather is hot' says the same as 'The weather is hot and the car is red'. This may seem obvious but there are other operators, like the minus operator in arithmetic, for which it does not hold: 'A minus B' is different from 'B minus A'.

The Associative Law allows us to move the brackets anywhere in a sequence of 'and's (or 'or's). Thus

$$(A \text{ and } B) \text{ and } (C \text{ and } D) = A \text{ and } (B \text{ and } C) \text{ and } D$$

In fact we can do without the brackets altogether, since the associative law guarantees that we shall get the same result however we group the propositions.

The third law expresses the properties of 'and' and 'or'. We can verify them by looking at the truth table for 'and' and 'or'. In fact the law enables us to construct the truth table, since it defines the value of 'and' for all possible operands. Note that from the law 'A and false = false', together with the Associative Law, we can deduce that a false operand anywhere in a long sequence of 'and's makes the whole sequence false. Similarily a true operand anywhere in a sequence of 'or's makes the whole sequence true. This is just the converse of our original definition.

The fourth law shows how negated operands combine with and cancel others. We observe that, whatever the value of A, the combination 'A and not A' is always false, since they cannot both be true. Also the value 'A or not A' is always true, but rather useless since it gives us no information about A. Isaac Asimov has a nice story about how an outer planet has a visit from a very senior politician, the Galactic Chancellor. At the end of the visit everyone feels reassured by his statements. However, someone transcribes all the statements and reads them into a computer. Eventually, after much simplification, using rules given later in this book, the machine prints out the total content as 'X or not X', and the inhabitants realise they have actually been told nothing!

The Distribution Law is discussed in the section below. The five laws together completely define a Boolean Algebra. From them it is possible to deduce some other useful laws:

Complement   :   not (not A) = A
Idempotent   :   A and A = A : A or A = A
Absorption   :   A and (A or B) = A

The proof of the *Absorption Law* is short but tricky. The reader is advised to try it before looking at the solution.

      A and (A or B)
    = (A or false) and (A or B)   {Property of 'or'}
    = A or (false and B)   {Distribution}
    = A or (B and false)   {Commutative}
    = A or false   {Property of 'and'}
    = A   {Property of 'or'}

It will be observed that every law exists in two dual forms, and this also extends, by induction, to every result. The *duality principle* states that every theorem in Boolean Algebra stays true if 'and' is replaced by 'or' and 'true' by 'false', and vice versa, everywhere throughout the theorem. Inspection of the previous laws will show that this is so.

1.6 DE MORGAN'S LAWS

A particularly useful law is De Morgan's Law, which the reader is urged to prove for himself by using a truth table. This enables us to negate formulae.

De Morgan   :   not (A and B) = (not A) or (not B)
                not (A or B) = (not A) and (not B)

By induction using the associative law, we see that

not(A and B and C and . . .) = (not A) or (not B) or (not C) or . . .

This gives us an easy way to remember the law. To negate a formula, *change the sign* and *change the operator* throughout the formula. For example

not(not A or B)   = not(not A) and not B
                  = A and not B

This must be one of the commonest exercises in logical manipulation, but in practice it is very easy to give up part way through a long statement, or forget to change an operator, with dire results later on!

Programmers in Pascal are familar with this transformation when writing 'while loops' with a compound condition. Thus by De Morgan the following conditions are equivalent:

while ((i<N) and (A[i] <>x) and not marked[i])

while not((i>=N) or (A[i] =x) or marked[i])

The first version expresses the condition to continue round the loop, whilst the second expresses the alternative conditions for leaving the loop, and then negates them.

1.7 THE DISTRIBUTION LAW – PROPOSITIONS IN NORMAL FORM

The Distribution Law gives us a way of multiplying out bracketed expressions. In many ways 'and' is analogous to multiplication in ordinary arithmetic; similarly 'or' corresponds to addition. (This is because the laws of Boolean Algebra are just like those of mathematical set theory, when we replace 'and' by set intersection, and 'or' by set union). If we write down the distribution law for arithmetic and for logic, we see the correspondence:

$$A * (B + C) = (A * B) + (A * C)$$

Distribution   :   A and (B or C) = (A and B) or (A and C)
                   A or (B and C) = (A or B) and (A or C)

However, the second form of the distribution law has no analogy in ordinary arithmetic, since

$$A + B * C \neq (A + B) * (A + C)$$

Thus it is usually less easy to visualise the rule this way round, because of our familiarity with arithmetic.

One of the commonest ways to simplify a formula is to use the distribution law to multiply it out, and then to collect up terms and cancel them out using the associative and commutative laws, just as in normal algebra. For example:

(A or B) and (not A or B)
= (A and not A) or (A and B) or (B and not A) or (B and B)
= false or (A and B) or (B and not A) or B
= (A and B) or (B and not A) or B   {Property of 'or'}
= (B or (B and A)) or (B and not A)   {Commutative}
=   B   or (B and not A)   {Absorption}
=   B   {Absorption}

Another use of the distributive law is to put formulae into normal form. By multiplying out and collecting up terms we can always put any formula of Propositional Calculus into one of two forms.

(1) *Conjunctive normal form.* The formula is written as a *conjunction* of clauses (C1 and C2 and . . . CN). Each *clause* is a disjunction of propositions or negated propositions (P1 or not P2 or P3 or . . . PN). This is useful in reasoning because if we know that the whole formula is true, then each clause must be true separately, and this makes the formula easier to deal with.

(2) *Disjunctive normal form.* The formula is written as a *disjunction* of expressions, each of which is a *conjunction* of propositions or negated propositions. This is often a convenient form in which to write boolean expressions for switching circuits, or conditions for something to happen. For example, if we wanted to express the statement that two members out of a committee of three people (Anderson, Baynes and Clark) voted for something but one voted against, then we can symbolise 'Anderson voted for it' by 'A', 'Baynes voted for it' by 'B', but 'Clark voted against it' by 'not C'. In order to express this and the two other possibilities as one compound proposition, in disjunctive normal form, we would write it as:

(A and B and not C) or (not A and B and C) or (A and C and not B)

From a truth table, we can see that each expression in brackets is true only for one particular combination of values of A, B and C. For any values of A, B and C apart from these three combinations, each expression will be false, thus making the whole formula false. Thus, for example, if this formula is true about the voting of the committee, then statements A, B and C cannot all be true, neither can they all be false, neither can more than one of them be false.

1.8 THE IMPLIES OPERATOR

We are now in a position to consider logical inference. This uses statements of the form 'if A then B'. That is, if we know that A is true we can deduce that B is true. However, if A is untrue we can make no inference about B; whether it is true or false the statement would be correct. The only way we can show that the inference statement is itself false would be to produce a case where B is known to be false when A is known to be true.

Thus we are in a position to construct a truth table (Table 1.3) for the formula 'if A then B', which, as we see, is false only for one case. We have also tabulated the values of the formula '(not A) or B' which we see are identical to those of 'if A then B'. This should not surprise us, because we can generate all the 16 possible boolean functions using 'and', 'or' and 'not', and so some such equivalent combination has to exist.

Table 1.3

A	B	if A then B	not A	(not A) or B
T	T	T	F	T
T	F	F	F	F
F	T	T	T	T
F	F	T	T	T

The 'if . . . then' operation occurs so frequently in logic that it has its own symbol, thus

$A \rightarrow B$

We read this as A *implies* B, or else as *if* A *then* B. The arrow reminds us that we can only reason in one direction; from knowing A we can deduce B but not vice versa.

Although classical logic can construct chains of inference using arrows, in order to use the resolution method we shall often need to rewrite it using the formula we have discovered:

$A \rightarrow B$ =   (not A) or B

An interesting result of this is the following equivalence:

$A \rightarrow B$ =   (not A) or B
    =   B or (not A)
    =   not (not B) or (not A)
    =   (not B) $\rightarrow$ (not A)

Thus if I say that 'if it rains then the crops will grow' it is entirely equivalent to say that 'if the crops don't grow then there has been no rain'. But it is not the same as saying that 'if the crops grow then there has been rain'. This is because the first statement leaves open the possibility of other causes of crops growing (e.g. sunshine; more fertiliser). It illustrates yet again that we can only use an implication in the direction of the arrow.

1.9 RULES OF INFERENCE: CHAIN RULE AND MODUS PONENS

In logic we use rules of inference to deduce true propositions from other true propositions. This is rather different from Boolean Algebra. The algebra allows us to manipulate formulae, whatever their truth values; the formulae are converted into other equivalent formulae independent of the truth values of their component propositions. However, with inference we rely on using formulae that are known to be true. Such formulae are sometimes called statements.

We believe that if our premises are true and self-consistent then, however often we apply rules of inference, we shall never be able to prove both that a proposition is true and that its negation is also true. If we could do this then our premises must be inconsistent, and as a result we could then prove every proposition both true and untrue, so our system of reasoning would be useless.

Just as for ordinary algebraic manipulation, Boolean Algebra is used to manipulate expressions, to simplify them, and to show their equivalence. However, the use of inference is much closer to the solving of simultaneous equations. We rely on the equations being true, and we make substitutions which preserve this truth and which lead to other equations.

The two classic rules of inference were discovered long ago, and one of them has a latin name 'modus ponens', which is commonly abbreviated to 'mod pons'. We can symbolise it as:

Modus Ponens

Given the truth of $\quad$ A
$\qquad$ and of $\quad$ A $\rightarrow$ B
$\qquad$ deduce $\quad$ B

Thus from two true propositions we deduce a third (**B**). The truth of the rule is obvious; it follows from the definition of the 'implies' operation.

However, the rule does not just apply to atomic propositions. It applies to any formula. For example

From ('Joe is fat' or 'Joe is heavy') $\rightarrow$ ('The entrance is small' $\rightarrow$
$\qquad\qquad\qquad\qquad\qquad\qquad\qquad\qquad$ not 'Joe can enter')
And 'Joe is fat' or 'Joe is heavy'
Deduce 'The entrance is small' $\rightarrow$ not 'Joe can enter'

The second rule allows us to deduce a new implication from two implications. We can symbolise it as

Chain Rule

Given the truth of $\quad$ A $\rightarrow$ B
$\qquad$ and of $\quad$ B $\rightarrow$ C
$\qquad$ deduce $\quad$ A $\rightarrow$ C

The rule is called the chain rule for obvious reasons. We follow a chain of reasoning starting from A, through B to C. The justification is clear: if whenever A is true then B is true, and if whenever B is true then C is true, it follows that whenever A is true then C is true. As an example suppose we are given three premises:

(1) $(P \to Q) \to ((P \text{ or } Q) \to (R \text{ or } Q))$
(2) $(R \text{ or } Q) \to (R \text{ or } S)$
(3) $P \to Q$

Then from 1 and 3 we deduce by modus ponens

(4) $(P \text{ or } Q) \to (R \text{ or } Q)$

Now from 4 and 2 we deduce by chain rule

(5) $(P \text{ or } Q) \to (R \text{ or } S)$

1.10 CHAINS OF INFERENCE

We are now ready to set up a formal system for proving the truth of formulae in the Propositional Calculus. First we need a grammar and a set of symbols, so that we can define precisely what we shall accept as a formula.

The symbols used in formal logic are:

$\land$ for and
$\lor$ or
$\to$ if ... then
$\leftrightarrow$ if and only if
$\sim$ not

We can then define the syntax for a formula as:

⟨formula⟩::= ⟨proposition⟩ | ~⟨proposition⟩ | ⟨proposition⟩⟨op⟩⟨formula⟩
    ⟨op⟩::= $\land$ | $\lor$ | $\to$ | $\leftrightarrow$
⟨proposition⟩::= ⟨atom⟩ | (⟨formula⟩)

We are here using a simple Backus–Naur (BNF) notation, which is used several times later in the book and in Appendix II. Any name in angle brackets stands for an instance of that named type of object. Each type of object is defined by appearing on the left-hand side of '::=', while on the right hand, separated by vertical bars, there appear the alternative ways of writing syntactically correct instances of that object. In this example we start with an ⟨atom⟩, which is an atomic proposition like 'P'; we can then make instances of a ⟨formula⟩ by negating it (~P), or by using an operator to combine it with another formula, e.g. $(P \lor Q, P \lor Q \to R)$.

We are allowed to put brackets round any instance of a ⟨formula⟩, in order to show which operators go with which arguments. However, the usual precedence rules allow us to leave out the brackets in many cases. These are that '~' has the highest precedence, followed by terms involving '$\wedge$', and then those involving '$\vee$', followed by '$\to$' and '$\leftrightarrow$' which have lowest precedence. Thus

$$A \wedge \mathord{\sim}B \vee C \to D \leftrightarrow X \vee Y = ((((A \wedge \mathord{\sim}(B)) \vee C)) \to D) \leftrightarrow (X \vee Y)$$

We also need two metasymbols. These are not part of formulae, but they are used for making statements *about* formulae. They are:

$\vdash$ meaning 'it is true that'
$\models$ meaning 'it is universally true that'

For example, we could say '$\vdash P \to Q$' asserting the truth of a particular proposition (that P implies Q). However, we can also make more general statements such as

$$\models P \to (P \vee Q)$$

for *all* propositions P, Q, regardless of their truth. This last statement is called a *tautology*. It plays the same role in logic as a theorem does in geometry.

The problem of proofs in logic is how to prove a formula B, the *conclusion*, given the truth of formulae A1 to An, the *premises*. We symbolise this as

$$A1, A2, \ldots An \vdash B$$

Basically there are two ways of proceeding.

(i) We can take all the different atoms used in the formulae A1, A2 ... An, B and then draw up a truth table for all possible combinations of truth values for these atoms. We then look along the table and check that whenever all the 'A's have value true then B has value true also. If we consider the example given above about using the chain rule, then A3 would be '$P \to Q$', and we would need to tabulate the 16 possible truth value combinations of P, Q, R and S, which are the atoms. This method always works but it is very long-winded. Instead we use it to justify the basic results used in the next method.

(ii) We write down the premises, and use rules of inference to deduce other true formulae. From these and the originals we deduce further formulae, and so on until we derive the conclusion. We call this a 'chain of inference'; it is the method commonly adopted for mathematical proofs. We shall now study how to do this.

1.11 TAUTOLOGIES AND INSTANTIATION

Besides the premises, we shall need to use *tautologies,* which are theorems of logic. Since they are true for all values of their atoms, it means we can substitute any formula for an atom and, provided we do it consistently all the way through, we shall still have a true formula. This is called taking an instance of the tautology, or *instantiating* it.

Let us list a number of useful tautologies

(a) $\models A \wedge (A \rightarrow B) \rightarrow B$
(b) $\models {\sim}B \wedge (A \rightarrow B) \rightarrow {\sim}A$
(c) $\models (A \rightarrow B) \rightarrow ((A \vee C) \rightarrow (B \vee C))$

We can take an instance of (c) by substituting P for A, R for B and Q for C, giving a result used earlier

$\models (P \rightarrow R) \rightarrow ((P \vee Q) \rightarrow (R \vee Q))$

Note that we cannot derive

$\models (P \rightarrow R) \rightarrow ((A \vee R) \rightarrow (B \vee R))$

as we have not substituted P for every occurrence of A. However, by substitution in (a), we could derive, for example

$\models (P \vee Q) \wedge ((P \vee Q) \rightarrow (R \vee Q)) \rightarrow (R \vee Q)$

In general the *rule of instantiation* says that if C(A) is a tautology, and we substitute a formula B for every occurrence of A in C, then C(B) is a tautology.

In order to prove a tautology there are two main methods:

(i)   Tabulate the value of the formula for all values of its atoms, and check that it is indeed true. The reader is urged to try this for (a) above.
(ii) Use Boolean Algebra to multiply out the formula, and see if it simplifies to a formula like $(A \vee {\sim}A)$, which is true for all values of A.

As an example let us use method (ii) to prove tautology (a) above:

$$(A \wedge (A \rightarrow B)) \rightarrow B$$
$$= {\sim}(A \wedge ({\sim}A \vee B)) \vee B$$
$$= ({\sim}A \vee (A \wedge {\sim}B)) \vee B$$
$$= (({\sim}A \vee A) \wedge ({\sim}A \vee {\sim}B)) \vee B$$
$$= (true \wedge ({\sim}A \vee {\sim}B)) \vee B$$
$$= {\sim}A \vee {\sim}B \vee B$$
$$= {\sim}A \vee true$$
$$= true$$

1.12 LOGICAL EQUIVALENCES AND SUBSTITUTION

Besides useing tautologies, we need to make substitutions for equivalent items. For example, we know that we can substitute $Q \vee P$ for $P \vee Q$, since they are equal. The symbol for equality used in logic is '$\leftrightarrow$'. It also means 'if and only if'. This follows from the truth table for it (Table 1.4).

We see that $B \leftrightarrow A$ has the same truth table as $(A \rightarrow B) \wedge (B \rightarrow A)$. We can read this as 'B if A and B only if A', or else 'B if and only if A'. Thus logical equivalence is the same as an implication that works in both directions, hence the symbol with the double-ended arrow.

Table 1.4

A	B	B ↔ A	A → B	B → A	(A → B) ∧ (B → A)
T	T	T	T	T	T
T	F	F	F	T	F
F	T	F	T	F	F
F	F	T	T	T	T

We can convert this into conjunctive normal form as

$$(\tilde{} A \lor B) \land (\tilde{} B \lor A)$$

If we multiply this out into disjunctive normal form we get

$$(A \land B) \lor (\tilde{} A \land \tilde{} B)$$

In other words, if A and B are equal, then they are both true or both false.

We can write down a number of tautologies involving logical equivalences, some of which we have met already. In fact all the equivalences of Boolean algebra can be written out this way.

(a) $\models$ (A → B) ↔ ($\tilde{}$B → $\tilde{}$A)
(b) $\models$ (A ∨ B) ↔ (B ∨ A)
(c) $\models$ A ∧ (A ∨ B) ↔ A

We can use an equivalence in two ways. Firstly we can write it down as two separate implications, e.g. the first one becomes

$\models$ (A → B) → ($\tilde{}$B → $\tilde{}$A)
$\models$ ($\tilde{}$B → $\tilde{}$A) → (A → B)

Secondly we can use the *Rule of Substitution* which says that if A ↔ B, then when we substitute B for A anywhere in a formula C, we do not alter the truth of the formula.

Thus if we have

$$(P \lor Q) \land ((P \lor Q) \to (R \lor Q)) \to (R \lor Q)$$

we can substitute (Q ∨ R) for (R ∨ Q) giving

$$(P \lor Q) \land ((P \lor Q) \to (Q \lor R)) \to (R \lor Q)$$

Note that we do not need to substitute for both occurrences of R ∨ Q.

1.13 PROOF BY ADOPTING A PREMISE

In this section and the next we shall look at three different strategies for proofs. The first is called 'adopting a premise'. The method can be summarised as 'to prove an implication of the form $A \to B$, assume the truth of the left-hand side, by adopting A as an extra premise, and try to prove B, the right-hand side'.

This method is often used in geometry. For example, to prove that if the two base angles of a triangle are equal then the two sides opposite them are equal, first assume the angles are equal and use this in your proof that the two sides are equal.

The method depends on some important theorems about proofs (Stoll 1961).

Th. {1}. $A \vdash B$ if and only if $\vdash A \to B$

This theorem says that a proof of conclusion B from premise A is equivalent to a proof of the formula $A \to B$ with no special premises. The theorem can easily be verified by considering truth tables.

Th. {2}. $A1, A2, \ldots An \vdash B$ if and only if $\vdash (A1 \wedge A2 \wedge \ldots An) \to B$

This theorem depends on the fact that if the premises $A1$ to An are separately true then their conjunction is true, and vice versa (property of 'and'). It also relies on the theorem just quoted.

Finally we need a very useful equivalence

$$\models (X \to (Y \to Z)) \leftrightarrow (X \wedge Y \to Z)$$

This is easily proved by Boolean Algebra as both sides reduce to $\sim X \vee \sim Y \vee Z$. We can now give a justification of adopting a premise:

if $A1, A2, \ldots An, P \vdash Q$
then $\vdash (A1 \wedge A2 \ldots \wedge An \wedge P) \to Q$ by {2}
then $\vdash (A1 \wedge A2 \ldots \wedge An) \to (P \to Q)$ by equivalence
then $A1, A2 \ldots An \vdash (P \to Q)$ by {2}

1.14 REDUCTIO AD ABSURDUM

When using the method of forming chains of inference, it is not always desirable to keep making inferences until the conclusion turns up. Typically this is what happens when we adopt B as premise to prove $B \to C$. We apply the chain rule and mod pons to B, with the other premises, and eventually deduce C. However, it is possible to get side tracked on the way and prove a great number of other propositions, including many that are irrelevant. This is known as 'forward chaining', and it tends to produce an explosion of intermediate results if it is used to any depth and mechanised for a computer.

Another alternative is to use one of our equivalences and try to prove $\sim C \to \sim B$ instead of $B \to C$. Then we shall adopt $\sim C$ and try to prove $\sim B$. Thus we assume the opposite of the consequent C (the right-hand side of the implication) and try to disprove the antecedent B. This allows us to work backwards using inference based on the consequent. It may give us a better clue as to what results are relevant. This is called 'backward chaining'.

We can also use a combination of the two methods known as 'reductio ad absurdum'. This means that in order to prove B → C we simultaneously assume both B and ˜C; that is, we assume the opposite of the conclusion.

$$˜(B → C) = ˜(˜B ∨ C) = B ∧ ˜C$$

We shall then be able to work forward from B, and backward from ˜C. If C is derivable from B then we shall have proved C, and assumed ˜C, so we have a *contradiction*, or else we derive ˜B from ˜C, and get a contradiction with B. In general we can work from both ends and derive both the truth of a proposition P, by working forward, and its opposite ˜P, by working backward. This proves that the premises are *inconsistent*. From this we deduce that the additional premise (B ∧ ˜C) must have been wrong, and hence that its converse (B → C) is true. This method is called 'reductio ad absurdum', meaning 'reduce to an absurdity'. It is quite commonly used in mathematics. For example, in geometry we could try assuming the two base angles of a triangle are equal but the sides opposite are unequal, and go on to show that if so, then the two angles assumed equal are unequal, or some other absurdity.

It should be noted that if B → C is false, then we shall never get a contradiction, no matter how long we reason. This again is a problem if the proof is mechanised, since the machine cannot tell when to stop. A famous case was the proof of Euclid's fifth postulate (parallel lines will never meet, if they are of finite length) which was believed to depend on the previous four. Many tried to prove it but failed. Lobatchevsky then tried assuming that the fifth postulate was false. To the surprise of many mathematicians this led to no contradiction with the other four, but instead produced a complete self-consistent geometry for a curved space. Theorems derived only from the first four postulates continued to hold in this space. Others, such as the sum of the angles in a triangle equalling 180 degrees, which depended on the fifth postulate, did not hold.

1.15 PROOF BY RESOLUTION

We shall conclude this chapter by introducing a completely general proof method, which also works for the Predicate Calculus. It depends on the use of a single inference rule, which is a great advantage, since it saves having to remember several inference rules and tautologies.

The resolution inference rule is

Resolution	Chain rule	Mod pons
From X ∨ A	From ˜X → A	A
and Y ∨ ˜A	and A → Y	A → Y
deduce X ∨ Y	deduce ˜X → Y	Y

It allows us to combine two formulae by eliminating a common atom 'A' from them. In fact it could be seen as the chain rule applied to formulae in conjunctive normal form, as we can see from the examples on the right above. The modus ponens rule is seen as a special case of this rule, where we take X to be false.

The rule can be justified from the tautology:

$$\models (X \vee A) \wedge (Y \vee \,\tilde{}A) \rightarrow (X \vee Y)$$

from this and previous theorems we have that

$$(X \vee A), (Y \vee \,\tilde{}A) \vdash (X \vee Y)$$

The tautology can be proved by Boolean Algebra thus

$$\begin{aligned}
&\tilde{}((X \vee A) \wedge (Y \vee \,\tilde{}A)) \vee X \vee Y \\
&= (\tilde{}X \wedge \,\tilde{}A) \vee (\tilde{}Y \wedge A) \vee X \vee Y \\
&= (X \vee (\tilde{}X \wedge \,\tilde{}A)) \vee (Y \vee (\tilde{}Y \wedge A)) \\
&= (X \vee \,\tilde{}A) \vee (Y \vee A) \\
&= X \vee Y \vee A \vee \,\tilde{}A \\
&= X \vee Y \vee \text{true} \\
&= \text{true}
\end{aligned}$$

To use the resolution rule we proceed as follows. We use reductio ad absurdum and assume the negation of the conclusion.

(i) Turn each premise and the negated conclusion (adopted as a premise) into conjunctive normal form thus:

(a) Remove $\leftrightarrow$ and $\rightarrow$ symbols by using

$$\begin{aligned}
A \leftrightarrow B &= (A \rightarrow B) \wedge (B \rightarrow A) \\
A \rightarrow B &= \tilde{}A \vee B
\end{aligned}$$

(b) Multiply out negation signs by De Morgan's law.
(c) Distribute $A \vee (B \wedge C) = (A \vee B) \wedge (A \vee C)$

(ii) Each premise is now a conjunction of one or more clauses as defined in section 1.7. Write each clause on a separate line (each is separately true as the conjunction is true).

(iii) Each clause now contains a disjunction of one or more propositions or negated propositions. They are thus in the right form to apply resolution. Take two clauses which contain the same atom with opposite signs, e.g.

$$\begin{aligned}
&X \vee Y \vee Z \vee \,\tilde{}P \\
&Y \vee P \vee W
\end{aligned}$$

Here P is the atom in question. Using resolution we treat P as 'A' in the inference rule, and eliminate it from the two clauses giving

$$(X \vee Y \vee Z) \vee (Y \vee W) = X \vee Y \vee Z \vee W$$

The rule is very easy to apply, since it can be seen as a simple cancellation process:

$$X \vee A, \,\tilde{}A \vee Y \quad \text{deduce } X \vee Y$$

$$A, \,\tilde{}A \vee Y \qquad \text{deduce } Y$$

(iv) We continue until we have derived both P and ~P. We can resolve these together to get the empty clause, expressing the contradiction, which completes the reductio ad absurdum method.

$$P, \text{~}P \quad \text{deduce false}$$

This is usually written as a small square, □

As an example consider the proof of

$$P \vee Q, P \rightarrow R, Q \rightarrow S \mathrel{|\!\!-} R \vee S$$

(i)   Convert the premises to normal form and write them on separate lines:

(1) $P \vee Q$
(2) $\text{~}P \vee R$
(3) $\text{~}Q \vee S$

(ii) Negate the conclusion and convert it to normal form:

$$\text{~}(R \vee S) = \text{~}R \wedge \text{~}S$$
(4) $\text{~}R$
(5) $\text{~}S$

(iii) Deduce the empty clause by resolution:

(6) $\text{~}P$ from 4 & 2
(7) Q 6 & 1
(8) $\text{~}Q$ 5 & 3
(9) □   7 & 8

1.16 ADVANTAGES OF RESOLUTION

Compared to classical logic the resolution method has several advantages.

(i)   We do not have to use equivalences to re-arrange $P \vee Q$ as $Q \vee P$ etc. . . . .
      This is partly because everything is put into normal form to start with, and partly because the resolution rule does not care about the position in the clause of the atom to be eliminated.
(ii) There is only one inference rule to remember.
(iii) It is easy to mechanise.

However, with long proofs it is possible to go round in circles, and the uniform notation tends to make all clauses look alike, so that it is hard to select the right one and remember what they all mean. We shall return to this problem in Chapter 2.

2

The Predicate Calculus

2.1 INTRODUCTION – PARAMETRISED PROPOSITIONS

The Propositional Calculus does not allow us to represent many of the facts and reasons that we use in everyday life. We need to generalise it by parametrising the propositions. Consider for example the statements:

All parts supplied by Mackintosh cost under five pounds.
Mackintosh supplies M8085 chips.

We should be able to deduce from this that M8085 chips cost under five pounds. However, we are unable to do this because the text of the second proposition does not appear directly in the first, even by rewording it. If instead the first proposition were to read:

'If Mackintosh supplies M8085 chips then M8085 chips cost under five pounds'

Then we could make the inference directly by modus ponens. We can symbolise this as

From   Macsupplies → CostUnderFive
And   Macsupplies
Deduce   CostUnderFive

To turn this into Predicate Calculus we parametrise the proposition by putting argument(s) after it in brackets. Thus we have

Macsupplies(M8085) → CostsUnder(M8085,5)
Macsupplies(M8085)

Here 'Macsupplies' and 'CostsUnder' are *Predicates*. The first means that Mackintosh supplies a given item, and the second that the item costs less than a given number of pounds. In general, a Predicate is a function of one or more arguments whose result is true or false (a boolean function). Thus Macsupplies(Coffee) is False, as is CostsUnder(M8085,0).

The introduction of parameters gives an enormous increase in usefulness. It has a similar effect to the introduction of arrays using subscripts into a programming language which only had simple variables, or the introduction of parametrised functions into a simplified version of Basic which only allowed unparametrised subroutine calls. In the case of arrays what is important is the introduction of a variable subscript as in $A[i]$, as against $A[3]$ or $A[1]$. In the case of procedures one parametrised declaration saves rewriting many separate variants of the same procedure.

In this chapter we shall explore the implication of allowing variables inside predicates, and we shall introduce the notion of quantifiers which govern the range of the variables. We shall see how to translate quite complicated statements from English into Predicate Calculus notation, and then we shall see how to use the Resolution Method of Chapter 1 to prove the correctness of these statements or to answer queries by finding values for variables to satisfy the statements.

2.2 THE UNIVERSAL QUANTIFIER ∀

We can make use of variables inside predicates to save writing down the conjunction of many similar statements. Thus instead of writing:

   Macsupplies(M8085) → CostsUnder(M8085,5)
   Macsupplies(M6800) → CostsUnder(M6800,5)
   and so on . . .

we introduce a variable x, and write just one statement

   (∀x) Macsupplies(x) → CostsUnder(x,5)

In the statement just given the symbol ∀ is a *Quantifier* and is used as *'for all'*. Thus the statement reads formally 'For all x if Macsupplies x then x costs under 5 pounds'.

The quantifier governs the scope of values of the variable name following it and says for how many of them the statement is true. If we use the universal quantifier, then we say it is true for every x in the universe. That is, we can substitute any value for x throughout the statement and it will be true.

We should really be more precise and describe a set of values that x can take. For example if Chips is the set of all silicon chips then we should say

   (∀x ∈ Chips) or alternatively (∀x:Chips).

However, a universe of discourse is usually understood from which the values are taken. In fact, for the given statement it doesn't matter if we choose a crazy value for x, since Macsupplies(x) will then be false and there will be no implication about the cost.

However, there is one important restriction. We do not allow predicates themselves to be treated as variables e.g. the use of P in:

$(\forall P,x)\ P(x) \rightarrow \sim(\sim Px)$

This is called a higher order expression. Instead we are using only the *First Order* Predicate Calculus, but henceforth the term 'First Order' is understood.

There are many examples of universally quantified statements in elementary mathematics. Consider the identities:

$(\forall x:\text{Real})\ \text{sqr}(x+1) = \text{sqr}(x)+2x+1$
$(\forall y:\text{Real})\ (y+1)\ (y-1) = \text{sqr}(y)-1$

Here 'sqr' denotes the square of a number, as in Pascal. These statements are true regardless of the values of x and y. However, the statement

$(\forall x)\ \text{sqr}(x+1) = 4$

is *not* true for all values of x, so we must use a different quantifier.

2.3 THE EXISTENTIAL QUANTIFIER ∃

The quantifier ∃ is used to state that *there exists* at least one value of a variable for which a statement is true. Thus we can correctly write

$(\exists x)\ \text{sqr}(x+1) = 4$

In fact there are two real values of x for which this is true (x=1 or x=−3).

We talk of variables as being universally quantified or existentially quantified according to the quantifier used. Every variable must be quantified, otherwise the statement is incomplete. For example, we could rewrite our earlier statement using mixed quantifiers as

$(\forall x)\ \text{Macsupplies}(x) \rightarrow (\exists y)\ (\text{Costs}(x,y) \wedge \text{Less}(y,5))$

This reads 'For all x if Mac supplies x then there is some y such that x costs y pounds and y is less than five'.

2.4 HINTS ON WRITING CALCULUS STATEMENTS

A useful rule to follow is that the universal quantifier goes with an implication and the existential quantifier goes with a conjunction. To see why this is so, consider some counter-examples

$(\exists x)\ \text{Macsupplies}(x) \rightarrow \text{CostsUnder}(x,5)$

This statement has almost no information content. It says that there is an object in the universe which, if supplied by Mac, costs under five pounds.

However, the object could perfectly well be anything not supplied by Mac (e.g. Coffee) in which case it doesn't matter what it costs since the implication will be true anyway! Instead we should say

$(\exists x)$ Macsupplies(x) $\wedge$ CostsUnder(x,5)

This says that there definitely is an object supplied by Mac and that this object costs under five pounds. However, we do not know what it is.

Consider another counter-example, e.g.

$(\forall x)$ Macsupplies(x) $\wedge$ Fragile(x)

This cannot be true! It says that every object in the universe is supplied by Mac and is fragile. The mistake was to use a conjunction instead of an implication. It should have been written

$(\forall x)$ Macsupplies(x) $\rightarrow$ Fragile(x)

One may have a conjunction of several predicates e.g.

$(\exists x)$ Macsupplies(x) $\wedge$ Red(x) $\wedge$ Fragile(x)

Notice that we do *not* say

$(\exists x)$ Macsupplies(Red(Fragile(x)))

This is wrong because Red and Fragile are predicates with boolean values, and we have to apply to them operations like 'and' and 'or', that are legal for boolean values. Nevertheless it is possible for the arguments of predicates to contain expressions including function symbols like 'plus' or 'sqrt', which give real or integer results, e.g.

$(\forall y:real)$ Less(y,plus(y,2))
$(\forall x:real)$ Less(1,x) $\rightarrow$ less(sqrt(x),x)

This last statement says that all numbers that are bigger than one are bigger than their square roots.

2.5 COMBINATIONS OF QUANTIFIERS

We must now consider the order of applying quantifiers in cases where several appear in one statement.

Consider the axiom expressing the transitivity of less:

$(\forall x)$ $(\forall y)$ Less(x,y) $\rightarrow$ $((\forall z)$ Less(y,z) $\rightarrow$ Less(x,z))

Here the order of the first two quantifiers doesn't matter since they are the same. In general

$(\forall x)$ $(\forall y)$ = $(\forall y)$ $(\forall x)$ = $(\forall x,y)$

The third form is shorter to write and reminds us that the order of the variables x,y is unimportant. We can also move the quantifier for z to the front of the statement since it does not affect the first predicate Less(x,y). This gives us:

$(\forall x,y,z)$ Less(x,y) → (Less(y,z) → Less(x,z))

Using our Propositional Equivalences (Chapter 1) we can write this as:

$(\forall x,y,z)$ Less(x,y) ∧ Less(y,z) → Less(x,z)
OR   (x<y) ∧ (y<z) → (x<z)

This is the more well-known form of the axiom, using the infix form of the 'less than' operator.

Similarly if we have several existential quantifiers they can be combined, e.g.:

$(\exists x,y)$ Less(x,3) ∧ Less(3,y) ∧ Eq(plus(x,y),6)

The last predicate Eq is true if the values of its two arguments are equal. The above statement would be satisfied by x=1, y=5 or x=2, y=4 etc.

2.5.1 Renaming of bound variables
However, we cannot always move quantifiers to the front of a statement without altering the meaning of the statement. Consider the statement

$((\exists x)$ Macsupplies(x)) ∧ $((\exists x)$ Less(x,3))

We cannot rewrite this as

$(\exists x)$ Macsupplies(x) ∧ Less(x,3)

This is because the two uses of x refer to different variables — they are independent statements. The x supplied by Mac is not necessarily the same x which is less than 3. We can overcome this by changing the name of the first 'x' to something else, e.g. y. We can do this because it is rather like a local variable in a subroutine; its scope is local to the brackets enclosing its quantifier. Within the brackets we can change its name to anything which does not clash with another used inside the same scope. We say that x is a 'bound variable', because it is bound to its quantifier. Thus we have:

$((\exists y)$ Macsupplies(y)) ∧ $((\exists x)$ Less(x,3))
$= (\exists x,y)$ Macsupplies(y) ∧ Less(x,3)

In general, when moving quantifiers, bound variables should be renamed if there is any danger of a clash. Care must also be taken about moving quantifiers which are inside brackets, e.g.

$(\forall y)$ $((\forall x)$ P(x)) → R(x,y)
does = $(\forall y,x)$ P(x) → R(x,y)

This is because of the negation operation concealed within the implies operation, which must be applied to $(\forall x)$ but not to $(\forall y)$. We can see this if we rewrite it as

$(\forall y)$ ~$((\forall x)$ P(x)) ∨ R(x,y)

In consequence one must adopt a precise strategy for rewriting calculus expressions, as explained below in section 2.13.

2.5.2 Mixed quantifiers

If we mix universal and existential quantifiers we must be careful about the order. Consider

$$(\forall y) ((\exists x) \, Eq(plus(1,x),y)$$

This is true, since it says that for any y, there is an x such that 1+x is equal to y. For example, if y is 7, then x is 6; if y is 0, then x is −1, and so on.

However, if the order of the quantifiers is reversed it becomes

$$(\exists x) ((\forall y) \, Eq(plus(1,x),y))$$

which is not true. This says that there is a single value of x such that for any y, y is equal to 1+x. Obviously this is not so.

The difference in the two formulae is that the choice of x is made after the choice of y (and dependent on it) in the first case, but before it (and thus independent of it) in the second case. Thus the order of the quantifiers is very significant.

If we move quantifiers in a statement such as:

$$((\forall x) \, P(x) \rightarrow Q(x)) \wedge (\exists y) \, R(y)$$

then we must put the existential one first since the original statement does not make it depend on x, i.e.

$$(\exists y) (\forall x) (P(x) \rightarrow Q(x)) \wedge R(y)$$

2.6 FORMAL SYNTAX

$$
\begin{array}{ll}
\langle const \rangle & ::= \langle identifier \rangle \\
\langle var \rangle & ::= \langle identifier \rangle \\
\langle fn \rangle & ::= \langle identifier \rangle \\
\langle pred \rangle & ::= \langle Upper\text{-}Case\text{-}identifier \rangle \\
\langle term \rangle & ::= \langle const \rangle \mid \langle var \rangle \mid \langle fn \rangle (\langle termlist \rangle) \\
\langle termlist \rangle & ::= \langle term \rangle \mid \langle term \rangle, \langle termlist \rangle \\
\langle atom \rangle & ::= \langle pred \rangle \mid \langle pred \rangle (\langle termlist \rangle) \\
\langle literal \rangle & ::= \langle atom \rangle \mid {}^{\sim}\langle atom \rangle \\
\langle operator \rangle & ::= \wedge \mid \vee \mid \rightarrow \mid \leftrightarrow \\
\langle varlist \rangle & ::= \langle var \rangle \mid \langle var \rangle, \langle varlist \rangle \\
\langle quantifier \rangle & ::= (\exists \langle varlist \rangle) \mid (\forall \langle varlist \rangle) \\
\langle formula \rangle & ::= \langle literal \rangle \mid {}^{\sim}(\langle formula \rangle) \\
& \quad \mid \langle quantifier \rangle (\langle formula \rangle) \\
& \quad \mid (\langle formula \rangle) \, \langle operator \rangle \, (\langle formula \rangle)
\end{array}
$$

Fig. 2.1 − Formal syntax of first order Predicate Calculus.

Figure 2.1 gives a formal syntax of the Predicate Calculus in Backus–Naur form as used for describing Programming Languages such as Algol60. This formally defines a *well-formed formula* (or WFF), i.e. one that is grammatically correct.

We see that a formula is built up from other formulae connected by the four operators conjunction, disjunction, implication and equivalence, together with negation, and that any formula may have one or more quantifiers in front.

The simplest case of a formula is a *literal,* which is an atom or a negated atom. An *atom* is just a predicate with 0,1 or more arguments which are called *terms.*

Terms may be constants (e.g. 2,true), variables (e.g. x,y) or functions with arguments (e.g. sqrt(x),plus(x,y)). Terms are precisely what one would allow as value parameters when calling a Pascal procedure, or as input parameters when calling a Fortran subprogram; the only difference is that the functions are usually written in prefix notation so that, for example, Less(3,5+x+y) becomes Less(3,plus(plus(5,x),y)).

This syntax does not show where brackets may be dropped because the order of applying operators may be inferred from the precedence rules. For example we usually write

$$(\forall x)\,(\forall y)\,P(x) \wedge Q(x) \rightarrow R(x) \quad \text{instead of}$$
$$(\forall x)\,((\forall y)\,((P(x) \wedge Q(x)) \rightarrow (R(x)))$$

2.7 SEMANTIC CONSTRAINTS OF THE CALCULUS

Just as in programming languages, there may be extra constraints on a grammatically well-formed expression which make it meaningful. We call these 'semantic constraints' or just 'semantics'. They are as follows:

(i)   Where a formula is made from ⟨quantifier⟩ ⟨formula⟩ it must not already contain another quantifier binding the same ⟨var⟩, i.e.

$$(\exists x)\,(\forall x)\,P(x) \text{ is illegal}$$

(ii) A Predicate (or a function) must take the same number of arguments wherever it is used.

(iii) The values of all constants and variables and the arguments of predicates and functions must be taken from a predefined universe (or domain of discourse) over which the predicates and functions are defined.

(iv) A *statement* in the calculus is a formula, all of whose ⟨var⟩s are quantified.

2.8 A SET-THEORETIC MODEL

Predicates are defined over a set of values which we call a universe of discourse **W**. If we confine ourselves to unary predicates (taking only one argument) then we can represent each predicate by the set of values of its argument for which it is true. This is called the *extension* of the predicate, and the set will be a subset of **W**.

Conversely if we take such a set, then the corresponding predicate is said to be the *Characteristic Function* of the set. This relies on the fact that predicates can produce only one of two values. Thus if we know the set of values in the universe for which they are true, then they must deliver false for all other values, and so we know their value for every item in the universe W.

If we know the extensions P and Q of any two predicates p(x) and q(x) then we can write down a table giving the extensions of any formula made by combining them, and hence by induction for all formulae (see Table 2.1). This is a formal way of defining the meaning of a Calculus expression.

Table 2.1.

Predicate Calculus formulae and their extensions

Formula	Extension
p(x)	P
q(x)	Q
p(x) $\wedge$ q(x)	$P \cap Q$
p(x) $\vee$ q(x)	$P \cup Q$
~p(x)	$W - P$ or $\bar{P}$
p(x) $\rightarrow$ q(x)	$\bar{P} \cup Q$
p(x) $\leftrightarrow$ q(x)	$(\bar{P} \cup Q) \cap (\bar{Q} \cup P)$
($\forall$x)p(x)	P = W
($\exists$x)p(x)	~(P = O)

We see the duality between conjunction and set intersection and between disjunction and set union. Thus p(x) $\wedge$ q(x) is true only for those x lying in the intersection of P and Q i.e. where p(x) and q(x) are both true.

Negation is represented by taking the complement with respect to the Universe. The extension for p(x)$\rightarrow$q(x) is just that for ~p(x) $\vee$ q(x). These are logically equivalent expressions, as shown in Chapter 1. It may seem a bit odd, but let us look at it in terms of extensions. Remember that the implication p(x)$\rightarrow$q(x) is true whenever p(x) is false (i.e. in ~P), and also whenever p(x) is true provided q(x) is true also (i.e. in P $\cap$ Q). This gives the extension

$$\bar{P} \cup (P \cap Q) = (\bar{P} \cup P) \cap (\bar{P} \cup Q) = W \cap (\bar{P} \cup Q) = \bar{P} \cup Q$$

The last two entries in Table 2.1 give a meaning to quantifiers in the model. The statement that p(x) is true for all x means that the extension P must include all x in the universe, i.e. P = W. The statement that there exists an x for which p(x) is true means that the extension must contain that x, and so cannot be equal to the null set.

2.9 NEGATING QUANTIFIERS

From this model we get an elegant proof of what happens when quantified formulae are negated, and thus we get a generalisation of De Morgan's law. If we say:

$$\sim(\exists x)p(x) \qquad \text{means} \quad \sim(\sim(P = O))$$
$$\text{i.e.} \quad P = O$$
$$\text{i.e.} \quad W{-}P = W{-}O$$
$$\text{i.e.} \quad \sim P = W$$
$$\text{but } (\forall x) \sim p(x) \quad \text{means} \quad \sim P = W$$

Thus

$$\sim((\exists x)p(x)) = (\forall x) \sim p(x)$$

By writing 'p' for '$\sim$p' and reversing the argument we have

$$\sim((\forall x)p(x)) = (\exists x) \sim p(x)$$

We thus arrive at a generalisation of De Morgan's law: To negate a quantified expression, *change* the quantifier, *change* the signs and *change* the operators. For example consider:

$$(\forall x) P(x) \rightarrow Q(x)$$

The negation of this is: $\sim((\forall x) \sim P(x) \lor Q(x))$ or
$$(\exists x) P(x) \land \sim Q(x)$$

Note that the quantifiers change, 'or' changes to 'and', and the signs of the literals are reversed.

The meaning is quite understandable. If I assert that for all x whenever $P(x)$ is true then $Q(x)$ is true (e.g. all red apples are sweet), then a counter-example would be a case where there is some x for which $P(x)$ is true but $Q(x)$ is not true (e.g. there is an apple which is red but not sweet); the negated statement states simply the existence of a counter-example.

2.10 EXAMPLES OF QUANTIFIED STATEMENTS

The basic method for translating from English into calculus form is to look for words like 'all', 'every' or 'any' which give rise to universal quantifiers and words like 'some' or 'a person' which give rise to existential quantifiers. These occur in combination, e.g. someone, somebody, somewhere, something, anyone, anybody, anywhere and anything. Consider the example:

All Australian cricketers admire some fast bowler.

We can write this as:

$$(\forall x) \text{ Australian}(x) \land \text{Cricketer}(x) \rightarrow ((\exists y) \text{ FB}(y) \land \text{Admires}(x,y))$$

Note that we write 'persons x who are Australians and who are cricketers' instead of the adjectival form 'Australian cricketers'. Note also the 'and' following the existential quantifier. As explained in section 2.4 if we wrote:

$$(\forall x) \text{ Australian}(x) \wedge \text{Cricketer}(x) \rightarrow ((\exists y) \text{ FB}(y) \rightarrow \text{Admires}(x,y))$$

then the statement would be very much weaker than that given. Note also that this is not the same as:

$$(\forall x) \text{ Australian}(x) \wedge \text{Cricketer}(x) \rightarrow ((\forall y) \text{ FB}(y) \rightarrow \text{Admires}(x,y))$$
$$\text{i.e. } (\forall x,y) \text{ Australian}(x) \wedge \text{Cricketer}(x) \wedge \text{FB}(y) \rightarrow \text{Admires}(x,y)$$

This says that all Australian cricketers admire all fast bowlers, instead of only some fast bowlers.

Note also that the statement is different from

$$(\exists y) (\forall x) \text{ Australian}(x) \wedge \text{Cricketer}(x) \rightarrow \text{FB}(y) \wedge \text{Admires}(x,y)$$

This says that there is a unique fast bowler admired by all Australian cricketers whereas we should use $(\forall x)$ $(\exists y)$ to say that different cricketers may admire different fast bowlers.

Sometimes the universal quantifier is expressed by negation. For example 'No cricketer is both a fast bowler and a high scorer'. We can write this as:

$$\sim((\exists x) \text{ Cricketer}(x) \wedge \text{FB}(x) \wedge \text{HighScorer}(x))$$

This is of course equivalent by De Morgan to

$$(\forall x) \sim(\text{Cricketer}(x) \wedge \text{FB}(x)) \vee \sim\text{HighScorer}(x) \text{ or}$$
$$(\forall x) \text{ Cricketer}(x) \wedge \text{FB}(x) \rightarrow \sim\text{HighScorer}(x)$$

which means 'if a cricketer is a fast bowler then he is not a high scorer'.

2.11 QUANTIFIED STATEMENTS ABOUT DATA

As we shall see in Chapter 7, the Predicate Calculus can be used to form queries about stored data. Basically we can store the extension of a predicate as a set of data values in a file on a computer. Thus we may have a file of cricketers, a file of fast bowlers and a file of batting averages. We can then ask 'Is there a fast bowler with an average over 60' by writing:

$$(\exists x,y) \text{ Cricketer}(x) \wedge \text{FB}(x) \wedge \text{Avge}(x,y) \wedge \text{Less}(60,y) \text{ ?}$$

Usually we also want to know who the cricketer is and what is his average. The computer can easily provide this since it actually computes the extension which contains the required information.

Another use of the calculus is to write down 'integrity constraints' on the data, which must be maintained whenever extra data is inserted. For example:

$$(\forall x) \text{ FB}(x) \rightarrow \text{Cricketer}(x)$$

This says that whenever we insert someone in the file of fast bowlers we must also add them to the file of cricketers. This is discussed more fully in Chapter 12.

The facts in the database can be written down directly as a series of instances of predicates applied to constants. Suppose the file of cricketers contained Hutton, Botham and Dexter. Then we could write:

Cricketer(Hutton) $\wedge$ Cricketer(Botham) $\wedge$ Cricketer(Dexter) $\wedge$ FB(Botham)

to represent this information.

2.12 EQUIVALENCE OF DIFFERENT FORMULAE

Since a number of superficially different statements can be manipulated to give rise to the same calculus formula it is challenging to see if we can convert any given formula into a canonical or normal form, so that a simple textual comparision will show whether or not the forms are equivalent. However, this comparison may fail for some equivalent formulae because:

(i)   The formulae may not be based on the same set of predicates and functions. It is possible to represent facts differently. For example we might represent that x is a fast bowler by the binary predicate Bowler(x,'Fast') or Bowler(x, 'Slow') instead of FastBowler(x) or SlowBowler(x). This has certain advantages, since one can quantify over the variables with values 'Fast' and 'Slow' but not over the predicates FastBowler and SlowBowler. Very much the same problem arises in Data Analysis for databases. Is a FastBowler a different entity from a SlowBowler or the same entity (bowler) with different attributes (fast or slow)? In general we cannot prove the equivalence of formulae based on different representations.

(ii) The formulae may be logically equivalent in that the truth of one implies the truth of the other, and vice versa, but this may require a chain of proof using extra axioms that express the properties of the given predicates. For example the statements

$$(\forall x,y) \text{ MacSupplies}(x) \wedge \text{Cost}(x,y) \rightarrow \text{Less}(y,6) \text{ and}$$
$$(\forall x,y) \text{ Less}(5,y) \wedge \text{Cost}(x,y) \rightarrow {\sim}\text{MacSupplies}(x)$$

are equivalent. This relies on the property of Less:

$$(\forall y,z{:}\text{Integer}) \text{ Less}(y,\text{plus}(z,1)) \leftrightarrow {\sim}\text{Less}(z,y)$$

2.13 CONVERSION TO CLAUSAL FORM

It is possible to convert any Calculus expression into Conjunctive Normal Form. This is rather similar to simplifying an algebraic expression made out of addition, subtraction and multiplication signs with constants, variables and brackets. It is possible to multiply this out and collect up terms so that we get a sum of products of variables and constants of ascending degree, e.g.

$$A + Bx + Cy + Dxx + Exy + \ldots$$

Similarly we can 'multiply out' a calculus formula using the distributive law so as to get a conjunction of *clauses* each of which is a literal or disjunction of literals thus:

$$A \wedge (B \vee P(x)) \wedge (C \vee Q(y)) \wedge (E \vee P(x) \vee Q(y)) \wedge \cdots$$

The advantage of this is that if the formula is asserted to be true then each clause must be true separately which makes the formula easier to deal with. It is also necessary for the Resolution Proof Method as explained in Chapter 1.

The syntax of the normal form may be expressed as an extension of that given in Fig. 2.1.

⟨normal form⟩ ::= ⟨conj form⟩ | ⟨quantifier⟩ ⟨normal form⟩
⟨conj form⟩   ::= (⟨clause⟩) | (⟨clause⟩) $\wedge$ ⟨conj form⟩
⟨clause⟩   ::= ⟨literal⟩ | ⟨literal⟩ $\vee$ ⟨clause⟩

The method of doing it proceeds in stages and is an extension of that given in Chapter 1, to allow for quantifiers.

(a) *Remove equivalences* Replace 'P↔Q' by '(P→Q) $\wedge$ (Q→P)'
(b) *Remove implications* Replace 'P→Q' by '~P $\vee$ Q'
(c) *Move the negation signs* Negation signs are moved from outside the brackets to just in front of atoms, using the generalised De Morgan's laws together with '~~P=P'. With a complex expression it is best to start with the outermost negation sign, since this will cancel inner negation signs thus saving the effort of multiplying these out.
(d) *Remove existential quantifiers* This can only be done after (c) because some universal quantifiers may become existential after negation, and vice versa. To do it we use a technique called 'Skolemisation' after the famous logician. If a variable x is quantified by (∃x) which is not itself within the scope of any universal quantifier then every occurrence of x which is quantified by (∃x) is replaced by an unknown *Skolem Constant,* say 'a'. The name is chosen to be different from any other and, by convention, starts with a lower-case letter from the first part of the alphabet. The constant 'a' represents one (unknown) value of x for which the statement is true. The crucial thing is that the *same* unknown value is substituted everywhere x is used. However, if (∃x) is within scope of universal quantifiers say (∀y,z) then instead of a constant 'a' we choose a *Skolem Function* 'f' of the universally quantified variables, e.g. 'f(y,z)'. This represents the fact that the choice of unknown can vary with y and z but for the same y and z we must choose the *same* unknown. Thus, e.g.

$$(\exists z)P(z) \wedge (\forall y) ((\exists x)\ Eq(y,plus(x,1)) \wedge (\exists x)\ Less(x,plus(x,y)))$$

becomes

$$P(a) \wedge (\forall y) (Eq(y,plus(f(y),1)) \wedge Less(g(y),plus(g(y),y)))$$

Here we have two different Skolem functions f and g for the two different uses of x. Fortunately examples of this complexity are rare!

(e) *Pull out universal quantifiers* It is now safe to move all universal quantifiers to the front of the formula. However, it may first be necessary to rename some variables as explained earlier (section 2.5).

(f) *Multiply out bracketed conjunctions* Any formula of the form P ∨ (Q ∧ R ∧ . . .) must be replaced by separate clauses (P ∨ Q) ∧ (P ∨ R) ∧ . . . this process is repeated until we are left with a conjunction of clauses.

2.14 THE RESOLUTION PRINCIPLE

If we have a number of axioms, and a formula F representing a conclusion, then we can form a new formula from the conjunction of the axioms with the negated formula (~F). We can then convert this formula into a number of clauses in normal form, using the method just given. Using the Resolution method of Chapter 1, together with the method of substituting for variables (Unification) explained below, we can repeatedly derive new clauses as logical consequences of existing ones. If the formula is deducible from the axioms then we shall be able eventually to derive both a clause P of one literal (from the axioms) and also its opposite (~P) (from the negated formula together with the axioms). From this we get the Null Clause, expressing the existence of a contradiction. Thus we deduce that the original formula F was true and derivable from the axioms.

It turns out that this is a completely general proof procedure for the first order Predicate Calculus, but alas it is not guaranteed to terminate! Just as humans can go round in circles trying to do proofs, so can computers. There are even some formulae which are known to be 'undecidable' (Stoll 1961); however clever your program is, they will force it into an endless loop! Fortunately most examples are not of this kind, and because of its generality, the Resolution method is very useful, both for verifying logical deductions and for answering questions.

2.15 USING RESOLUTION FOR QUESTION ANSWERING

Suppose that, as discussed in section 2.11, we have a database file containing the following facts about parenthood, using the predicate $F(x,y)$ to mean that x is the father of y:

$$F(john,harry) \land F(john,sid) \land F(sid,liz)$$

Thus we have three *unit clauses* each containing one literal. They do not contain any variables or implications, and so just represent basic facts of the kind which would be held in a database.

Suppose we introduce the predicates $M(x)$, $S(x,y)$ and $B(x,y)$ to represent respectively that x is (a) male, (b) the sibling of y, and (c) the brother of y. We can write down the following axioms about family relationships:

$$(\forall x,y) \quad F(x,y) \rightarrow M(x)$$
$$(\forall x,y,w) \; F(x,y) \land F(x,w) \rightarrow S(y,w)$$
$$(\forall x,y) \quad S(x,y) \land M(x) \rightarrow B(x,y)$$

These state that (i) all fathers are male; (ii) if children have the same father then they are siblings; (iii) a brother is a male sibling.

Suppose we ask the question $(\exists z)$ B(z,harry)? To answer this by resolution we negate the question giving $(\forall z)$ ~B(z,harry). We now convert the axioms into normal form and write each clause on a separate line (each is separately true).

(i)   ~F(x,y) $\vee$ M(x)
(ii)   ~F(x,y) $\vee$ ~F(x,w) $\vee$ S(y,w)
(iii)   ~S(x,y) $\vee$ ~M(x) $\vee$ B(x,y)
(iv)   F(john,harry)
(v)   F(john,sid)
(vi)   F(sid,liz)
(vii)   ~B(z,harry)

We have missed out the universal quantifiers, since it is understood that anything that is not a constant is universally quantified. The constants are recognisable since either they start with a letter from the first part of the alphabet, or they are names like john, sid, harry and liz.

In order to do resolution we must substitute terms for variables systematically throughout a pair of clauses, so that an instance of a literal in one clause clashes with one in the other. We can do this because each variable is universally quantified. For example, if we substitute john for x and sid for y in (ii) we get:

~F(john,sid) $\vee$ ~F(john,w) $\vee$ S(sid,w)

We can resolve this with (v) to give a new clause (viii):

(viii) ~F(john,w) $\vee$ S(sid,w)   from (v) & (ii) {john/x, sid/y}

The comment on the right gives the two clauses used in the resolution and what substitution was used.

Continuing we get:

(ix)   S(sid,harry)   from (iv) & (viii) {harry/w}
(x)   M(sid)   from (vi) & (i) {sid/x, liz/y}
(xi)   ~S(sid,y) $\vee$ B(sid,y)   from (x) & (iii) {sid/x}
(xii)   B(sid,harry)   from (ix) & (xi) {harry/y}
(xiii) □   from (xii) & (vii) {sid/z}

Thus we deduced the unit clause (xii), which says that sid is harry's brother, from the axioms and the facts in the database ((iv), (v), (vi)). This contradicts our negated query which says that harry has no brothers.

If we want to know who harry's brother is then we must keep track of the substitutions. This can be done by the device of introducing a special literal — the 'Answer Literal' (Green 1969). Thus instead of ~B(z,harry) we write:

(viia) ~B(z,harry) $\vee$ Answer(z)

Instead of resolving to produce the null clause we resolve until we get the

Answer clause which 'remembers' the instantiation for z required to resolve with B(z,harry). Thus the last lines above would read:

(xiii) Answer(sid)   from (xii) & (viia) {sid/z}

Thus the answer is that Sid is Harry's brother. Depending on the information we might not get a unit clause but instead, e.g. Answer(sid) ∨ Answer(fred).

Even if we do the resolution in a slightly different order we shall still get the same answer. Suppose we start again at line (xi) but this time using (viia) instead of (vii):

(xi)   ~S(x,harry) ∨ ~M(x) ∨ Answer(x)   from (viia) {x/z} & (iii) {harry/y}
(xii) ~S(sid,harry) ∨ Answer(sid)   from (x) & (xi) {sid/x}
(xiii) Answer(sid)   from (xii) & (ix)

However, if we do the substitutions in a different sequence we get into difficulty:

(viii) ~F(john,w) ∨ S(harry,w)   from (iv) & (ii) {john/x, harry/x}
(ix)   S(harry,sid)   from (v) & (viii) (sid/w)

The problem is that we have proved S(harry,sid) when we need S(sid,harry) to resolve with (xii). We can overcome this by introducing the extra axiom:

(∀x,y) S(x,y) → S(y,x)

or in normal form

(xiv) ~S(x,y) ∨ S(y,x)

Unfortunately we can loop endlessly on this if not careful:

(xv)   S(sid,harry)   from (ix) & (xiv) {harry/x, sid/y}
(xvi) S(harry,sid)   from (xv) & (xiv) {sid/x, harry/y}
(xvii) S(sid,harry)   from (xvi) & . . . and so on

This shows the need to plan proofs carefully as discussed below if we are to have any hope of mechanising them.

2.16 HEURISTICS FOR PROOF

If we want to make a computer program that will do resolution for us and search for the answer then we must give it some rules of thumb, or 'Heuristics', to help search for a derivation of the null clause. This is discussed more fully in (Chang and Lee 1973), and also in (Robinson 1979) but the most useful methods are:

(i) *Unit preference* It is best to use at least one unit clause in resolution, since this reduces the length of the resultant clause. If instead we resolve (say) two clauses of three literals each then we get a result of four literals and so on, which gets ever further from the null clause.

(ii) *Set of support* One must use specific facts from the problem, not just general axioms to answer specific questions. Thus we can just resolve clauses (i) to (iii) to prove ever more general theorems about family relationships but this will never produce a specific answer. The answer must include the use of clauses from (iv) to (vi), and those derived from them. We can keep a note of the ancestry of a clause, and so check on this.

(iii) *Choose unique literals* In the example above it is clear that the only occurrence of B was in clause (iii) so that this must be resolved with ~B in (vii). By contrast there are many instances of ~F, and it is better to start by resolving with literals like B, so as to get partially instantiated shorter clauses which give clues for further substitutions.

(iv) *Planning* A human will usually plan out a proof first by drawing diagrams and getting the basic pattern of proof before filling in the details. It may thus be necessary to axiomatise information about which axioms are most useful. This is 'meta-information'. Bundy *et al.* (1979) has used this technique very successfully in Prolog to carry out proofs in a 'planning space', and then to use the results to form the framework of a proof and govern the choice of which axioms and substitutions to use, and in what sequence.

2.17 SUBSTITUTION AND UNIFICATION

The Resolution method requires one to make substitutions in clauses so that two literals of opposite sign will contain identical atoms. Since these atoms may contain uninstantiated variables, it is possible to make extra substitutions which instantiate them and still keep the two literals equal and opposite. The process of finding a substitution which makes two literals clash is called *Unification.* Consider the unification process for the two literals:

$$P(a, x, f(g(y))) \text{ and } {\sim}P(z, f(z), f(u))$$

We gradually build up a *substitution* S which is a set of pairs of terms and variables for which they are to be substituted. We have already seen substitutions written in the question answering example, e.g. $S = \{harry/x, z/w\}$. In general one writes $S = \{t1/v1, t2/v2,. . .\}$ where all the vi are different variables, and each term ti is different from its vi. We work from left to right looking for terms or parts of terms which do not match. Thus we get successively:

	Match $P(a,x,f(g(y)))$	with ${\sim}P(z,f(z),f(u))$
$S = \{a/z\}$	Match $P(a,x,f(g(y)))$	with ${\sim}P(a,f(a),f(u))$
$S = \{a/z, f(a)/x\}$	Match $P(a,f(a),f(g(y)))$	with ${\sim}P(a,f(a),f(u))$
$S = \{a/z, f(a)/x, g(y)/u\}$	Match $P(a,f(a),f(g(y)))$	with ${\sim}P(a,f(a),f(g(y)))$

This method gives the most general unifier (Robinson 1979). We have instantiated z, x and u but not y. A more restrictive unification might use, e.g.

$$S = \{a/z, f(a)/x, g(a)/u, a/y\} \text{ giving } P(a, f(a), f(g(a))).$$

The process is important in the Prolog language since it provides a generalis-ation of the procedure call mechanism used in conventional programming languages. Normally the arguments of the procedure call are expressions which are substituted for the formal parameters which may only be variable names. However, Prolog allows the formal parameters themselves to be terms and the process of calling a 'Logic Procedure' proceeds by matching the terms in the call with the terms in the procedure heading, using the unification method. If the unification fails, because no substitution will make the rest of the literals match, no call is made but an attempt will be made to match an alternative procedure definition if one is present. This is sometimes called 'Pattern Directed Invocation', and is an important notaion for the newer programming languages.

2.18 SUMMARY

The Predicate Calculus is much more powerful than the Propositional Calculus, and it provides a way of expressing most things we wish to say or to reason about. We can express quite complex statements by using predicates, quantifiers, variables and function symbols, and we can express simple facts just as pre-dicates, with constants as arguments. Thus we can express knowledge, both general axioms and facts, in one common formalism, which is very important for 'Expert Systems' (Stefik *et al.* 1982). We have also seen how to convert Calculus statements into normal form, and how to use the Resolution method to prove their correctness, and to find values for the (existentially quantified) variables which will satisfy the statements. This has applications to database question answering, as we shall see in Chapter 7 and later. It is also the basis for the Prolog language, which we shall study in Chapter 4. However, we need to be able to manipulate sets of data, which we shall often represent as lists, and before we can formalise this in the Predicate Calculus, we shall need to under-stand how to perform list processing operations using recursion. This is commonly done by using the applicative languages, which are based on the Lambda Calculus; these are the subject of the next chapter.

3

Lambda expressions and list processing

3.1 INTRODUCTION

Whilst one class of database query languages, discussed in Chapter 7 is based on the predicate calculus, others are based on 'Applicative' or 'Functional' languages. This chapter provides a background to these languages, which make extensive use of function application. They express results in terms of functions applied to objects, which are themselves the results of functions, and so on. Where we use a loop or iteration in a conventional program, the corresponding functional form uses recursive function calls, which are explained below.

The crucial point about the applicative languages is that they do not use 'destructive assignment'; thus once a variable has acquired a value, it is never changed or overwritten. Where an ordinary program operates by assignment on arrays, the corresponding functional form, as we shall see, produces new list structures; these may share parts of old ones but they do not overwrite them, thus preserving the old values intact. We shall be particularly interested in this method of processing list structures, since it is also suitable for describing operations on lists in the predicate calculus, as we shall see in Chapter 4.

Another reason for interest is that we can use algebraic substitutions both to simplify and optimise applicative programs. We cannot use this technique if the values of variables are changed by destructive assignment. It follows that programs in functional form look much more like ordinary algebraic expressions, which we are used to simplifying and working with. As we shall see in Chapters 8 and 9, it is possible to write database queries in this form by using 'Relational Algebra'; this specifies the answer to a database query in terms of application of functions, instead of a sequence of instructions, and is much easier to deal with.

Other theoreticians are interested in functional languages, because it is easier to prove the correctness of functional programs by standard mathematical techniques, and also because they are more suitable for execution on parallel hardware. We shall not stress these particular features, which are described in detail elsewhere (Henderson 1980).

In this chapter we shall look at a particular functional notation called the *Lambda Calculus* which was introduced by the logician Alonzo Church in the 1930s and developed and popularised by P. J. Landin in the 1960s. The Lambda Calculus is mainly concerned with function application and the evaluation of *Lambda expressions* by techniques of substitution. It provides a very concise notation for functions, especially in list processing, and has been used as the basis of the list processing languages LISP and POP–2. Two classic papers on this are 'Recursive functions of symbolic expressions and their computation by machine' (McCarthy 1960), which describes an early version of LISP, and 'The mechanical evaluation of expressions' (Landin 1964, 1966), which describes a way to implement a general interpreter for lambda expressions.

We start by examining the abstract idea of a function in terms of set theory and mappings, in order to see the relationship between the abstract notation used by mathematicians and the concepts used in programming languages, and also the concepts of relational databases as described in Chapter 6. We then go on to see how we can carry out the standard constructs of structured programming (composition, alternation and iteration) in lambda expressions, and how to write recursive functions. Next we shall introduce the basic operations of list processing and see how to express them in functional form. We conclude by seeing how to write a number of standard list processing functions, which we shall need in Chapter 4.

3.2 FUNCTIONS VIEWED AS MAPPINGS BETWEEN SETS

A function of one argument is a rule which associates with any value lying in the *domain* of that argument another value lying in the *range* of the function. We are familiar with elementary numerical functions, like sin(x) or sqrt(x), which take a value in the domain of real numbers (or positive real numbers in the case of square root), and deliver a result in the range of real numbers (or in the range −1 to +1 in the case of sine). Note that a function is defined to deliver only one value (which may however be a structure with components). Thus we have to define sqrt(x), as in Pascal and Fortran, to deliver the positive number which, when squared, is equal to x; it cannot sometimes deliver the positive and sometimes the negative solution.

The notion of a function has been taken over in programming languages. There are usually a number of built-in functions which are provided with the language, e.g. sine, cos, sign, sqrt etc. The programmer can also usually define his own functions. These may work on a wider variety of data types than the real numbers, usually integer, real, boolean, and character. They may also work on structures such as records, arrays, lists, and files of records, as in Pascal, Algol 68 and PL/1, and they may return pointers to structures as results. This is all in accordance with the concept of a domain of values outside which the function is undefined. In programming languages the domain is usually specified by a data type, which is a set of values, and in Pascal it is the job of the compiler to check that no function is applied to a value of the wrong type, which would be outside its domain.

Our examples of domains up to now have been of infinite sets, e.g. the set of all real numbers, or of all integers. However, there are functions over finite sets. For example, in Pascal, the function chr(n) takes an integer in the range 0 to 127, and returns the character which has that ordinal number. We may also have a boolean function such as eof(f), which takes one of a limited number of files as argument, and returns a boolean value, true or false, depending on whether we have read up to the end of file f. Again, the predicates of logic, which we considered in Chapter 2, are boolean functions.

Some functions are not defined for all values in their domain; we call these *partial functions*. For example a function that works on days of the month can deal with a record representing the 30th of January but not with one representing the 30th of February. However, in Pascal we cannot write a type declaration which will specify the domain so precisely as to stop a function being entered with the 30th day of the second month as argument. A partial function implemented as a program may do one of two things. It may print an error message (e.g. 'invalid day for this month') and exit, or else it may go into a loop from which it never returns. In either case it does not deliver a result. We shall find that there are also partial functions which are applicable to database record types, as we shall see when we discuss the Functional Data Model in Chapter 10.

Since a function is a rule associating pairs of values, there are many ways to represent it. In programming languages we are used to representing the rule as an algorithm. However, if we are dealing with a small finite set of values then we can represent the function as a *set of pairs* of values. That is, we store the argument of the function and the value of the corresponding result, paired together in a table. To find the value of the function, we look up the argument in the table and read off the result (just as in tables of sines and other trigonometric functions). We can of course use this method on a computer, by storing the table as an array in the body of a function, which is defined in a program; such functions are usually referred to as 'table-driven'. In the case of databases the items concerned are held on secondary storage and the argument value is found by looking for a matching value in the database, usually with the aid of an index, or from a calculated starting point as explained in Chapter 11. The stored result value is often held physically close to the argument value, or else found by following a pointer, as described in the same chapter. We shall examine this view of a database as holding 'stored functions' when we consider the Functional Data Model in Chapter 10. For the moment we wish to concentrate on the idea that a function may be viewed as a set of ordered pairs and see how to formalise this notion.

3.2.1 Ordered pairs

An ordered pair ⟨x,y⟩ is an object with two components x and y. The order is

important, so that for example ⟨2,3⟩ is different from ⟨3,2⟩. A function f may
be viewed as a set of ordered pairs where the values of the first component are
taken from a set called the domain D and the values of the second component
cover a set called the range R. We talk of the function f as mapping values in D
to values in R and write it as

   $f : D \Rightarrow R$

   Let us consider an example where D is the set of integers 0. . .5, and R is the
set of integers 0 and 1, and f maps even values on to 0 and odd values on to 1.
We can draw the sets D and R as ovals enclosing values, and use arrows to
represent the mapping of individual values as shown in Fig. 3.1. We view f as
the set of ordered pairs:

   $f = \{⟨0,0⟩,⟨1,1⟩,⟨2,0⟩,⟨3,1⟩,⟨4,0⟩,⟨5,1⟩\}$

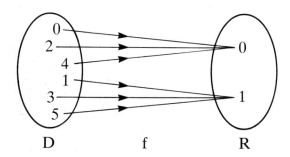

Fig. 3.1 — A function as a mapping.

The set itself is unordered and could equally well be written

   $f = \{⟨0,0⟩,⟨2,0⟩,⟨4,0⟩,⟨1,1⟩,⟨3,1⟩,⟨5,1⟩\}$

Given a function as a set of ordered pairs, we can obtain the domain and
range sets simply by collecting up all the values of first or second components thus

   $D = \{0,1,2,3,4,5,\}$ $R = \{0,1\}$

   In general, we say in Predicate Calculus notation that the domain D and
range of a function f satisfies

   $(\forall x)$ $(x \in D) \leftrightarrow (\exists y) (⟨x,y⟩ \in f)$
   $(\forall y)$ $(y \in R) \leftarrow (\exists x) (⟨x,y⟩ \in f)$

Here the symbol $\in$ means 'is a member of', as in standard set notation.
   In order that a set of ordered pairs should represent a function, they must
associate only one value with any argument value. Thus

   $\{⟨0,1⟩,⟨0,0⟩,⟨0,3⟩,⟨1,2⟩, ... \}$

is not a function, since it associates three values with 0. In general we can write this condition as

$$(\forall x,y,z)\,(\langle x,y\rangle \in f)\, \wedge\, (\langle x,z\rangle \in f)\, \rightarrow (y=z)$$

A function may map many values from a domain on to the same range value, as in the example of 'f' in Fig. 3.1; that is, it can be a 'many-to-one' mapping. It cannot be a 'one-to-many' mapping. It may, however, be a *one-to-one* mapping. In this case each value in the domain is associated with a unique value in the range and vice versa. For example the function which associates $1 + x$ with each value of x is one-to-one. Such functions can be *inverted* merely by drawing the arrows in the mapping diagram the other way and using R as the domain of the new function f~ and D as its range. The function is called the inverse of f and it satisfies

$$(\forall x)\; f^{\sim}(f(x)) = f(f^{\sim}(x)) = x$$

For example if the function g associates $1 + x$ with x so that

$$g = \{\langle 0,1\rangle,\langle 1,2\rangle,\langle 2,3\rangle,\ldots\}$$

then the inverse associates $x - 1$ with x so that

$$g^{\sim} = \{\langle 1,0\rangle,\langle 2,1\rangle,\langle 3,2\rangle,\ldots\}$$

Thus we obtain the inverse function just by reversing each ordered pair. Note that if the function were not one-to-one then this would produce a one-to-many mapping, which would not be a function.

3.2.2 Functions of multiple arguments

We now need to generalise our definition so as to allow functions of multiple arguments. We do this by the device of bundling up the 'n' arguments into an ordered *n-tuple,* which we can consider as one argument. Consider the subtraction function diff(x,y). We treat it as a mapping from the 2-tuple $\langle x,y\rangle$ onto the integers. Considered as a set of ordered pairs, it can be written thus:

$$\text{diff} = \{\langle\langle 5,3\rangle,2\rangle,\langle\langle 6,3\rangle,3\rangle,\langle\langle 4,5\rangle,-1\rangle\ldots\}$$

If instead we have a function of four arguments 'h(x,y,z,w)', then we use a mapping from 4-tuples $\langle x,y,z,w\rangle$. We are familiar with this device in programming. If we wish to cut down the number of arguments to a procedure or function, and they are all of the same type, then in Fortran we can pass an array as a parameter, and store the values in the array instead of passing them separately. More generally, if we allow the arguments to be of different types, then in Pascal we can pass a record as a parameter, and store the values as separate components of the record. In fact in mathematics the n-tuple is the abstraction corresponding to a record in computing. Its components are each drawn from domains of a particular type, as for a record. The only difference is that its components are identified by position instead of by name. The relational data model, considered in Chapter 6, works with sets of n-tuples, with correspond to files of records held on the computer.

3.2.3 The Cartesian product

In order to define the type of an n-tuple more precisely we need the notion of a 'Cartesian product'. Given sets D1 and D2 then the set of all possible ordered 2-tuples $\langle x,y \rangle$, taking x from D1 and y from D2, is defined to be the Cartesian product of D1 and D2. For example the Cartesian product of D1 {1,6} with D2 {2,4,7} is $\{\langle 1,2 \rangle, \langle 6,2 \rangle, \langle 1,4 \rangle, \langle 6,4 \rangle, \langle 1,7 \rangle, \langle 6,7 \rangle\}$, which has $2 \times 3 = 6$ values. If there are m different values in D1 and n in D2 then there will be $m \times n$ values in their Cartesian product. Thus it is written using a large X as 'D1 X D2' and read as 'D1 cross D2'. We can extend this to N sets giving D1 X D2 X D3 X . . . DN, whose elements are tuples with N components, the first from D1 and so on. The Cartesian product operation is associative, but it is not commutative.

We can now write an example type description for a function of four arguments, taken from three distinct domains as

f4: integer X real X char X integer $\Rightarrow$ boolean

In Pascal we would write this as

function f4(A1:integer; A2: real; Ae:char; A4:integer):boolean;

We can now define a *relation* over N domains, as a subset of the Cartesian product over those domains, i.e. it is a set of n-tuples giving associations between values from the domains. Formally speaking, a function is a special case of a relation, where no two tuples with the same values for the first $N - 1$ domains have different values for the Nth domain (which acts as the range of the function). A function of one argument can be viewed as a set of ordered pairs, which is a special case of a relation of 2-tuples. Thus, considered as a relation, f is a subset of $D \times R$. We shall return to this correspondence in Chapter 6, when we look at binary relations.

3.3 COMPOSITION OF FUNCTIONS: THE COMPOUND STATEMENT

Suppose we have a function $f:D \Rightarrow R$ and a function $g:R \Rightarrow S$ then we can define a new function $g.f:D \Rightarrow S$, which is the *composition* of g and f, such that

$$(g.f) (x) = g(f(x))$$

If we look at it in terms of mappings then we see that we are merely extending arrows and removing the intermediate set (see Fig. 3.2).

Composition of functions is associative, so that $(g.f).h = g.(f.h)$. However, it is not commutative, that is, in general $g.f \neq f.g$. If the functions concerned are one-to-one, then we can define an inverse to the composed function just by reversing the arrows, so that

$$(g.f)^{\sim} = f^{\sim} . g^{\sim}$$

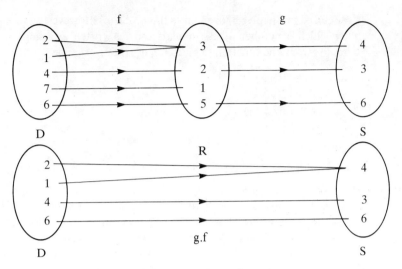

Fig. 3.2 – Composition of mappings.

Let us now see how this relates to the use in Pascal of the compound statement, which contains a sequence of statements bracketed between 'begin' and 'end'. Consider the following piece of Pascal:

```
function f1(x:D):R;
begin f1 := 2 * x + 5 end;
function f2(y:R):S;
begin f2 := 3 * y – 7 end;
function f3(z:S):T;
begin f3 := 8 – z end;
```

{main program}	{version 2}	{version 3}
begin	begin	begin
x := 3;	x := 3;	writeln(f3(f2(f1(3))))
y := 2 * x + 5 ;	y := f1(x);	end;
z := 3 * y – 7;	z := f2(y);	
w := 8 – z;	w := f3(z);	
writeln(w);	writeln(w);	
end;	end;	

We see above the three different equivalent forms of the main program. The first two versions work by successive assignment, using a compound statement. The third version uses no assignment, and just builds up an expression by function application. If we could extend Pascal to use function composition we could write this as:

writeln((f3.f2.f1) (3));

This simple syntax does not extend to the composition of functions with more than one argument (the use of 'Curried functions', as in the KRC language discussed in Chapter 5, overcomes this problem). However, we do see the principle by which a number of assignments can be written as a single expression with results from one function fed into the next. For example

    y := f1(x,3);
    z := f2(y,x);
    w := f3(z,y+2);
    writeln(w);

becomes

    writeln(f3(f2(f1(x,3),x), f1(x,3)+2));

Written in *prefix* form, that is, with the functional symbols before the arguments, this is rather hard to read because of the brackets. However, let us take the case where f1 is addition, f2 is multiplication and f3 is subtraction and write the expression in *infix* form, with the corresponding function symbols (+, *, −) between their arguments. We then get a more normal looking arithmetic expression:

    writeln(((x+3)*x) − (x+3+2));

The only snag with this example is that the value of 'x+3' is computed twice. There are ways of avoiding this in functional notation, as we shall see later in this chapter.

3.4 RESTRICTION AND UNION OF FUNCTIONS: THE 'IF' STATEMENT

We have seen how to represent compound statements. Another key construct in structured programming is the conditional statement, e.g. 'if P then S1 else S2', where P is a boolean and S1 and S2 are statements. In functional programming, we use a *conditional expression* instead, which has one of two values V1 or V2, depending on whether its boolean argument P is true or false. Thus for example we write

    y = (if x > 0 then x else −x)

for an expression whose value is the unsigned value of x. If we used a conditional statement we would instead use two alternative assignments to y thus:

    if x > 0 then y := x else y := −x;

Another example finds the greatest of two numbers, x1 and x2:

    (if x1 > x2 then x1 else x2)

Note that we cannot leave off the 'else', as we are able to do in ordinary programming.

In general a conditional expression can be thought of as defining a new function G in terms of two existing functions F1 and F2:

    G(x) = if P(x) then F1(x) else F2(x)

If x falls in the set for which P(x) is true, then G(x) behaves like F1(x); otherwise it behaves like F2(x). If we now consider the functions in terms of mappings, then we see that we are performing the disjoint union of two sets of ordered pairs. We are, so to speak, 'adding together' the definitions of F1 and F2 to form G.

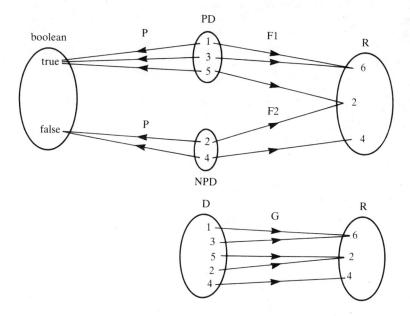

Fig. 3.3 – Union as addition of mappings.

Figure 3.3 shows the process of forming G from F1 and F2 as an addition of mappings. If we view it in terms of ordered pairs then

F1 = {⟨1,6⟩,⟨3,6⟩,⟨5,2⟩}
F2 = {⟨2,2⟩,⟨4,4⟩}
G = F1 union F2 = {⟨1,6⟩,⟨3,6⟩,⟨5,2⟩,⟨2,2⟩,⟨4,4⟩}

3.4.1 Use of the restrict operator

In general F1 may apply to a wider range of integers, including those in the range of F2. In order to make the functions disjoint we must use the *restrict* operator to reduce the set of pairs F1, so that its domain is just the extension of P (as defined in Chapter 2), which we call PD. (The extension of not P we will call NPD.) Then, considering F1 as a set of pairs with domain D, we can derive a subset of F1, consisting of just those pairs whose domain is PD by:

F1 restrict P = (PD X R) intersect F1

Here the Cartesian product PD X R contains every possible ordered pair that can occur in functions from domain PD onto R. We intersect this with F1, in order to eliminate any other ordered pairs outside the domain PD.

Thus in general the conditional expression

if P(x) then F1(x) else F2(x)

corresponds to G(x), where G is given by the union of functions:

G = (F1 restrict P) union (F2 restrict not P)

We should note that the union of the functions is defined even if F is a partial function for some values outside its restricted domain. For example

if x = 0 then 1 else 1/x

is a total function even though 1/x is undefined at x = 0. Thus, when evaluating a conditional expression, we must be careful to evaluate the predicate P(x) first, and then either F1 or F2; we must not evaluate F1 and F2 first, and then choose the result. This would be inefficient anyway, but if we represent a conditional expression as though it were a function of three arguments

cond(P(x), F1(x), F2(x))

then the normal method of evaluating all arguments before calling the function 'cond' would fail.

3.5 FORMS OF APPLICATIVE SYNTAX: THE LAMBDA NOTATION

So far we have dealt with expressions involving application of functions and the use of conditionals. However, function application only allows us to apply existing functions, so we need a constructor for new functions. In the Lambda Calculus this is done using the greek symbol lambda; the process is known as 'function abstraction'. Let us see some examples.

We can make a function g of one argument (x) by prefixing the argument by 'lambda', and following it by '.' and then an expression for the result:

g = lambda x. 2*x + 3

We can apply it to various integers to produce results e.g.

g(10) = 23   g(1) = 5 etc. . . .

We can make a function h by

h = lambda x. if x > 4 then g(x) else −x

and apply it giving:

h(10) = 23   h(1) = −1

We do not have to name a lambda expression in the way that we name functions in programming languages. In fact a lambda expression denotes an unnamed function. Just as 2 * 3 denotes an integer and chr(48) denotes a character, so 'lambda x. x*3' denotes a function from integers to integers. We do not have to name the function, and in fact we can put a lambda expression anywhere in an expression we could put a function symbol, thus:

(lambda x.x*3)((lambda y. if y > 4 then y + 2 else 1) (5))
= (lambda x.x*3) (7) = 21

We can now write a syntax for expressions thus

⟨exp⟩	::=	⟨const⟩ |	e.g. 2, true
		⟨var⟩ |	e.g. x
		(⟨exp⟩⟨op⟩⟨exp⟩) |	e.g. (2+x), (3−x)
		⟨fn⟩(⟨exp-list⟩) |	e.g. f(3,2+x)
		⟨fn⟩	e.g. f, lambda x.x+2
⟨exp-list⟩	::=	⟨exp⟩ | ⟨exp⟩,⟨exp-list⟩	
⟨fn⟩	::=	⟨function symbol⟩ |	
		lambda ⟨parlist⟩.⟨body⟩	
⟨body⟩	::=	⟨exp⟩	
⟨parlist⟩	::=	⟨var⟩ | ⟨var⟩,⟨parlist⟩	

Fig. 3.4 − Applicative syntax using lambda expressions.

We see that a lambda expression consists of the symbol lambda followed by a list of one or more parameters, followed by a dot which separates them from the body of the lambda expression. The body can itself be any expression, including another lambda expression. In general an expression is made up from constants, variables, infix operators ⟨op⟩, function symbols and lambda expressions. Lambda expressions may take functions as arguments and yield functions as results. For example consider

G = lambda P.(lambda x. if P(x) then 2*x else x/2)

(G(lambda y. y>2)) (5) =
(lambda x. if (lambda y.y>2) (x) then 2*x else x/2) (5) =
    2 * 5 = 10

Here G is a function-producing function. When applied to a function it produces another function. We may also have functions which take integers as arguments and produce functions, and vice versa. For example

H = lambda n.(lambda x.x−n)
FF = lambda f. 2*f(8) − f(f(8))

In programming languages we are used to functions that take functions as arguments, as in FF, but not to those such as G and H that produce functions as results. Only languages based on the lambda calculus, such as LISP and POP−2, have this ability to create new functions at run-time.

We can define our combinator '.' for function composition, as in 'f.g', by the lambda expression

    lambda f,g.(lambda x.f(g(x)))

We can now see how to use the process of function abstraction to write expressions which avoid evaluating items twice. For example, if we consider the expression we looked at earlier

    $((x+3)*x) - ((x+3)+2)$

we could write it as

    (lambda p,q. q*p $-$ (q+2)) (x,x+3)

The point is that x+3 is evaluated once only and then used in several places. Here 'function abstraction' consists of turning an expression '(q*p $-$ (q+2))' into a function, by prefixing it with 'lambda p,q'.

3.6 WRITING RECURSIVE DEFINITIONS IN LAMBDA NOTATION

We have seen how we could use lambda expressions to write an applicative expression which computes the same result as a sequence of assignments and conditional statements. However, we cannot perform the equivalent of iteration, which is the one construct of structured programming that we have not covered. To do this we must allow recursive definitions for lambda expressions. We do not require any new syntax, except that which gives a name to a lambda expression, so that we can apply it to itself. Also, in order to make the recursion terminate, we shall need to use conditional expressions.

For example, we can write the definition of the factorial function as

    fac = lambda n. if n = 0 then 1 else n * fac(n$-$1)

Thus

    fac(3) = 3*fac(2) = 3*2*fac(1) = 3*2*1*fac(0) = 3*2*1*1 = 6

We may note in passing that this example is commonly used in textbooks on recursion because of its simplicity. However, in practice it is unlikely to be of any value above n = 8, since it breaks the limits for storage of integers! A definition of the combinatorial function C(n,r) (the number of choices of r items from n) by

    combin = lambda n,r. fac(n) div (fac(r) * fac(n$-$r))

would almost certainly cause integer overflow! However, we can write a much better definition recursively as

    combin = lambda n,r. if r = 1 then n
                    else (n*combin(n$-$1,r$-$1)) div r

This is also much closer to an inductive definition as used in mathematics, or to the kind of definition used in Prolog.

3.6.1 Downgoing and upgoing recursion

There are two styles for writing recursive functions, which we shall call 'down-going' and 'upgoing'. The 'downgoing' style keeps breaking the problem down recursively into a simpler version, until a terminal case is reached. Only then can it start to build up the answer, as intermediate results are passed back to the calling functions. The version of 'fac' given earlier was written using this technique. In 'upgoing' recursion the intermediate results are computed at each stage of the recursion, thus building the answer up and passing it in a 'work-space parameter', until the terminal case is reached. At this stage the answer is already complete and it has merely to be passed back to the top level calling function. We can write an 'upgoing' version of 'fac' thus:

$$fac = lambda\ n.\ facn(n,1)$$
$$facn = lambda\ n,w.\ if\ n = 0\ then\ w\ else\ facn(n-1\ ,n*w)$$

Here 'w' is the 'workspace parameter' used to build up the results. Since the original function has only one parameter we have to define an auxiliary function 'facn' with the extra parameter and we also have to initialise the parameter by the first call of facn.

The evaluation can be done by substitution:

$$
\begin{aligned}
fac(3) = \ &facn(3,1) = \\
&facn(2,3*1) = \\
&facn(1,2*3*1) = \\
&facn(0,1*2*3*1) \\
&= 1*2*3*1 = 6
\end{aligned}
$$

Here we see the result being built up in the workspace parameter, and we note that the value is known at each stage, even though we have written it as e.g. $2 * 3 * 1$. Instead, with the downgoing version of fac, we get intermediate results like $3 * 2 * fac(1)$, which cannot be evaluated till we know $fac(1)$.

3.7 RECURSIVE LIST PROCESSING

A *list* is a sequence of items, which we shall write separated by commas and enclosed in square brackets, thus: [1, 5, 9, 8]; [jam, butter, honey]. The length of a list is the number of items in it, which is usually unknown until run-time; thus it is very difficult to allocate fixed storage for lists, as one does for arrays.

Instead of asking for the nth item of a list, as one can for an array, we access the elements in sequence, one at a time, by using the two basic operations 'car' and 'cdr'. For a list l, the function car(l) returns the leading item, while the function cdr(l) returns the remainder of the list, without the first item. Thus:

$$car([jam, butter, honey]) = jam$$
$$cdr([jam, butter, honey]) = [butter, honey]$$

Hence car(cdr(l)) gives the first item of the remainder, which is the second item of l. Similarly car(cdr(cdr(l))) gives the third item of l.

Thus a list is a sequential data structure which can be accessed one item at a time, rather like a sequential file. A list of integers, or names, or other atomic items, is called a *linear list;* it is not suitable for direct access. However, a list can contain lists which contain other lists and so on, thus representing a *tree* whose branches form sub-trees such as:

$$[\ [bread, \ [jam,honey]] \ , \ [chips,[fish,sausage,egg]] \ ]$$

It is possible to organise information in such a tree structure so that it can be found quickly, by looking at only a fraction of the items. In particular there are structures called binary trees and B-trees, which serve this purpose and can be used to index and locate data in a database. We will not say any more about them, but they are described in Wiederhold(1977) and Date(1981).

3.7.1 Sequential access by recursion

The nice thing about lists is that they have a recursive structure, since the 'cdr' of a list is normally another list. Hence we can write simple and elegant recursive functions that operate on lists. For example, suppose that we want to write a function 'select(n,s)', whose result is the nth item of the list s:

select = lambda n,s. if n=1 then car(s) else select(n−1, cdr(s))

Thus, for example,

```
select(3, [jam,butter,honey])
= select(2, cdr([jam,butter,honey]))
= select(1, cdr(cdr([jam,butter,honey])))
= car(cdr(cdr([jam,butter,honey])))
= car(cdr([butter,honey])) = car([honey]) = honey
```

However, this function will fail if there are fewer than 'n' items in the list. In order to test for this we need the standard predicate *null(s)*, which returns the value 'true' if s is the empty list, and there are no more items. The *empty list* is written as [], signifying a list with no items. It is illegal to apply the functions car and cdr to it. It behaves very like the empty set in set theory; or like an empty file, with just an end file marker, in data processing. Thus a better version of the function 'select' would be:

```
select = lambda n,s. if null(s) then []
            else  if n ⩽ 1  then car(s)
            else               select(n−1, cdr(s))
```

Here we have chosen to signify the absence of an item by returning [] in its place; e.g. select(5,[jam,butter,honey]) = [].

3.7.2 List construction

Besides accessing the elements of a list, we need to be able to construct lists.

This is done by using he constructor function *cons(x,s)*, which makes a new list whose first item is 'x' and whose remainder is 's':

cons(paste, [jam,butter]) = [paste,jam,butter]
cons(paste, [])   = [paste]

If we wish to construct a list from its separate elements, then we start with the empty list and keep adding them on with 'cons', thus:

cons(jam, cons(butter,[])) = cons(jam, [butter]) =[jam,butter]

People are often confused by a list such as [honey], containing only one item. This is *not* the same as the atomic item 'honey'; nor is it the same as the list [[honey]], which is formed by cons([honey],[]). The result of doing 'car' on each of these is different.

3.7.3 Implementation

Since a list consists of a variable number of items, it is conveniently represented by a *linked* representation, using a pointer to a *list cell* containing the first item, which is followed by a pointer to the cell containing the second item, and so on, as in Fig. 3.5. Notice that every application of 'cons' produces a new list cell, which is shown in the figure as a rectangular box with two compartments. Two such cells may share a pointer to the same sub-list or remainder list, as in the figure, where two cells share the same remainder list [butter,honey]. This is called a common sub-list, or shared sub-structure. It is very important in applicative programming not to overwrite the contents of this shared list structure, as otherwise both lists will be altered. If we wish to make a new list, by inserting an extra item, then we must copy the leading list cells, and then 'cons' the new item onto the pointer to the remainder. For example, consider the function insert(x, n, s), which inserts at item 'x' into the 'n'th position of the list 's', as shown in Fig. 3.5.

insert = lambda x,n,s. if null(s) or n=1 then cons(x,s)
              else cons(car(s), insert(x, n−1, cdr(s)))

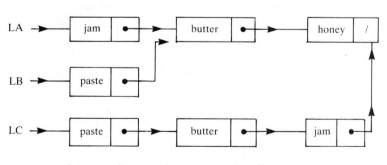

LA = cons(jam, cons(butter, cons(honey, [])))

LB = cons(paste, cdr(LA))

LC = insert(jam, 3, LB)

Fig. 3.5 − Pointer representation of lists.

3.7.4 Representing lists in Pascal

For those familiar with Pascal we give below the definitions of the functions 'car', 'cdr' and 'cons'. The function 'cons' uses 'new' to allocate storage for a record of type 'pconsrec', representing the list cell, into which it places the item and the remainder pointer. The functions 'car' and 'cdr' just extract the values from the components 'hd' and 'tl' of the record respectively. We use the Pascal null reference 'nil' to represent the empty list. Further examples can be found in Grogono (1980), and Moore (1980).

```
type pconsrec = ↑ consrec;
     consrec = record
                    hd : integer;   {the head}
                    tl  : pconsrec  {the link or tail}
                end;

function cons(x : integer; y : pconsrec) : pconsrec;
var res : pconsrec;
begin
     new(res);
     res ↑ .hd:=x; res ↑ .tl:=y;
     cons:=res;
end;

function car(y : pconsrec) : integer;
begin car:=y ↑ .hd end;

function cdr(y : pconsrec) : pconsrec;
begin cdr:=y ↑ .tl end;
```

Using these definitions we can write in Pascal a definition of 'insert':

```
function insert(x:integer; n:integer; s:pconsrec) :pconsrec;
begin
  if (s=nil) or (n⇐s) then insert := cons(x,s)
  else insert := cons(car(s), insert(x, n−1, cdr(s)))
end;
```

This is very like the lambda calculus version, except that it uses conditional statements starting with 'insert :='.

Note that the Pascal definition of 'car' can only deliver an object of type integer. Our lambda calculus version is more general than this, since it will allow 'cons' to construct trees, for which 'car' may deliver either a list or (at the tip) an integer; this is awkward to express in Pascal.

The following three axioms can be written down about car, cdr and cons.

$$(\forall x,y) \; car(cons(x,y)) = x$$
$$(\forall x,y) \; cdr(cons(x,y)) = y$$
$$(\forall y) \quad not(y = [\,]) \rightarrow (cons(car(y),cdr(y)) = y)$$

3.8 STYLES OF RECURSIVE FUNCTIONS

If we look back at the upgoing and downgoing versions of the factorial function considered previously, we see that one big difference between the two versions is that the result is calculated in a different sequence. In one case we get $3*2*1*1$ and in the other $1*2*3*1$. Because multiplication is commutative it makes little difference in this case. However, with another function, such as the list constructor 'cons', it produces different results. Consider two versions of a function to copy a list:

$$dcopy = lambda\ s.\ if\ s = [\ ]\ then\ [\ ]$$
$$else\ cons(car(s),\ dcopy(cdr(s)))$$

$$ucopy = lambda\ s.\ ucop(s,[\ ])$$
$$ucop\ \ = lambda\ s,w.\ if\ s = [\ ]\ then\ w$$
$$else\ ucop(cdr(s),\ cons(car(s),w))$$

If we follow the evaluation of these two versions on the list $[2, 5, 7]$ we have:

$$dcopy([2, 5, 7]) = cons(2,dcopy([5, 7]))$$
$$= cons(2,cons(5,dcopy([7])))$$
$$= cons(2,cons(5,cons(7,dcopy([\ ]))))$$
$$= cons(2,cons(5,cons(7,[\ ])))$$
$$= cons(2,cons(5,[7])) = cons(2,[5, 7])$$
$$= [2, 5, 7]$$

This copies the list in the correct sequence. If we now evaluate the upgoing version we get:

$$ucopy([2, 5, 7]) = ucop([2, 5, 7],[\ ])$$
$$= ucop([5, 7],cons(2,[\ ]))$$
$$= ucop([7],cons(5,[2]))$$
$$= ucop([\ ],cons(7,[5, 2]))$$
$$= [7, 5, 2]$$

Thus the copy is produced in the reverse order! If we think about it this is inevitable, because the upgoing version has to start constructing the list with the first members before it knows the last members. The downgoing version delays construction until it knows the last member.

3.8.1 Hints for writing recursive definitions

The process of writing a recursive function definition proceeds in stages. The definitions always look easy by hindsight but they are not always so easy to think up. People used to assignment programming have an initial difficulty, especially with downgoing functions. The difficulty seems to be that, at a stage where we do not know if our definition of the function will work, we have to recall the function using that same definition. The trick is to use the same method that is used for establishing the correctness of a recursive function, namely to assume that we already have a function that works for $n - 1$ or cdr(l), and use this version to construct a definition that works for the next case (i.e. n or l). The stages for writing functions in the two styles are as follows.

Downgoing recursion
(1) Write the definition for the terminal case e.g. the number 0 or the empty list or a list of one element.
(2) For the non-terminal case assume you have a definition that works for a case nearer the trivial case (n−1 or the remainder of a list). Use this to construct an expression for the next case up.
(3) Combine 1 and 2 with a conditional expression. Test it with examples.

Upgoing recursion
(1) Invent a function with extra workspace parameter(s), especially one to build up the result.
(2) For the terminal case set value of function = workspace parameter.
(3) For the non-terminal case recall the function with the new parameters expressed in terms of the old.
(4) Call the function with starting values for workspace parameters.
(5) Test it with examples and adjust starting values if necessary.

3.8.2 Tree recursion

There is another type of recursion, which has to be used even in assignment programming. We call this 'tree recursion'. It is used to traverse a tree structure, that is, a list whose elements may themselves be lists, and so on. In order to determine the tips of such a structure we need an extra predicate *atom(l)*, which is true if l is an element which has no components (i.e. the selectors car and cdr cannot be applied), but false if the element l is a list. Thus atom([2 5 7]) will be false but atom(2) will be true. Note also that atom([]) is true, since we cannot apply car or cdr to the empty list. Thus 'atom' is false for all lists except the null list.

Let us now consider an example which uses downgoing recursion to copy a tree.

    tcop = lambda t. if atom(t) then t
        else cons(tcop(car(t)),tcop(cdr(t)))

Consider another example to count the number of tips in a tree.

    ntip = lambda t. if null(t) then 0 else if atom(t) then 1
        else ntip(car(t)) + ntip(cdr(t))

For example:

    ntip([[jam,bread],[butter]])
    = ntip([jam,bread]) + ntip([[butter]])
    = ntip(jam) + ntip([bread]) + ntip([butter]) + ntip([])
    = 1 + ntip(bread) + ntip([]) + ntip(butter) + ntip([]) + 0
    = 1 + 1 + 0 + 1 + 0 + 0 = 3

Looking at these two examples we may write down some hints for tree recursion.

Tree recursion (downgoing)
(1) Use atom(t), and maybe also null(t) to test for the terminal case.
(2) For the general case assume that your function works on both car(t) and cdr(t), and write an expression that combines them.

3.8.3 How to manage without assignment and 'goto'

It is time to look back at the class of lambda expressions that we can write, and to compare them with ordinary programs. A beginner who is brought up on a version of BASIC sees the use of 'goto' and assignment as fundamental, yet we have managed to do without them. How is this?

Instead of changing the values of variables by assignment, we are re-calling functions with changed values for their parameters. Instead of using 'goto' for jumping forward in conditional statements or looping backwards in iteration, we have used conditional expressions and recursion.

With hindsight we can see destructive assignments and jumps ('goto's) as low level concepts, which are used to get programs running on current (von Neumann) hardware with small memories. Those familiar with implementing recursion will realise that it takes up space on a stack, and that the binding mechanism used to address the position of the current variable on this stack could slow down execution. Instead, it is much quicker on conventional hardware to keep the address of a variable fixed and to overwrite its value; likewise it is quicker to jump back to repeat an instruction than to execute a procedure call.

It is in fact possible to compile upgoing recursive functions and translate them into a version using iteration and assignment. This was pointed out by McCarthy in his original classic paper. Many LISP compilers do this; the process is known as 'removing tail recursion'. This process is rather satisfying, since it allows us to express our abstract description in functional form, yet attain reasonable speed on current hardware.

As an example, consider the definition of a function to compute the sum of the squares of the first n elements in a list:

```
ssql = lambda n,s. ssf(n,s,0,1)
ssf  = lambda n,s,w,i. if i > n then w
       else ssf(n,cdr(s), w + sqr(car(s)),i+1)
```

The corresponding iterative version in Pascal would be:

```
function ssql(n:integer; s:list):integer;
var w,i : integer;
begin
   w := 0; i := 1;
   while not (i>n) do
   begin
      w := w + sqr(car(s));
      s := cdr(s);
      i := i + 1
   end;
   ssql := w
end;
```

Hence we see how, instead of recalling the function with new parameters, we alter the current values by assignment and jump back to repeat the code from the beginning of the 'while' loop.

3.9 SOME SET AND LIST PROCESSING FUNCTIONS IN LAMBDA NOTATION

We have seen recursive functions to copy lists and trees. In this section we look at some other classic functions, and then in the next chapter we will consider how to write equivalent versions in Prolog notation.

First consider the 'append' function, which concatenates two lists together to make one list of all the items in sequence. For example: append([jam,bread], [butter]) = [jam, bread, butter].

    append = lambda la,lb. if null(la) then lb
                  else cons(car(la),append(cdr(la),lb))

This uses downgoing recursion. Note that it copies the cells of list la, using 'cons' to construct new ones, but it does not copy the cells of lb. Instead it uses a shared pointer to the list structure. We can evaluate it thus:

    append([jam, bread],[butter])
    = cons(jam,append([bread],[butter]))
    = cons(jam,cons(bread,append([],[butter])))
    = cons(jam,cons(bread,[butter]))
    = [jam, bread, butter]

3.9.1 Member

Next consider the function 'member(x,s)', which is true if x is a member of the list s. For example, member(honey, [jam, bread, honey]) is true. If s represents a set then we are testing for set membership ($x \in s$). Note that the definition does not say anything about the types of x or of s, as it would be in Pascal. One of the reasons for the popularity of Lambda-Calculus-based languages like LISP and POP–2 is that a single definition of 'member' does for a wide variety of types of data structure, whereas in Pascal many such definitions are required. The price, of course, is paid in extra run-time type tests.

    member = lambda x,s. if null(s) then false
                  else if x = car(s) then true
                  else member(x,cdr(s))

There are two interesting variants of this algorithm. In the first case let us use an 'orelse' operator, which is defined to behave like a logical 'or', but which is evaluated left to right, so that

    A orelse B   =   if (A = true) then true else B

Such an operator was suggested by McCarthy. Then we can define member, without using conditional expressions, as:

member = lambda x,s. not null(s) andif(x=car(s) orelse member(x,cdr(s)))

where

A andif B   =   if (A = false) then false else B

defines left-to-right evaluation of 'and'.

Note the ordering of the tests with 'andif' and 'orelse', so that we do not apply 'car' or 'cdr' to an empty list.

Another variant of the algorithm applies where the list s is ordered, e.g. integers or strings in ascending sequence.

member = lambda x,s. if (null(s) orelse x $<$ car(s)) then false
          else (x=car(s) orelse member(x,cdr(s)))

This version relies on the ordering of the list so that if x $<$ car(s) it must be less than all remaining elements of the list. Thus it will fail sooner for items that are not in the list.

3.9.2 Intersection

Now consider a function intsec(la,lb) which produces the intersection of two lists considered as sets.

intsec = lambda la,lb. if null(la) then nil
          elseif member(car(la),lb)
          then cons(car(la),intsec(cdr(la),lb))
          else intsec(cdr(la),lb)

Here, for example,

intsec($[1, 2, 3]$,$[1, 5]$)
= cons(1,intsec($[2, 3]$,$[1, 5]$))
= cons(1,intec($[3]$,$[1,5]$))
= cons(1,intec($[]$,$[1,5]$))
= cons(1,$[]$) = $[1]$

The function works by taking each element of the first list and looking for a match in the second list, using 'member'. It is very similar to one of the algorithms used for a join of relations (Chapter 8), since in fact 'join' is a generalised intersection.

We can write a more efficient algorithm if we know that both lists are ordered.

intsec = lambda la,lb. if null(la) or null(lb) then nil
elseif car(la) = car(lb) then cons(car(la),intsec(cdr(la),cdr(lb)))
elseif car(la) $<$ car(lb) then intsec(cdr(la),lb)
else   intsec(la,cdr(lb))

The functions for set union and set difference can be written similarly. A predicate to test whether one list is a subset of another is easily written:

subset = lambda la,lb. if null(la) then true
    else(member(car(la),lb) andif subset(cdr(la),lb))

A predicate to test set equality can then be written as

equal = lambda la,lb. subset(la,lb) andif subset(lb,la)

We can write a more efficient version if the lists are ordered

equal = lambda la,lb. (null(la) andif null(lb))
   orelse (not null(lb) andif
     (car(la) = car(lb)) andif
      equal(cdr(la),cdr(lb)))

As with most of these examples, one has to be careful when dealing with the null case.

3.10 SUMMARY

We have seen how the abstract notions of ordered n-tuples and mappings, as used by mathematicians, relate to our notions of functions, as used in programming. We have also seen the definition of a relation, which is extensively used in database theory. We have studied the use of lambda expressions, using conditional expressions and recursion, which enable us to write programs without destructive assignment. We have seen how to represent list structures in terms of the functions 'cons', 'car' and 'cdr', and the predicates 'null' and 'atom'. Finally we have seen how to write lambda expressions to manipulate list structures without overwriting them, and we have used two different styles of recursive functions.

The use of function composition and application will be important in considering 'functional programming' in Chapter 5, and the database query languages that use this style, in Chapters 8 and 10. The use of list processing without assignment will allow us to define list processing in the predicate calculus, and to apply it in a language like Prolog, as explained in the next chapter.

4

Representing programs
by clauses: Prolog

4.1 HISTORY OF LOGIC PROGRAMMING

In this chapter we shall explore how Predicate Calculus and resolution can be used as the basis of a remarkable programming language, Prolog, which also has applications to database queries. Early attempts to use a resolution theorem-prover as a universal engine proved awkward. Green *et al.* (1969) developed one such engine (QA4), but a lot of work had to be done on massaging clauses by hand, and careful selection of axioms, to guide the theorem-prover. As an alternative, Hewitt and Sussman at MIT developed PLANNER (Hewitt 1972), which adapted the list processing language LISP to use 'backtrack' programming; this explored chains of alternative hypotheses in a depth-first fashion, by going down branches until it encountered failure, and then going back up to a previous node and down another branch, and so on. At first sight this is very different from resolution, but then Colmerauer and others (1973) developed Prolog, a language for 'logic programming'. This was implemented using backtrack programming, but it could also be viewed as a resolution theorem-prover working on a restricted set of clauses, the so-called 'Horn clauses'. This interpretation reinforced the view, powerfully advocated by Kowalski (1979), that algorithms are made out of 'Logic + Control'.

This chapter starts by explaining the syntax of Prolog, and how to understand pieces of Prolog in terms of a search for data values to satisfy goals and sub-goals, which can be achieved in various alternative ways. We then see how to represent list processing operations in Prolog, using the notation of Chapter 3, and how to deal with more general structures containing records. We study the connection between resolution and the evaluation of Prolog, which shows its close relationship with the Predicate Calculus. We conclude by studying how to write various pieces of Prolog to process sets and lists.

4.2 ELEMENTS OF THE PROLOG LANGUAGE

Prolog allows us to write definitions of predicates in a restricted predicate calculus notation, which we can then execute, rather as if they were Lambda Calculus functions. Consider the predicate 'between(X,L,U)', which expresses the fact that the integer X lies between L and U, or is equal to one of them. Thus 'between(5,5,10)' is true and 'between(4,5,10)' is false. We shall define it recursively in Prolog as follows:

> between(X,L,U) :– X=L,L≤U.
> between(X,L,U) :– L<U, L1 is L+1, between(X,L1,U).

or in an alternative notation:

> between(X,L,U) if X=L and L≤U.
> between(X,L,U) if L<U and L1 is L+1 and between(X,L1,U).

The first definition says that X lies between L and U if X is equal to the lower bound L, and L is less than or equal to the upper bound U. The second definition is an alternative, to try if the first one fails. It says that X lies between L and U, if L is less than U, and if X lies between L+1 and U. It would actually be much quicker to test 'L<X and X≤U' instead of calling 'between' recursively, but the reason for using recursion will soon become apparent.

   If we wrote the definition of 'between' in Predicate Calculus notation, then we should just write it the other way round, thus:

> $(\forall X,L,U)$ eq(X,L) $\wedge$ le(L,U) $\rightarrow$ between(X,L,U)
> $(\forall X,L,U)$ lt(L,U) $\wedge$ between(X,plus(L,1),U) $\rightarrow$ between(X,L,U)

Here 'eq', 'le' and 'lt' are prefix forms of the predicates '=', '≤' and '<' respectively. In the Prolog version, the special predicate 'is' checks that the integer on the left is equal to the value of the arithmetic expression on the right. Thus, for example, '14 is 2+3*4' would be true. In the predicate calculus version we assume that the predicates 'eq', 'le' and 'lt' will work both on arithmetic expressions and on integers.

4.2.1 Execution of a Prolog query

Let us now see how our definition of 'between' is executed. In order to do this we need to know how to type a query to a Prolog interpreter. The query is written as one or more predicates (with arguments), separated by commas and terminated by a full stop. Unlike in predicate definitions, any variables are existentially quantified, and the interpreter will attempt to find values for them that satisfy the conjunction of the predicates. If it cannot find any such values, it fails and prints 'NO'. Queries are typed interactively in response to the prompt '?–' thus:

> ?– between(7,5,10).

The Prolog interpreter starts by trying the first definition of the predicate, and substituting the values for the variables; it then checks '7=5' which fails. Next it tries the second definition and checks '5<10', which succeeds, and goes on to check if 'between(7,6,10)'. This is like a recursive call, and again the first definition fails, this time on '7=6'; the other definition causes it to check if 'between(7,7,10)', and this time the first definition succeeds and the whole chain of inference is successful and the terminal prints 'YES'.

We have described it as a piece of reasoning, yet it is very close to the evaluation of a Lambda Calculus definition, thus:

$$\text{between} = \text{lambda } X,L,U. \text{ if } X=L \text{ and } L\leqslant U \text{ then true}$$
$$\text{else if } L<U \text{ then between}(X,L+1,U) \text{ else false}$$

For example, between(7,5,10) = between(7,6,10) = between(7,7,10) = true

4.2.2 Constructing alternative solutions

Execution of Prolog definitions is not always so simple. Consider what happens if we type:

?– between(Z,5,7).   { i.e. $(\exists Z)$ between(Z,5,7)? }

This time the first definition is matched by unification, as in Chapter 2, and Z is matched with X, and 5 with L. It then finds a value for X, and thus for Z, and prints:

Z= 5   YES

However, there are other possible solutions. If we ask for another possible value of Z (in most implementations, by typing ';'), then it will try the other definition and attempt to find data satisfying 'between(Z,6,7)'; this succeeds and it prints:

Z= 6   YES

After another semi-colon it prints 'Z= 7' and, after another, it attempts 'between (Z,8,7)', fails on both definitions and prints 'NO'.

This ability to construct values for what we normally consider to be 'input parameters' is special to Prolog. In a normal programming language, a call to 'between(Z,5,7)', with the value of Z undefined, would produce an error message, or else a misleading answer; in neither case would a value be found for Z. However, Prolog does not have magic powers! It cannot always find values to satisfy things. For example, if we give 'between' the more obvious definition:

between(X,L,U) :– L$\leqslant$X, X$\leqslant$U.

then the system will not construct data to satisfy '5$\leqslant$Z'; instead it reports an error. Our original definition is thus better for constructing answers, but it is worse for checking them, since it just enumerates all the integers between L and U! Hence the test 'between(10 000, 1, 10 000)' would be very slow! Unfortunately it is all too easy to write definitions like this in Prolog, which are very concise, yet end up doing an exhaustive trial and error search.

4.2.3 Prolog syntax

In general any calculus formula involving atomic predicates of the form:

atom1 $\wedge$ atom2 $\wedge$ ... atomN $\rightarrow$ atom

can be written in Prolog the other way round, terminated by '.' as:

atom :– atom1, atom2, ... atomN.

This may be read as:

atom if atom1 and atom2 and ... atomN

Here we use 'atom' to denote a predicate applied to arguments, as in the Predicate Calculus syntax given in Chapter 2.

The syntax of Prolog is thus extremely simple. It consists of a number of statements, starting on separate lines, and made up as follows:

⟨statement⟩ ::= ⟨atom⟩ . | ⟨atom⟩ :– ⟨atomlist⟩ .
⟨atomlist⟩   ::= ⟨atom⟩ | ⟨atom⟩ , ⟨atomlist⟩ | (⟨atomlist⟩ ; ⟨atomlist⟩)
⟨atom⟩   ::= ⟨pred⟩ | ⟨pred⟩ (⟨explist⟩)
⟨explist⟩   ::= ⟨exp⟩ | ⟨exp⟩ , ⟨explist⟩
⟨exp⟩   ::= ⟨const⟩ | ⟨var⟩ | ⟨fn⟩ (⟨explist⟩) | ⟨exp⟩ ⟨fn⟩ ⟨exp⟩
⟨query⟩   ::= ⟨atomlist⟩ .

In most versions of Prolog, constants start with a digit or a *lower-case* letter, while *variables* start with an *upper-case* letter, or else an underscore symbol. Variables used in statements (as opposed to queries) are universally quantified. Note that in the basic version of Prolog we cannot use negation. Also, as we shall see, there is strictly no need for 'or', but it is provided as a convenience, by typing a semi-colon instead of a comma. Note also that, just as in the first order predicate calculus, predicates cannot take other predicates as arguments (though there are ways round this). The advantage of this restricted form of the calculus is that we can use a simplified form of the resolution proof procedure, which is like evaluating recursive functions; this is explained in more detail later.

4.3 EVALUATION VIEWED AS GOAL-DIRECTED DEPTH-FIRST SEARCH

It is possible to view a piece of Prolog as a description of a sequence of goals to be achieved, and this gives us a good insight into the evaluation mechanism (Colmerauer 1983).

Thus the piece of Prolog

P(X) :– G1(X), G2(X,Y), G3(Y).
P(X) :– G4(X,Z), G5(Z).

can be interpreted as follows. In order to succeed with goal P, first prove goal G1, then goal G2, then goal G3; if any of these fail (say G3) then backtrack and see if a previous goal (G2) can be proved using a different instance of variable Y, and then re-try the current goal (G3); repeat this until the current goal succeeds, or else backtrack to one further (G1) and re-try the subsequent goals (G2,G3). If you can backtrack no further on this clause, then try the next clause and attempt its goals in order (G4,G5), and so on. If any clause succeeds, then report success and the current instantiation of the variables; but be prepared to treat this as failure and to be asked to go on and find the next combination of goals that succeeds.

As a simple example of this consider the definition:

P(X) :− between(X,5,7), between(X,7,10).

The first goal succeeds with X=5, but the second goal fails with this value for X. The first goal is then re-tried, and succeeds with X=6, but again the second goal fails. It is tried again, and succeeds with X=7, and this time both goals succeed.

We call this method 'goal-directed depth-first search'. It is very similar to 'backtrack programming' as used for solving a classic problem: the 'Eight Queens' Problem (Wirth 1971). For this problem there is a conjunction of eight separate goals to be achieved. Each goal is to plant a queen on one of the eight files of a chess board so that it attacks none of the queens on previous files. Unfortunately the position chosen for a queen to achieve its goal may interfere with the achievement of subsequent goals. For each goal there are at most eight ways of succeeding (one for each rank). One version of the program iterates over the eight files of the chess board, periodically backtracking to a previous board file and undoing the positions of the queens. Another version is written recursively; each time a queen is planted successfully the recursive function calls itself with a deeper level of recursion which terminates when it succeeds at level 8. If it fails at any level then it returns to the previous level, which tries the next position for its queen, and re-tries the recursive call.

The problem about using the depth-first mechanism is that the Prolog programmer gets to rely on knowing the order of evaluation, and takes short cuts which make Prolog look less like Predicate Calculus.

The commonest short cut is to leave out tests when one knows that previous clauses must have failed. For example consider the following predicate defining the price of the bus fare Y for X stages.

price(X,Y) :− X < 4, Y = 10.
price(X,Y) :− X < 6, Y = 20.
price(X,30).

This reads very much like a piece of Pascal e.g.

if X < 4 then Y := 10
else if X < 6 then Y := 20
else Y := 30.

We rely on the order of evaluation, and if instead we were to re-order the clauses as below, we would always get the answer 30 for the bus fare!

price(X,30).
price(X,Y) :− X < 6, Y = 20.
price(X,Y) :− X < 4, Y = 10.

A solution suggested by Clocksin and Mellish (1981) is to put in explicit tests:

price(X,Y) :− X ≥ 6, Y = 30.
price(X,Y) :− X ≥ 4, X < 6, Y = 20.
price(X,Y) :− X < 4, Y = 10.

Another debatable question is the use of the 'cut' pseudo-goal. This can be illustrated by the following definition:

price(X,Y) :− X < 4, !, Y = 10.
price(X,Y) :− X < 6, !, Y = 20.
price(X,30).

To understand this it is necessary to grasp the notion of a *choice point*. This is a goal which can succeed in more than one way; it is as if the interpreter comes to a multi-way branch in the road and tries each branch in turn, remembering which it has eliminated. The '!' stands for a pseudo-goal which controls the search. It says − if you have got this far then erase all choice points created since entering the 'price' goal, including the choice of which of the three clauses to use. In this case the advantage is that if, for example, the goal price(3,X) is attempted, then it succeeds with Y = 10, and if the system later backtracks past this point, then it cannot try the second clause and also succeed with Y = 20, since the alternative branches at each choice point have been removed. The use of 'cut' very much depends on taking a procedural view of Prolog and it is discussed further by Kowalski (1982). 'Cut' is very much like 'goto' in procedural languages; it is necessary, but unsafe, and makes programs hard to read. Attempts are being made to introduce higher order constructs such as 'not' and 'case' which will replace it (Townsend 1982), just as the constructs of structured programming have rendered 'goto' redundant.

4.4 EXAMPLE QUERIES ON A PROLOG DATABASE

We have seen how Prolog can be used to define predicates in terms of implications. However, the syntax given earlier does not require that a predicate be defined using a ':−' symbol. If the right-hand side is empty, then we can just leave off the ':−' and treat the definition as a single positive atomic literal, giving one instance of the predicate as a fact (e.g. 'cricketer(botham).' as in Chapter 2). Facts like these are normally stored in a database and we wish to see how Prolog could be used to answer queries on a database of such facts (we shall be exploring this further in Chapter 7).

The attraction of Prolog is that one can use the unification mechanism both to retrieve facts and to make inferences on them. It is also possible to retrieve related facts, much as in relational algebra (Chapter 8). Let us see some examples of this. Suppose we have the following facts about suppliers and parts:

        supplies(widco,widgets).
        supplies(bronco,screws).
        supplies(elco,toolkits).
        supplies(elco,washers).
        supplies(X,screws) :— supplies(X,toolkits).
        price(90,widgets).
        price(25,toolkits).
        price(10,screws).
        price(15,washers).

We can ask a question just to retrieve basic facts

        "Who supplies widgets?"
        ?— supplies(X,widgets).
          X= widco YES

We can also ask a question based on inference. One of the clauses says that if someone supplies toolkits then they will supply screws. Thus if we ask who supplies screws we get two answers, one direct from the database and one through inference.

        "Who supplies screws?"
        ?— supplies(X,screws).
          X= bronco YES;
          X= elco YES

We can also ask a question based on related facts. (This corresponds to using the selection and join operations of relational algebra, described in Chapter 8). Thus:

        "Who supplies parts whose price is less than 20?"
        ?— supplies(X,Y), price(P,Y), P $<$ 20, write(X).
          bronco;
          elco;
          elco

In this example the first goal succeeds with X = widco and Y = widgets, the second goal succeeds with P = 90 and the third fails. The first goal succeeds again with X = bronco and Y = screws, and the next two goals succeed. We also ask the system to 'write' (i.e. print) the value of X, instead of relying on it to print values for all the variables.

Note that elco appears twice: once on account of selling screws, and again for selling washers. If we wish to eliminate duplicates then we must arrange to construct a list, so that we can remember previous answers and check for duplicates; this problem is considered further at the end of the chapter.

4.5 AXIOMATISATION OF LIST PROCESSING OPERATIONS

Before we can understand how to write definitions in Prolog which describe list processing, we need to study how to define these operations in Predicate Calculus notation, and to see how the resolution method can be made to construct lists, in answer to questions. This is very similar to the goal-directed method used by Prolog.

We start by considering the definition of 'append', which we have already seen in lambda notation. In order to write it as a predicate, we need to write a version with an extra parameter. Thus 'App(X,Y,R)' is true if R is the concatenation of the lists X and Y; it is false otherwise. We can define the properties of App by two axioms :—

$(\forall L)$ App(nil,L,L)
$(\forall X,L1,L2,R)$ App(L1,L2,R) $\rightarrow$ App(cons(X,L1),L2,cons(X,R))

The first axiom says that concatenating the null list onto the front of a list doesn't change that list. The second axiom says that if R is the concatenation of two lists then if we cons X onto the front of the first list, the concatenation of the new lists will be the same as concatenating the old lists and then 'consing' X onto the front of it. For example:

append(cons(honey,[butter]),[jam]) = cons(honey, append([butter],[jam]))

Let us see how we can use resolution to deduce the answer to a question from these axioms.

$(\exists Z)$ App(cons(1,cons(2,nil)),cons(3,nil),Z) ?

That is 'Does there exist a Z such that if we take the list [1,2] and concatenate it to the list [3], the result is Z?'. The answer is of course 'yes Z=[1,2,3]', i.e. Z=cons(1,cons(2,cons(3,nil))). We will now show this by resolution using the answer literal as in Chapter 2.

(i)   First put the axioms in normal form.
      (1) App(nil,L,L)
      (2) App(cons(X,L1),L2,cons(X,R)) $\lor$ ~App(L1,L2,R)

(ii) Negate the query and add an Answer clause.
      (3) ~App(cons(1,cons(2,nil)),cons(3,nil),Z) $\lor$ Ans(Z)

(iii) Deduce the answer clause by resolution. {Note the use of unification to match the terms involving cons(a,b) which is treated just as the function symbol f(a,b), as in the unification example at the end of Chapter 2.}

(4) ~App(cons(2,nil),cons(3,nil),R) ∨ Ans(cons(1,R))
        from 2 & 3 { 1/X, cons(2,nil)/L1, cons(3,nil)/L2, cons(1,R)/Z }
(5) ~App(nil, cons(3,nil), R) ∨ Ans(cons(1,cons(2,R)))
        from 2 { 2/X, nil/L1, cons(3,nil)/L2 }& 4 { cons(2,R)/R }
(6) Ans(cons(1, cons(2, cons(3, nil))))
        from 5 & 1 {cons(3, nil)/L, cons(3,nil)/R }

Although the process seems mysterious, we are actually following a process of backward chaining and using resolution to implement it. We can symbolise it as

    from   ~Q
    and   P → Q
    deduce   ~P

Thus we know from clause 3 in the resolution proof (the negated conclusion) that there is no result Z where the first list starts 'cons(1'; thus (from clause 2), either the first list starts with 'cons(1', (we assume not), or there is something wrong with the remainder. This is the basis of clause 4. We then apply the same argument to the remainder and so on until we get to the terminating case with the null list, given in clause 1.

4.6 THE MECHANISM FOR GENERATING ALTERNATIVE ANSWERS

The Prolog system is able to answer existentially quantified questions directly and to keep track of substitutions and the use of equality without the device of an 'answer literal', which we used. For example if we type the definition of App in Prolog notation (we have to use a lower-case name 'app'), followed by a question:

    app(nil,L,L).
    app(cons(X,L1),L2,cons(X,R)) :– app(L1,L2,R).

    ?– app(cons(1,cons(2,nil)),cons(3,nil),R).

    R=cons(1,cons(2,cons(3,nil)))   YES

The really startling thing is when we put an unknown in place of a different parameter of App. For example suppose we ask

    ?– app(Z,cons(3,nil),cons(1,cons(2,cons(3,nil)))).
    Z= cons(1,cons(2,nil))   YES

This shows the difference from the usual procedure call mechanism in programming languages, as noted earlier in our discussion of 'between'. If we supply values for some of the parameters, then the system will often be able to construct values for the rest. It does not always work, but in general it works for data structures; thus if we write a piece of Prolog to make checks by selecting components of a given structure, then the same piece of Prolog can usually be used to build an instance of a structure that will satisfy the test.

Let us see how the inference can be done by resolution. We have

(1) App(nil,L,L).
(2) App(cons(X,L1),L2,cons(X,R)) ∨ ~App(L1,L2,R).
(3) ~App(Z,cons(3,nil),cons(1,cons(2,cons(3,nil)))) ∨ Ans(Z).
(4) ~App(L1,cons(3,nil),cons(2,cons(3,nil))) ∨ Ans(cons(1,L1)).
     from 2 & 3
     {cons(1,L1)/Z, cons(3,nil)/L2, 1/X, cons(2,cons(3,nil))/R }
(5) ~App(L1,cons(3,nil),cons(3,nil) ∨ Ans(cons(1,cons(2,L1)))
     from 2 & 4
     {cons(3,nil)/L2, 2/X, cons(3,nil)/R, cons(2,L1)/L1 }
(6) Ans(cons(1,cons(2,nil)))
     from 1 & 5
     {nil/L1, cons(3,nil)/L }

Clause 6 gives the expected answer. Note that L1 in each clause is a universally quantified object and that L1 in clause 5 is independent of L1 in clause 4. We could have renamed them to make this more obvious, as explained in Chapter 2.

The secret is in the unification pattern matching, which is a two-way process. If we look at the atom 'App(cons(X,L1), L2, cons(X,R))' in clause 2, we see that in the first example we unified cons(X,R) with an unknown and used it to construct the result, while in the second example we unified cons(X,R) with a given structure and used it to dissect the structure. This ability to use a single definition either as a generator, or else as a test, is very powerful; it is one of the reasons why Prolog programs are so concise.

Let us see what happens if we try another example.

    ?– app(cons(P,L),cons(P,nil),cons(1,cons(2,cons(1,nil)))).

Here P is an unknown list item. The Prolog system replies

    P = 1
    L = cons(2,nil)
    YES.

However, if we try

    ?– app(cons(P,nil),cons(P,nil),cons(1,cons(2,cons(1,nil)))).

then the Prolog interpreter replies 'NO'!
The first resolution with clause 2 gives

    ~App(nil,cons(1,nil),cons(2,cons(1,nil))) ∨ Ans(1)

However, this cannot unify with either clause for App at the next iteration. There is no alternative way of doing the first resolution so the system fails.

What happens if we try Prolog with an ambiguous question? For example

    ?– app(X,Y,cons(1,cons(2,nil))).

We get

> X = nil
> Y = cons(1,cons(2,nil)).
> YES

If we reject this answer, by typing ';', meaning 'or else?' the we get the alternative.

> X = cons(1,nil),   Y = cons(2,nil)
> YES

If we reject this we get another alternative.

> X = cons(1,cons(2,nil)), Y = nil
> YES

Finally if we reject this the system answers NO! The reader is advised to try generating these answers by resolution. The first answer is produced just by resolving with clause 1. The second is produced by resolving instead with clause 2 and then using clause 1 with the derived clause. The third is produced by using clause 2 with the derived clause and so on. We see that the alternative answers are enumerated systematically in an order which depends on the order of the original clauses. This is explained below.

4.7 FUNCTIONS AS RECORD CONSTRUCTORS

We have seen how to use the definition of App to construct lists. We will now see how to use the selector functions car and cdr which were defined in our original axioms for lists. We then go on to consider more general structures. Suppose we want to evaluate

> car(cdr(cons(1,cons(3,nil))))

We can do this by resolution, which illustrates the generality of the pattern matching, but it is rather long-winded. First we have to rewrite the query by naming the intermediate expressions. We rewrite it as

$$(\exists R1,R2,R3) \; Eq(R1,cons(1,cons(3,nil))) \land Eq(cdr(R1),R2) \land$$
$$Eq(car(R2),R3) \land {\sim}Ans(R3)$$

We can read this as: 'Does there exist an R3 such that R3 is car(R2) and R2 is cdr(R1) and R1 is the list [1,3]?' We negate this and then introduce an equality axiom and two axioms about car and cdr given earlier.

(1) ${\sim}Eq(R1,cons(1,cons(3,nil))) \lor {\sim}Eq(cdr(R1),R2) \lor$
$\quad {\sim}Eq(car(R2),R3)) \lor Ans(R3)$
(2) $Eq(X,X)$
(3) $Eq(car(cons(X,Y)), X)$
(4) $Eq(cdr(cons(X,Y)), Y)$
(5) ${\sim}Eq(cdr(cons(1,cons(3,nil))), R2) \lor {\sim}Eq(car(R2),R3) \lor Ans(R3)$
$\quad$ from 1 & 2

(6) ~Eq(car(cons(3,nil)),R3) $\lor$ Ans(R3) from 5 & 4
(7) Ans(3) from 6 & 3

4.7.1 Problems of using selector functions in Prolog

Although we have made use of the selector symbols car and cdr in the above example, they are not defined in Prolog. Unfortunately we cannot define them as functions, because Prolog only allows us to define predicates, and although we may use functions inside terms, their properties are only implicit through pattern matching. Further, we cannot extend the definition of the standard Prolog equality predicate '=' by clauses such as '=(car(cons(X,Y)),X).'. We could instead define special predicates 'iscar' and 'iscdr' as follows, but it is rather inefficient. Here we use 'iscar(X,Y)' to mean 'Y=car(X)' in functional notation.

        iscar(L,Car) :— L=cons(Car,Cdr) .
        iscdr(L,Cdr) :— L=cons(Car,Cdr) .
        app(Y,L2,Z) :— iscar(Y,X), iscar(Z,X), iscdr(Y,L1), iscdr(Z,R),
                       app(L1,L2,R).

It is much better to say e.g.

        app(cons(X,L1),L2,cons(X,R)) :— app(L1,L2,R).

The interesting thing about this method of introducing lists into Prolog is that it just makes use of terms which are built up using the function symbol cons and pattern matching. There is nothing special about the name 'cons'; it could be replaced everywhere with, for example, 'ff' and the method would still work!

4.7.2 Prolog syntax for lists

The two-component constructor function 'cons' occurs so often that a special version of it is provided in Prolog, but the name '.' is used in place of 'cons'. This can be written either in infix or prefix form, or else in a more convenient syntax, as in Chapter 3, with list elements enclosed in square brackets and separated by commas.

        . (X,Y) = X.Y = [X|Y]
        . (1, .(2, .(3,[]))) = 1.2.3.[] = [1, 2, 3]

We can use this notation both to rewrite the definition of App given earlier and also to apply it and get the result printed in square brackets.

        app([],L,L).
        app(X.L1,L2,X.R) :— app(L1,L2,R).

        ?— app([1,2],[3],Z).

              Z = [1,2,3]
              YES

        ?— app([[the,cat],[bit]],[[the,dog]], Z).

              Z = [[the,cat],[bit],[the,dog]].
              YES

With this syntax people are often confused about the use of the vertical bar before the *last* tail of the list. In Pascal this can only be nil, but in Prolog and LISP it can be any atomic item. By convention we leave out the bar if it is followed by nil, in the square-bracket notation. Thus:

$$[2, 3] = .(2,.(3,[\,])) = [2, 3 \mid [\,]\,]$$
$$\text{car}([2, 3]) = 2$$
$$\text{cdr}([2, 3]) = .(3,[\,]) = [3]$$

However, if the tail is an atom we must use the bar:

$$[2 \mid 3] = .(2,3)$$
$$\text{car}([2 \mid 3]) = 2$$
$$\text{cdr}([2 \mid 3]) = 3$$

4.7.3 General record structures

With the aid of these symbols we can build all the structures of LISP, which is based on list cells of two components. However, Prolog allows a function to take any number of arguments (as long as it is the same number each time!). Thus we can name any number of functions to be used as constructors, to build up data structures, which are the equivalent of Pascal records. These can have any number of components, including other data structures; thus we can build trees where the nodes are records of various types, and the tips are integers or atomic symbols. Let us see an example, using the record constructor 'person' with various predicates:

```
employs(cIBM,person(fred,25,'m')).
forename(person(X,Y,Z), X).
age(person(X,Y,Z), Y).
sex(person(X,Y,Z), Z).

?– employs(cIBM,P), forename(P,fred), sex(P,S).

S = 'm'
P = person(fred,25,'m')
YES
```

Here 'employs' is a predicate saying that a company (cIBM) employs a particular person. We used 'person' as a record constructor, just like 'cons', but taking three components. We then define the selector predicates 'forename', 'age' and 'sex' by three axioms, just like 'iscar' and 'iscdr'. Finally we ask the system a question about the sex of a person, whose name is fred and who is employed by cIBM.

We do not need to declare record constructors before they are applied, as in Pascal, because Prolog does no type checks at compile time. Instead the type checking takes place at run time through unification.

4.7.4 Type checking and unification

Consider the case where there is another unit clause about 'employs', but this time referring to a different type of employee:

　　　employs(cIBM, robot(r2d2)).

The matching process to answer the query just given would match 'P' with 'robot(r2d2)' and it would then attempt to resolve the two clauses

　　　forename(robot(r2d2),fred).
　　　forename(person(X,Y,Z), X).

However, it could not unify the function symbols 'robot' and 'person' and so the resolution would fail and the system would then try another clause for 'employs' to get a different instantiation for 'P'. Thus we can see that unification acts as a form of run-time type checking which ensures that it is impossible to apply the predicate 'forename' to an object not made by the constructor 'person'. Pascal achieves the same result by checking the type information at compile time.

　　　Note that the same resolution method is also capable of constructing a record based on 'selector' predicate information. For example

　　　?– forename(P,fred), sex(P,'m'), age(P,25), employs(C,P).

　　　C = cIBM
　　　P = person(fred,25,'m')
　　　YES.

Here the system has constructed a record P and then looked up an 'employs' clause which matches that record in order to find the company (cIBM).

　　　Note that it is not necessary to give all the information to construct the record. For example

　　　?– sex(P,'m'), age(P,25), employs(C,P).

will produce a sequence of companies with male employees aged 25. However, the companies will be repeated in the sequence for each employee found who works for them.

4.7.5 Tree structures

The components of a structure may themselves be other structures. For example instead of giving the age in years we might give a person's date of birth as a structure containing the year, month and day, e.g.:

　　　employs(cIBM, person(fred,date(61,Feb,26),'m')).

This kind of structure is very useful in recording the result of parsing sentences as described by Pereira and Warren (1980), Clocksin and Mellish (1981). For example:

　　　?– sentence(T,"the cat sat on the mat", " ").
　　　T = sent(nounph(article(the),noun(cat)),verb(sat), ...)
　　　YES

Here the record constructors are nounph, noun, verb, article etc., and the nested bracketed structure represents the parse tree.

4.8 RESOLUTION RELATED TO DEPTH-FIRST SEARCH

We have noted that the methods of finding answers in Prolog are similar to those in resolution. In order to see why this is so, we must first study the resemblance between clauses in normal form, and Prolog predicate definitions.

4.8.1 Horn clauses

We recall that a clause is a disjunction of literals and that literals can have either positive or negative atoms. Suppose we allow clauses to have *at most one positive literal*. This class of clauses is known as 'Horn clauses'. The following are examples of Horn clauses:

$$P(a)$$
$$R(a,f(b))$$
$$R(x,f(x)) \lor \sim P(x)$$
$$T(y) \lor \sim P(y) \lor \sim Q(y) \lor \sim S(x,y)$$

The first two examples contain simple facts or universal propositions. They are 'unit clauses'. The last example is of the form

$$P1 \land P2 \land \ldots \land PN \to Q = Q \lor \sim P1 \lor \sim P2 \lor \ldots \sim PN$$

where the 'P's and 'Q'are all atoms.

Suppose instead that Q is a conjunction of two atoms, of the form $Q1 \land Q2$. Then we can rewrite it as two Horn clauses thus:

$$(P1 \land P2 \land \ldots PN) \to Q1 \land Q2$$
$$= \quad \sim(P1 \land P2 \land \ldots PN) \lor (Q1 \land Q2)$$
$$= \quad (\sim P1 \lor \sim P2 \lor \ldots \sim PN \lor Q1) \land (\sim P1 \lor \sim P2 \lor \ldots \sim PN \lor Q2)$$

Similarly, suppose instead that the left-hand side in a disjunction of two atoms. Then again we can rewrite it as two Horn clauses thus:

$$(P1 \lor P2) \to Q = \sim(P1 \lor P2) \lor Q$$
$$= (\sim P1 \land \sim P2) \lor Q$$
$$= (Q \lor \sim P1) \land (Q \lor \sim P2)$$

By induction, any combination of 'ands' and 'ors' on the left-hand side can be expanded and rewritten as Horn clauses. The only combination which is not allowed is of the form:

$$P \to Q1 \lor Q2 = Q1 \lor Q2 \lor \sim P$$

Here Q1, Q2 are positive literals or clauses beginning with positive literals.

As we shall see, the advantage of Horn clauses as regards resolution is that there is 'only one way in', namely through the positive literal, when we are looking for something against which to resolve a negative literal. This leads to a systematic depth-first left to right method of trying resolutions and making substitutions, which closely resembles backtrack programming.

4.8.2 Evaluation in Prolog viewed as theorem proving

We shall now see how to view a Prolog system as a resolution theorem-prover, working on Horn clauses. We shall first explain the formal basis of this, and then see how it resembles backtrack programming.

Consider an example using a number of clauses thus:

(1) ~A(z)
(2) A(x) ∨ ~P(x) ∨ ~Q(x,y)
(3) A(x) ∨ ~R(y) ∨ ~Q(y,x)
(4) P(a)
(5) Q(b,c)
(6) R(a)
(7) R(b)

Let us assume that (1) comes from the negated query, and let us start with it. It can only match a positive literal at the start of Horn clause (2) or (3) so we shall work through them in order starting with (2). This gives us

~P(z) ∨ ~Q(z,y)

We now look for clauses matching the first literal P and find (4) giving

~Q(a,y)

However, this fails to unify with 5 and there are no alternatives. We now backtrack to consider the other alternative clause to resolve with (1), namely (3). This produces

~R(y) ∨ ~Q(y,z)

We now look for clauses matching the first literal R. The first choice is (6) which leads to '~Q(a,z)' which has no match. The second choice is (7) which leads to ~Q(b,z), which clashes with (5), giving the null clause and the answer z=c.

Thus we are systematically trying out possible substitutions and matches in our search for derivations of the null clause. The sequence is:

(i)   Start with a query containing all negative literals.
(ii) Take the first Horn clause with a matching positive literal, which unifies with the leading negative literal, and substitute throughout.
(iii) Take the derived clause and work from left to right, matching the negative literals. If one matches a non-unit clause then proceed depth first to eliminate all the negative literals in this clause, just as for the original clause.
(iv) If any negative literal cannot be matched or eliminated by resolution, then backtrack and try the next alternative Horn clause in sequence, with fresh substitutions. If there is no such clause then fail.

(v) If all literals at the top level have been matched, then the null clause has been derived and the proof succeeds. Report the substitutions used.

The method is known as 'depth-first, left to right'. It is a well-known method for systematically enumerating a tree of possibilities. Nilsson (1980) calls this an 'and/or' tree. At some nodes we have to succeed with all the literals in a clause (an 'and' node); at other nodes we can succeed with any one of the alternative Horn clause definitions (an 'or' node).

4.9 SPECIAL PREDICATES IN PROLOG

4.9.1 Evaluable predicates

Prolog differs from resolution in various ways. The first is by the use of 'evaluable predicates'. Some predicates succeed directly by evaluation instead of resolution. Thus, for example, the following are known by the system to be true without further matching (we give infix and prefix forms).

$$6 \text{ is } 2 + 4$$
$$\text{is } (6,+(2,4))$$
$$5 > 3$$

The 'is' predicate is a special form of equality which evaluates any term made up of integers and the function symbols of arithmetic (+, −, *, div) and treats it as an integer constant. This saves a lot of work proving arithmetic equalities via Peano's axioms! Likewise the greater-than predicate saves matching an enormous number of unit clauses (one for every pair of integers!).

There are other predicates which work by side effects. They always succeed. For example 'write':

$$?- Z \text{ is } 2 + 2, \text{write}(Z).$$
$$4$$

$$?- \text{age}(P,X), \text{write}(X).$$
$$25$$

The predicate has the side effect of printing the value of its argument on the current output stream. The value is printed according to the type of argument, which may be an integer, character or list.

One drawback of evaluable predicates is that they cannot be used as generators. For example '$X > 5$' will not generate the sequence 6,7,8. . . , as we saw when discussing 'between' earlier on.

4.9.2 Use of meta-level predicates

It is possible to write a more efficient definition of 'between', which does not try using predicates such as '$<$' with uninstantiated variables. We use the meta-level predicate 'nonvar(X)', which succeeds if X is currently instantiated; it means 'X is not an unknown'. This is really a control mechanism in disguise and rather beyond the scope of first order predicate calculus. The definition would be:

between(X,L,U) :– nonvar(X), nonvar(L), nonvar(U), !, L $\leqslant$X, X$\leqslant$U.
between(X,L,U) :– X=L, L$\leqslant$ U.
between(X,L,U) :– L$<$U, L1 is L+1, between(X,L1,U).

Another example of the use of meta-level constructs is the use of predicates as arguments. It has been said before that a question must be a conjunction of positive literals; then its negation will consist only of negative literals, which can all be eliminated with the Horn clauses. Suppose, however, that we want to ask a question involving a negative.

We can use the meta-level predicate 'not', which takes a clause as argument, and succeeds if its argument clause fails and vice versa:

?– employs(cIBM,P), not((age(P,X),X$>$26)), not(sex(P,'f')).
P = person(fred,25,'m');
P = person(joe,21,'m');
etc . . . .

The secret is that the predicate '(age(P,X))' is tested with P instantiated as some person, say fred. If it fails (because 25$>$26 fails), then not((age. . .)) succeeds. Thus if a clause C succeeds then not(C) fails, causing backtracking, but if C fails then not(C) succeeds. We can actually define 'not' in Prolog by using 'cut' and the goal 'fail', which always fails. We rely on being able to pass whole clauses, including predicates (like age(P,X)), as arguments to 'not'. This is not strictly allowed in first order calculus; however Warren (1981a) has justified it by treating the predicates as though they were simply function symbols making up a data structure (actually representing a clause), when they are used as arguments. The definition of 'not' is:

not(X) :– X, !, fail.
not(X).

However, there is a catch with this method. Suppose we write

?– not(age(P,96)), not(sex(P,'f')), employs(cIBM,P).

The first clause may cause P to be instantiated to some person but since it fails the instantiation will be undone before 'not' makes it succeed. Thus the next predicate in the clause will start with an uninstantiated version of P, and may produce a different instance. In other words the 'not' predicate works differently according to whether the value of P is known or otherwise, which is unsatisfactory. Clark (1978) has used a modified Prolog interpreter, which delays attempting any 'not' goals until they get instantiated, whilst it tries other goals in the clause, in order to overcome this problem.

4.10 CONVERTING FROM LAMBDA NOTATION TO PROLOG

Both lambda calculus and Prolog are based on recursion. Hence there is a certain similarity in programming style. The main difference is that with Lambda Calculus we define the value of a function as an expression, but in Prolog we supply this expression as a term which is one argument of the predicate. It is rather like the difference between returning a result from a routine, either by assigning it to the name of a function, or by assigning it to a result parameter of a procedure or subroutine.

The other main difference is in the use of predicates as 'guards' at the start of clauses, in place of conditional expressions. Let us look at the example of append:

> append = lambda la,lb. if null(la) then lb
>   else cons(car(la),append(cdr(la),lb))

A simple translation to Prolog would produce two clauses

> append(La,Lb,R):− La = [], R = Lb.
> append(La,Lb,R):− La=[Car|Cdr], append(Cdr,Lb,LR), R=[Car|LR].

Note that we have to invent extra variables such as LR to hold the result of the recursive call to append. We also use pattern matching to match the car of La with the variable Car and similarly for Cdr.

We can shorten this definition by substituting expressions for the formal parameters instead of explicit use of the '=' predicate. This gives something very close to the original definition:

> append([],R,R).
> append([Car|Cdr],Lb,[Car|LR]):− append(Cdr,Lb,LR).

Let us consider another example, that of finding the largest element of a list. If we use upgoing recursion then we can write it as

> lmax = lambda l. wlmax(l,0)
> wlmax = lambda l,x. if null(l) then x
>   else if car(l) > x then wlmax(cdr(l),car(l))
>   else   wlmax(cdr(l),x)

In Prolog this becomes

> lmax(L,R):− wlmax(L,0,R).
> wlmax(LX,X,R):− LX = [], R = X.
> wlmax(LX,X,R):− LX = [Car|L], Car>X, wlmax(L,Car,R).
> wlmax(LX,X,R):− LX = [Car|L], Car⩽X, wlmax(L,X,R).

We can interpret wlmax(LX,X,R) as saying that the largest number, out of all the elements of LX and the number X, is R. The downgoing version of lmax can be written as

> lmax = lambda l. if null(cdr(l)) then car(l)
>   else greater(car(l),lmax(cdr(l)))

This becomes:

    lmax(L,R):− L = [Car] , R = Car.
    lmax(L,R):− L = [Car|Cdr] , lmax(Cdr,M), greater(Car,M,R).

    greater(X,Y,R):− X > Y,R = X.
    greater(X,Y,R):− X ≤ Y,R = Y.

As a final example of a problem requiring upgoing recursion consider a function to turn an ordered list of digits into a decimal number (there is no way of doing this by downgoing recursion unless you form another intermediate list).

    lnum = lambda l. dlnum(l,0)
    dlnum = lambda l,n. if null(l) then n
                  else dlnum(cdr(l),10*n+car(l))

for example

    lnum([1, 6, 2] = dlnum([1, 6, 2],0) =
    dlnum([6, 2] , 1) = dlnum([2] , 16) = dlnum([] , 162) = 162

In Prolog this becomes

    lnum(L,R) :− dlnum(L,0,R).

    dlnum([],N,N).
    dlnum(Car.Cdr,N,R):− X is 10*N + Car, dlnum(Cdr,X,R).

4.11 SOME BASIC SET AND LIST PROCESSING PROCEDURES

We have already seen how to use the App predicate to construct lists. Let us look at some other predicates which can be satisfied by the construction of lists. In particular we will see how to formulate a question in Prolog which would build up a list of answers without duplicates.

Let us first define the predicate 'member(X,L)' which succeeds if X is a member of list L.

    member(X,X.L).
    member(X,H.L) :− member(X,L).

The first clause says that X is a member of a list starting with X. The second clause looks recursively down the remainder of the list if the first clause fails. Both definitions fail if L is the null list.

Let us now define a predicate returning a list of solutions given by a predicate q(X).

    listp(L2,R) :− q(X), not(member(X,L2)),listp(X.L2,R).
    listp(L2,L2).
    ?− listp([],R), write(R).

This method is very inefficient. Every time q(X) succeeds it attempts listp again with an extra item on the list in the first argument. This will start trying q(X) again from the beginning, only it will reject all values found so far because of the clause not(member(X,L2)). Only when all possibilities of q(X) are on the list, and thus cause failure, will it try the second clause which just uses the second parameter to pass back the result list.

The basic reason for this problem is that when we call q(X) recursively we are not giving it any information on the basis of which to generate the next item. Suppose we have an improved version of q called 'nextq(Xold,Xnew)' which, given the last value found for X, will return the next value. For example suppose we want the list of all the integers less than 7. We would use a definition of nextq thus and a corresponding version of listp

    nextq(X,Y) :– Y is X + 1, Y < 7.
    listp([],R) :– nextq(0,X), listp([X],R).
    listp(L2,R) :– L2 = (X.L), nextq(X,Y), listp(Y.L2,R).
    listp(L2,L2).

  ?– listp([],R), write(R).

    [6,5,4,3,2,1]

In general we would have to pass three parameters and use nextq(Oldstate, Newstate,Xnew) where Oldstate and Newstate are structures used as state vectors. We also have a problem with starting off the recursion by providing an initial state. All this is rather tedious, and an alternative method based on updating the knowledge base with 'assert' and 'retract' is described in the next section.

Let us look at some operations on sets represented as lists so that we can compare them with examples given in Chapter 3 in functional notation. First let us write down predicates describing the intersection, union and difference of their first two arguments.

    intsec([],S2,[]).
    intsec(X.S1,S2,X.R) :– member(X,S2), intsec(S1,S2,R).
    intsec(X.S1,S2,R) :– intsec(S1,S2,R).

    union([],S2,S2).
    union(X.S1,S2,R) :– member(X,S2), union(S1,S2,R).
    union(X.S1,S2,X.R) :– union(S1,S2,R).

    diff([],S2,[]).
    diff(X.S1,S2,X.R) :– not(member(X,S2)),diff(S1,S2,R).
    diff(X.S1,S2,R) :– diff(S1,S2,R).

These can almost be read off directly, for example, 'The intersection of the null list and a list S2 is the null list'; 'The union of a list whose head is X and remainder S1 with a set S2 is R, if X is a member of S2 and the union of S1 with S2 is R'.

4.12 DATABASE AND SET OPERATIONS IN PROLOG

The resolution interpretation of Prolog using Horn clauses has the following limitation. At no time is the current clause, which has just been derived by resolution, resolved against a previously *derived* clause. Each step just takes the current clause, considered as a list of remaining goals and resolves it against an *existing* Horn clause. This is called 'linear input' resolution. Furthermore no existing Horn clause is ever resolved against another existing Horn clause. One consequence of this is that one cannot derive and store 'lemmas', i.e. short proofs or chains of proofs which may be needed again, but instantiated with other variables. Likewise one cannot hold onto a stored form of a previously derived clause in order to save proving it again.

4.12.1 Use of 'assert' and 'retract'

This has been partly overcome by the introduction of two new primitive meta-level predicates. These are *assert(X)* and *retract(X)*, where X is a clause. These allow one to introduce or remove Horn clauses during the course of the proof, and thus to affect its course. Together with other facilities, like 'cut' and 'nonvar', they give extra control facilities to the programmer, though these are somewhat ad hoc. There is no systematic theory on how to use them, as there is with the theory of which heuristics can be safely used with resolution. In some ways they can be used to produce the effect of assignment to global variables in a programming language, since they allow one to change the state of the database of clauses.

For example, consider the following definition of a random number generator:

```
seed(99).
rand(X) :−
        seed(S), retract(seed(S)),
        X is S,
        SS is (S*7) mod 101,
        assert(seed(SS)).
```

Each call of rand as a goal causes the current unit clause for seed to be matched, and the value of its argument retrieved. This argument is returned as the next pseudo-random number and the clause for seed is retracted, i.e. removed from the database of Horn clauses. A new random number in the range 0 to 100 is then generated, and this is asserted. Thus, next time rand is called, the state of the database will have changed, and a new clause for seed will be found and, in its turn, replaced. Successive clauses will be seed(87), seed(3), . . . The whole process is remarkably similar to a Pascal procedure:

```
var s:integer;
procedure rand(var x:integer);
begin x:=s; s:=s*7 mod 101 end;
```

We can use 'assert' and 'retract' to get over the problem of making a list of all instances of X satisfying q(X), introduced in the preceding section. This is done with a unit clause memo(L), rather like seed() in the preceding example, which remembers the current list of values.

```
listp(L) :− assert(memo([ ])), q(X), addlist(X), fail.
listp(L) :− retract(memo(L)).

addlist(X) :− memo(L), member(X,L), ! .
addlist(X) :− retract(memo(L)), !, assert(memo(X.L)).
```

We start by remembering an empty list. We then attempt q(X) and, if this succeeds, we add it to the memo list; we then force a failure, which causes us to backtrack and try the next solution for q(X). The backtrack mechanism continues from where it left off in attempting q(X), and thus we do not need to remember any state information for q as in the previous example. We do, however, need to remember the state of the list of solutions, which is held by memo(). The next solution is added to memo, and the process continues until q(X) fails. We then try the other clause for 'listp', which uses 'retract' to match its arguments with 'memo', and thus to instantiate the result variable L, before removing the 'memo' clause altogether.

The 'addlist' predicate works very like 'rand', but instead of calculating a new integer it makes a new list with one extra element. The first clause makes it test to see that the element is not already in the list. If it is, it exists immediately by 'cut', which stops addlist backtracking and trying the second clause.

4.12.2 Constructing sets of answers
Clocksin and Mellish have a more general predicate 'findall(X,G,L)', which they suggest may be used for collecting lists of instances of variables, and which saves one programming up ad hoc versions. Warren has suggested a similar predicate 'setof(X,G,L)', which we shall use in Chapter 9; it is given below. It says that L is the list (i.e. set) of values of X satisfying G (which may be a conjunction of predicates).

The 'setof' predicate is based on a variant on 'listp' where we assert many versions of 'memo', one for each instance. This is more efficient if there are many solutions, because one can use the indexing facilities for Prolog to find the appropriate clause quickly, if it exists, instead of searching slowly down the list, using 'member'. This version is adapted from 'findall':

```
listp(L)         :− setof(X,q(X),L).
setof(X,G,L)     :− asserta(memo(mark)), call(G), addlist(X), fail.
setof(X,G,L)     :− collectup([],L).

addlist(X)       :− memo(X),! .
addlist(X)       :− asserta(memo(X)).

collectup(S,L)   :− getnext(X), !, collectup(X.S,L).
collectup(L,L).

getnext(X)       :− retract(memo(X)),!,X \==mark.
```

The main difference is the use of 'collectup', which keeps finding occurrences of memo, by the use of 'retract', until it finds 'memo(mark)' which was the first one placed. This makes it possible for the definition of 'q' itself to use 'setof', and hence 'memo', as it will add its own marker before adding and removing further 'memo' clauses. The method relies on the use of 'asserta', instead of 'assert', as this adds new clauses before existing ones, so that we are manipulating a stack of 'memo' clauses, with markers at intervals to show the start of each new recursive call.

4.13 SUMMARY

We have studied how to use Prolog in various ways: to retrieve unit clauses from a database, to explore alternative goals with backtracking, and to do recursive list processing. We have seen that Prolog statements can be interpreted as statements in the Predicate Calculus, and that a Prolog interpreter can be thought of as carrying out a resolution proof procedure, using a restricted depth-first left-to-right method. However, large Prolog programs need to incorporate other facilities, such as 'cut' and 'assert', whose semantics are not so obvious.

As a tool for list processing, Prolog has the advantage of powerful pattern-matching facilities, combined with the ability to construct trees of records of various types. The facilities for constructing lists of items satisfying general predicates are important in database query languages, and we will use them in Chapters 7, 8 and 9.

5

Representing programs in functional notation

5.1 FUNCTIONAL PROGRAMMING

The previous chapter introduced the Lambda Calculus notation, as popularised by Landin. In recent years new languages have been developed, based on the Lambda Calculus, which emphasise two things: (a) the use of 'higher order' functions which produce functions as results and pass them to other functions, (b) a syntax which is closer to that used in mathematics for equations, so as to facilitate correctness proofs by substitution and induction. A language which is particularly nice in this respect has been developed by D.A. Turner and is called KRC (Turner 1981); it descended from an earlier language SASL (Turner 1976). We shall use KRC for a number of examples in this chapter. For a fuller description with further examples the reader is referred to (Turner 1981). Another similar language is HOPE (Burstall *et al.* 1981).

Because of their emphasis on the use of higher order functions, the programming style used with such languages is called 'functional programming'; a seminal paper on the use of such languages was given by Backus (1978). However, the programs are still applicative, and based on function application and function composition as in the Lambda Calculus. Both styles maintain *referential transparency,* so that a variable or an expression always denotes the same value, within a given scope. Evaluating the same expression in a different sequence must always produce the same result. In particular, evaluating one expression cannot be allowed to have a side-effect on the value of a variable, and thus to change the value of another expression; such side-effects can happen in conventional programming with assignment, for example in Pascal, where a function definition can contain statements which change the values of global variables.

Hence we shall use the term *functional programming* to mean applicative programming in a language based on functions (often higher order), which is referentially transparent.

This very important property means that equality is always *substitutive*; that is, we can always substitute one expression anywhere by a variable or another expression that is equal to it, without changing the value of the whole expression that contains it. This is fundamental to much mathematical reasoning and to many proofs. In Chapter 8 we shall introduce an applicative database query language: 'Relational Algebra'. Because it has the substitutive property, it is possible to transform queries, by rewriting and substitution, so as to change the method of computation without altering the value of the result. Proofs of the correctness of these transformations are also possible using the techniques developed by Turner. Similar work on other types of program has been done by Darlington (1974). Because of the facility for performing program transformations which are provably correct, developments in functional programming will have a strong influence on database query languages. In fact, Buneman has developed a functional query language for databases, FQL (Buneman, Frankel and Nikhil 1982) which is described later in this chapter.

5.2 FUNCTIONAL SYNTAX: KRC

Let us now see some function definitions in KRC and compare them with similar ones in lambda notation.

First let us look at a simple function 'greatest', defined in lambda notation as:

greatest = lambda x,y. if $x > y$ then x else y

In KRC this becomes

greatest x y = x , $x > y$
greatest x y = y , $x \leqslant y$

We notice that the parameters 'x y' are put immediately after the function name, without any brackets or commas, and that the body of the definition starts after the equals sign. Note also that, instead of using a conditional expression, we give two alternative definitions, rather in the style of Prolog. Each definition is followed by *guard* condition, such as '$x > y$', which says whether it is applicable. In general any number of different cases may be listed, using guards which should be exclusive and exhaustive.

Let us now define a simple recursive function such as 'factorial'. (We shall see later that there are more elegant ways of doing this).

fac 0 = 1
fac n = n*fac (n−1) , $n > 0$

We note that a function is applied simply by putting its argument after it, separated by spaces. In this case we need brackets round the argument expression (n−1) to avoid confusing it with '(fac n) − 1'.

Lists are dealt with very simply by using the infix operator ':' which represents the list constructor 'cons' (see Chapter 3). Thus 'a:x' in KRC would be written as 'A.X' in Prolog. The null list is represented by '[]'. A list of several items, e.g. (a:b:c:[]), can be written separated by commas, as in lambda notation: [a,b,c]. Just as in Prolog, expressions involving lists can be written in place of formal parameters. Thus the function to sum the elements of a list looks very similar to a Prolog version,

lsum[] = 0   lsum([],0).
lsum (a:r) = a + lsum r   lsum(A.R, S) :− lsum(R,W), S is A+W

    KRC version   Prolog version

                                    function lsum(s:list):integer;
lsum = lambda s. if s=[] then 0   begin if s=nil then lsum:=0
   else car(s) + lsum(cdr(s))   else lsum:=s ↑.hd+lsum(s ↑.tl)
                                      end;

    Lambda Calculus version   Pascal version

Fig. 5.1 – Comparison of syntax for declarations.

as in Fig. 5.1. We see here the principal differences between the versions we have seen so far. The Pascal version does more type checking and uses assignment to pass back the result; the list selectors 'hd' and 'tl' are applied postfix. The Lambda Calculus version uses list selectors applied as functions in the prefix position; the expressions following 'else' or 'then' denote the result. The KRC version also uses expressions, but misses out brackets where possible, and writes two alternative definitions rather like Prolog, instead of using 'if'. The Prolog version names its result variable and has to use extra variable names to pass intermediate results. Both KRC and Prolog versions use pattern matching to access the list components; the matching in Prolog, using unification, is more general. All versions are recursive.

    We note that the definitions in KRC can be read just like mathematical equations and that we can evaluate them by substitution, just as for lambda expressions. e.g.

lsum [1, 4, 7] = lsum(1:4:7:[])
            = 1 + lsum(4:7:[])
            = 1 + 4 + 7 + lsum []
            = 1 + 4 + 7 + 0 = 12

    We can also write an alternative version of lsum using the explicit selectors 'hd' and 'tl' for head and tail (or car and cdr) respectively.

hd (a:r) = a
tl (a:r) = r
lsum [] = 0
lsum s = (hd s) + lsum (tl s)

5.3 FUNCTIONS THAT CONTROL ITERATION: MAPLIST, LIT

To save ourselves repeatedly writing definitions that recurse down lists we shall use higher order functions, which take functions as arguments. The classic one is 'maplist', which copies a list, replacing every element by a given function of that element, e.g.

> maplist square $[1, 2, 5] = [1, 4, 25]$
> where square x   = x * x

The definition of maplist in KRC is

> maplist f [] = []
> maplist f (hd:rest) = (f hd) : maplist f rest

Another crucial function is the list iteration function 'lit', which is also called 'fold' in KRC. This allows us to apply a function 'f' to each element of a list and to a second parameter, representing the result obtained so far, starting with value 'z'. Effectively it allows us to iterate up a list, building up a value from 'z'. Thus

> lit (f, z, [a1, a2, a3]) = f(a1,f(a2,f(a3,z)))

The definition in KRC is:

> lit f z [] = z
> lit f z (h:t) = f h (lit f z t)

We can thus define lsum by

> lsum s = lit plus 0 s

so that

> lit plus 0 $[1, 4, 7]$ = plus 1 (plus 4 (plus 7 0)) = 12.

KRC allows one to create a list by means of a 'generator'. Thus for example [1..n] generates the list of integers from 1 up to n in sequence. Using this and the multiply operator 'times', we can give another definition of the factorial function as:

> fac n = lit times 1 [1..n]

KRC does not require type declarations, and does all its type checking at run time. Thus a list may be a list of tuples, representing a relation (see Chapter 6), or a list of records, representing a file. If we wish to form a list of records, restricted to only those satisfying some predicate 'p', we can write it as

> restrict p [] = []
> restrict p (h:t) = h : restrict p t , p h
>   =   restrict p t

Note that we do not give an explicit guard in the last line of the definition of 'restrict'. Just as with Prolog, or as with the final else clause in an 'if statement', it represents all cases not satisfying the previous guards. We can compare this with a version in lambda notation:

restrict = lambda p,s. if s = [] then []
    else if p(car(s)) then cons(car(s), restrict(p,cdr(s)))
        else restrict (p,cdr(s))

We can use 'lit' to define functions for checking that a whole lot of tests are true. First suppose that the results of the tests are formed into a list of booleans: [true, true, false, . . .]. Then, if we call the list 'bl', the tests will all be true if the following expression is true:

(lit and true bl)   =   car(bl) and car(cdr(bl)) and . . . and true

Thus, if we want to define a function 'forall', such that 'forall p s' is true if the predicate p is true for every element of a list s, then we just use 'maplist p s' in place of 'bl':

forall p s = lit and true (maplist p s)

If we were writing 'forall' in calculus notation, we would say

$(\forall p,s)$ forall(p,s) $\leftrightarrow$ $((\forall x)$ member(x,s) $\rightarrow$ p(x))

Note that, since p is a predicate, this is not first order predicate calculus. Thus 'forall' expresses universal quantification over a predicate. The corresponding predicate 'forsome', using existential quantification, would be defined in calculus notation by

$(\forall p,s)$ forsome(p,s) $\leftrightarrow$ $((\exists x)$ member(x,s) $\wedge$ p(x))

The corresponding function would be defined in KRC by

forsome p s = lit or false (maplist p s)

Thus by substitution we get, for example

forsome p [1, 4, 7] = p(1) or p(4) or p(7) or false

5.4 FUNCTION-PRODUCING FUNCTIONS

We have so far seen functions that take functions as arguments. We now want to see those that produce functions as results.

The combinator '.' for function composition, as used in Chapter 3, Section 3, is available in KRC, so that (f.g)x = f(g x). Thus we can write, e.g.

msq s = maplist square s
mf = lsum.msq

Here mf is a function to sum the squares of the elements of s. Thus e.g.

mf s = (lsum.msq) (s) = lsum(msq s) = lsum(maplist square s)
mf [1, 2, 5] = lsum [1, 4, 25] = 30

5.4.1 Partial application

It is rather annoying to have to name the intermediate function msq, which forms a list of squares of the elements in the original list. Also we might want to form a function whose definition involved an expression or variable which is only available inside the context of another function. Thus we need an expression whose value is a new function and which can be introduced into any context. Such an expression can make use of 'partial application', a technique introduced in the POP–2 language (Burstall *et al.* 1971). The technique consists of applying a function of n arguments only to values for the first n–m. The result is a new function which takes just m arguments and produces the same result as the original function applied to all n arguments. Thus we can now write, e.g.

msq = maplist square {maplist partially applied to square}

Hence by definition of partial application, msq is a function of 1 argument, such that

msq x = maplist square x

However, we do not have to name 'msq' at all. Instead we can just write

mf = lsum.(maplist square)

This definition is very much in the spirit of functional programming. We note that there are no explicit parameters, and that new functions are produced by composing old ones.

Another nice example involving partial application is the definition of the intersection of two sets represented at lists:

intersection S1 S2 = restrict (member S1) S2

Here we have defined the order of the parameters of member to be convenient for partial application, so that e.g. (member S X) is true if X is a member of set S.

We can also rewrite our definition of 'forall' as

forall p = (lit and true).(maplist p)

In this definition we say that forall is a function of one argument 'p', which produces as result a different function of one argument, which is equal to the composition of two partially applied functions.

5.4.2 Curried functions

It might be thought that we would have to put extra brackets when applying 'forall', to show that forall is a function of one argument, thus:

'(forall p) [1 4 7]' instead of 'forall p [1 4 7]'.

However, this is not necessary in practice, since all functions in the language are *Curried,* and thus take one argumetn at a time. This technique, introduced by Curry (1958), solves the problem of using combinators with multi-argument functions, which was referred to in Chapter 3. We just replace a function of n arguments by a function of one argument, whose result is a function of (n−1) arguments. This function is applied in turn to the next argument, producing a function of (n−2) arguments, and so on. Thus for example we replace

$$f = \lambda x, y, z. \; x+y-z \quad \text{by} \quad \lambda x. (\lambda y. (\lambda z. \; x+y-z))$$

thus

$$f(a) = \lambda y. (\lambda z. \; a+y-z)$$

Hence we see that the use of Curried functions makes partial application trivial. Similarly, in KRC notation, we can treat

$$(f \; a \; b \; c) \quad \text{as} \quad (((f \; a) \; b) \; c) \quad \text{or as} \quad (f \; a) \; b \; c$$

A similar idea is used in Pascal, where a multi-dimensioned array $A[x,y,z]$ can be treated as an array of sub-arrays, and for example, we can form an array of one less dimension by applying the array to a single subscript, thus:

$$r := A[a,b,c] \quad \text{or equivalently} \quad B := A[a]; r := B[b,c]$$

5.5 THE COMBINATORS OF CURRY AND TURNER

We have noted that some of the function definitions given above have the remarkable property that they do not involve any variables. Turner has pointed out that this can give us a new method of implementing applicative languages. The early proposal by Landin (1966) for implementing an interpreter for the Lambda Calculus involved a complicated scheme for keeping track of the current instantiation of variables and functions, using an SECD (Stack, Environment, Control, Dump) machine, which runs rather slowly.

The problem with variables is that the same name may be used in two different contexts. The classic form of this problem is the evaluation of an expression such as

$$(\lambda x. (\lambda y. \; y+x)) \; (y+2z)$$

Here y occurs twice, once as a bound variable (in $y+x$) and also as a free variable (in $y+2z$). Theoretically you should rename the bound variable, so as to avoid the clash, but this is tedious to mechanise.

Most LISP interpreters use a simpler version of the SECD scheme, called 'dynamic binding', in order to speed up execution. Unfortunately it has the undesirable (and originally unintended) effect of making it possible for non-local names in a function to reference new variables, introduced after the function was defined! This changes the meaning of the function, and thus loses referential transparency. A similar problem occurs in POP–2, although adherents of the language extol it as a virtue!

Turner's solution, demonstrated on a **SASL** implementation, is to remove all the bound variables, by translating the expressions into an equivalent form which uses function composition with 'combinators'. Following the work of Curry (1958), he has shown that three primitive combinators are needed as follows: (Turner 1979).

I = lambda x.x   {the identity function}
K = lambda x,y.x   {Make a constant x into a function;
                                    also a way to forget a parameter}
S = lambda f1,f2.   {Composition and a way to copy
     (lambda x. f1(x,f2(x)))   a parameter}

or in **KRC** syntax:

I x = x
K x y = x
S f g x = f x (g x)

Thus a function such as 'lambda x. x + 2' is represented as:

S (S (K plus) (K 2)) I

Essentially the combinators act as a kind of glue to stick the program together and every function name and constant now occurs as an argument of a combinator. Functions now receive their argument values based on their position in the matrix of combinators, and not on the names of the arguments. In fact a language such as **SASL** is translated into combinations of about twelve primitive combinators. Although an interpreter for combinators is slow, there is some hope of executing the combinators directly, using special-purpose chips, which it is hoped will make a language like **SASL** or **KRC** run competitively with **LISP** (or even Fortran!). It should be stressed that the use of combinators is an implementation technique, and not something which is seen by the user.

Three extra combinators are useful which were earlier suggested by Curry in a classic work on combinators (Curry and Feys 1958). In **KRC** notation these can be defined as:

B f g x = f (g x)
C f x y = f y x
Y f   = f(Y f)

The combinator B is the standard one for function composition. The 'fixpoint combinator' Y is used for making recursive functions by making them refer back to themselves. The trick is not to make the recursive definition explicitly self-referencing, but instead to make it reference some unknown function as an extra parameter. We then use Y to partially apply this definition back to itself! The reader is advised to try it for himself using

F = lambda fac.(lambda n. if n = 0 then 1 else n * fac(n−1))
   then (Y F) 6 = factorial 6 = 720.

5.6 FUNCTIONS THAT GENERATE SETS

KRC allows one to write expressions whose values are sets, by using the 'set abstraction' notation of Zermelo-Frankel. These are called ZF expressions. The original notation is

$$\{f\ x\ |\ x \in S\}$$

that is to say 'the set of values of f(x) where x is an element of some set S'. In general one can write an expression on the left-hand side, and one or more 'generators' on the right-hand side, which generate values for variables from various sets. The generators are separated by semi-colons. In KRC notation this becomes, for example

$$\{\text{square } x\ |\ x \leftarrow [1..10]\ ; x \bmod 3 = 0\}$$

Here we are saying that we want the squares of x, where x is taken from the set of integers from 1 to 10, and we also impose the condition that x should be divisible by 3. This gives the result [9, 36, 81]. Note that we use a left arrow in place of an 'element of' sign. It is possible to use generators for more than one variable, and later generators can make use of the values of earlier generators. Furthermore the sets from which the values are taken may themselves be ZF expressions, or functions involving them, or even functions recursively involving the same ZF expression. Turner gives a very nice example defining the permutations of some set x:

$$\text{perms } [] = [[\,]\,]$$
$$\text{perms } x\ = \{a : p\ |\ a \leftarrow x; p \leftarrow \text{perms}(x--[a]\,)\}$$

Here '--' is the set difference operation. The definition says that the result is a set of lists. Each list starts with a member 'a' of 'x', followed by the permutations 'p' of the remainder of 'x'. Of course this can be inefficient, but ultimately we would look for equivalence transformations that produce an equivalent (but more complicated) ZF expression, which evaluates faster. The impressive thing is the conciseness and elegance of the language.

Expressions which produce sets as values are very important in formulating database queries, since we are often looking for multiple results. When we come to look at relational algebra and relational calculus, we shall see that they produce relations as results; these are, of course, sets of tuples. Strictly speaking KRC works in terms of lists, which are sequences, rather than sets. If we wish to form an explicit set, we can do it by writing a function that will remove duplicates, which is a potentially expensive operation for a large set.

We can write our earlier 'restrict' function in ZF notation as

$$\text{restrict } p\ S = \{x\ |\ x \leftarrow S\ ; p\ x\}$$

We can generate the cartesian product of two sets of tuples, where each tuple is represented as a list, and we use the concatenation operator '++' as the infix form of 'append' by:

$$\text{cart } S1\ S2 = \{x ++ y\ |\ x \leftarrow S1\ ; y \leftarrow S2\}$$

One case of the 'join' operation, defined in Chapter 6, requires one to take the cartesian product of two sets of tuples, but to choose only those tuples where the two leading values match, and to keep only one copy of the leading value. We can do this by:

join S1 S2 = {x ++(tl y) | x ← S1 ; y ← S2 ; hd x = hd y}

5.7 LAZY EVALUATION

The time at which one should evaluate the arguments of an applicative expression has been debated for some years. In a language such as Pascal, or even LISP, the rule is to evaluate all the parameters and store the value somewhere (e.g. on a stack) before executing the body of the function. Thus if a parameter involves a recursive call, we get a kind of 'depth-first' evaluation, where execution of the body must be delayed until the recursive evaluation of the parameters is complete.

However, this method can have disadvantages. In a particular case, the body of the function may not use the value of a parameter, so it is a waste of time evaluating it; worse still the evaluation may loop for ever, or fail and produce an error message. For example consider the function defined by

gif x p q = p, x = 0
      = q

If we evaluate 'gif y 1 (1/y)' when y is zero then we shall get an error, by evaluating (1/0), when the function does not use the parameter.

More interesting still, suppose we wish to work with generators for infinite sets; for example in KRC we can write [1. .] meaning the set of all integers from 1 upwards. Now suppose we want to evaluate 'first 4 [1. .]' where first is defined as

first 0 x = []
first n (a:x) = a : (first (n−1) x)

The answer should be [1, 2, 3, 4], but if we have to evaluate [1. .] before executing 'first' then we shall never get there!

The solution is provided by 'lazy evaluation' (Henderson and Morris 1976) which means 'don't evaluate something until you have to, and even then only evaluate just as much as you need and no more'. In everyday life this attitude might be typified by statements like 'never do today what you can put off till tomorrow' or 'don't speak until you're spoken to'.

Thus we represent the infinite list [1. .] by a token. When we apply the function 'hd' to this token it delivers 1, and when we apply 'tl' it delivers a new token, which is a promise to generate more items starting from 2, if asked. In the case of our example with 'first', the function tl is applied four times, finally leaving a promise to deliver the list [5. .], but this is never called on. A similar idea using 'dynamic lists' or 'streams' was present in POP−2 (Burstall et al. 1971), following a suggestion by Landin (1965).

Lazy evaluation saves using a lot of intermediate storage, particularly in the case of lists. For example, suppose we define the function 'oddsq' to give a list of squares of values, but only those squares which are odd numbers. . .

> oddsq = (restrict odd).(maplist square)
> odd n = (n mod 2) > 0

If we try to evaluate oddsq [1. .100] by standard techniques, as for example in Pascal if we evaluated

> restrict(odd,maplist(square,mklist(1,100)))

then the function mklist would eat up heap space for a list of integers from 1 to 100, and then maplist would eat up more space for a list of 100 results, and then restrict would produce a list of 50 or so results.

If we do it instead by lazy evaluation, then maplist will not generate all 100 results at once but will just pass over one result at a time and suspend itself until more is asked for. If we remind ourselves of the definition of maplist it is

> maplist f [] = []
> maplist f (a:x) = (f a) : maplist f x

Thus if we apply 'maplist square' to [1. .100] then we get '(square 1): maplist square [2. .100]', and only when hd is in turn applied to this do we get the next element (square 2), and so on.

The result is that at any time we only need space for tokens representing the suspended functions, and not for the whole stream or list. The list could be infinite and yet we could still evaluate

> first 4 (oddsq [1. .])

The use of lazy evaluation is particularly important with functional languages, such as FQL, that work on databases. Typically the intermediate results involve large numbers of tuples, and it is much better if one has to store only a few at a time. Of course, if one of the functions forces a sort operation (e.g. in order to remove duplicate tuples), then it is necessary to store the entire result and lazy evaluation will not help.

Early implementations of relational algebra used a 'pipeline' technique, which has the same effect (Todd 1976). Each function behaves as a separate process or program. Every time it has produced a bufferful of tuples, it is suspended until other processes suck the buffer dry, when it is woken up again. (The idea is similar to that of a 'pipe' between processes in UNIX.)

Turner has discovered an interpreter for combinators that has the additional property of lazy evaluation. Basically one pays no extra execution cost for this. However, with the method of evaluating lambda expressions by an SECD machine, the overhead of introducing lazy evaluation is substantial; it actually performs worse than the combinator technique (Turner 1979).

5.8 FUNCTIONS THAT OPERATE ON STREAMS: EXAMPLES FROM FQL

We have seen that KRC has expressions that evaluate to sets, represented as lists. The FQL language (Buneman and Frankel 1979) works on streams, which are lazily evaluated lists of items. The items may be integers, reals, strings or tuples. Like KRC, it is remarkably concise. Unlike KRC, which contains bound variables, expressions in FQL are variable-free, and are built up using five combinators.

5.8.1 Use of generators and function composition

FQL is designed for work on databases, and queries usually start with a function of no arguments that produces a stream of items of a particular type, from those stored in the database. For example the function !INSTRUCTOR acts as a generator and produces a stream of INSTRUCTORs. Each instructor is represented by a data-base identifier (DBKEY), which may be thought of as a reference to a record held on secondary storage. If we want a stream of names of instructors, then we must apply to each instructor the function NAME, which returns a text string giving the desired information, accessed from the record.

We could do this in applicative notation by using maplist, introduced earlier, thus:

> maplist(NAME,INSTRUCTOR( ))

In functional notation we can do the same by composing the function

> maplist(NAME).INSTRUCTOR

Note that INSTRUCTOR is a function of no arguments, so the composed function also takes no arguments and needs to be applied to something to start it off, e.g. to an empty argument list.

In FQL this is written using a small circle as the combinator '.' reversed

> !INSTRUCTOR ○ *NAME

Here the asterisk in front of NAME turns it from a function that works on single instructors to one that works on streams of instructors, i.e. it produces the effect of partially applying maplist to it.

We can keep composing further functions, particularly a 'restrict' function that acts like the one we met earlier. In FQL we might write:

> !INSTRUCTOR ○ | ([AGE,30] ○ LT) ○ *NAME

Read informally this means: start with a stream of instructors; to each one apply the AGE function and remove those that do not satisfy the test AGE < 30; finally generate a stream of names for these instructors.

Although the notation seems odd at first sight, one can visualise it as a sequence of boxes or processes, with streams flowing from left to right along pipes joining the boxes. Each box transforms the stream in some way either by filtering it or replacing its contents. The final result stream should just contain integers or strings or booleans, which can be printed. Each function composition acts like a pipe and, because of lazy evaluation, the streams flow steadily and do not build up into a big lake between processes, which would overflow storage.

The 'Restrict' function is denoted by a vertical bar. In applicative notation we would write the above as:

Maplist(NAME,restrict(lambda x.AGE(x)<30, INSTRUCTOR( )))

Just as with Turner's combinators, FQL notation uses no variables. Thus instead of a lambda expression involving the bound variable x, FQL uses a composition of functions.

5.8.2 The tupling operator

Functions in FQL only take one argument, and do not use partial application as in KRC. Instead, functions of more than one argument take a list of arguments. Thus an important operator is the 'tupling operator', which is denoted by square brackets and commas; it takes any given number of arguments and produces a list of that length. Tuples may have tuples as components. The selectors on tuples are written as #1, #2 etc. An example of a tuple is the tuple of functions [AGE,30]. Here we treat the numeric constant 30 as a constant function 'lambda x. 30', i.e. when applied to anything it produces the integer 30 as result. Thus we can apply a tuple of functions [f1, f2, f3] to a value x, producing a tuple of results [r1, r2, r3] where r1 = f1(x), r2 = f2(x) and r3 = f3(x). We can also apply a function such as LT (less than) to a tuple of two integers, and produce a single result (in this case a boolean). Other functions can be applied to tuples and produce tuples.

The advantage of introducing tuples is that it gives one a very general power of computation. This can be applied, not just to database items, but also to integers. Thus it is possible for example to compute the Fibonacci series, as shown in (Buneman *et al.* 1982):

[0,1] ∘ & [#2,+] ∘ *#1

Here the ampersand operator repeatedly applies the function [#2,+] to [0,1] producing the stream of result tuples:

[1,0+1],[1,1+1],[2,1+2],[3,2+3], . . .

The function *#1 then produces a stream of first components (1,1,2,3,. . .); this is the Fibonacci series.

In general, if we have a function f and a value (x), then &f applied to x produces the sequence f(x),f(f(x)), f(f(f(x))) and so on. Thus if f is 'add 1', the successor function on integers, then '0 ∘ &(add 1)' generates the sequence of natural numbers 0,1,2,. . . .

5.9 FUNCTION SUMMARY

We are now in a position to give a formal definition of the five basic operations of FQL and the types of their inputs and results. This summary is taken from

(Buneman *et al.* 1982). Where we write e.g. f: $A \rightarrow B$ we mean that f is a function from an object of type A to a result of type B.

Compose:

$$\text{Given } f: A \rightarrow B \text{ and } g: B \rightarrow C \text{ then } f \circ g: A \rightarrow C.$$

Extend:

Given f: $A \rightarrow B$ then *f: $*A \rightarrow *B$ where
$*A$ represents a sequence of objects of type A.

Restrict:

Given p: $A \rightarrow BOOL$ then |p: $*A \rightarrow *A$.

Tuple:

Given f1: $A \rightarrow B1$, f2: $A \rightarrow B2$, etc.
then $[f1,f2, \ldots ,fN] : A \rightarrow [B1,B2, \ldots ,BN]$.

Generate:

Given f: $A \rightarrow A$ then &f: $A \rightarrow *A$.

5.9.1 Database functions

Besides the functions like AGE and NAME, which give printable facts about an instructor, there may be other functions which give references to other records stored in the database. Let us use the database described in Chapter 10, and illustrated in Fig. 10.1. There, for example, DEPT gives a reference to the record concerning the university department in which the instructor works. This department has a printable name DNAME. Thus we can produce a sequence of names of all departments (including repetitions of the same name) by '!INSTRUCTOR ○ DEPT ○ DNAME'

We can also use the inverse of a function via the '↑' operator, for example ↑DNAME will return the reference to the department with the given name. Sometimes the inverse will produce multiple results as a stream. Thus the function ↑DEPT, when applied to a department, will give a stream of all instructors working in that department. The efficient implementation of such a function depends of course on the physical organisation of the database, as will be discussed in Chapter 11, but Codasyl databases will support this efficiently. Thus we could produce a list of names of all instructors in the Computing Department by, e.g.

'Computing' ○ ↑DNAME ○ ↑DEPT ○ *NAME

Note that the first two function compositions are used to pass single values across, and only the third is used to pipe a stream.

We shall consider the application to databases further later in the book, especially when we discuss Shipman's Functional Data Model in Chapter 11, but for the moment we are interested in seeing how to write programs by function composition, and the types of construction and syntax that are used. FQL is particularly interesting in its use of lazy evaluation, combined with function composition, for streams of tuples which are potentially very large.

The details of how lazy evaluation is performed efficiently and how to avoid re-evaluating functions and common sub-expressions are very well explained in the paper by Buneman *et al.* (1982).

It is possible to define functions in FQL, including recursive functions. It is also possible to construct lists, which are just a particular form of stream, by using the list constructor 'cons'. Thus FQL has the power of pure LISP.

5.10 GENERALISED TYPES FOR FUNCTIONS: EXAMPLES FROM HOPE

One criticism of the applicative and functional languages that we have studied so far, apart from FQL, is that they make little or no use of the concept of *type*.

The fashion in this was set by LISP, which asks for no type declarations from the programmer, and does only certain basic essential type checks at run time. At the other extreme we have languages such as Pascal, that ask for precise type information on everything, and endeavour to check as much as possible at compile time. The snag with this approach is that standard list processing functions, such as 'member' and 'maplist', have to be rewritten for every different record type used in list construction. Each variant of e.g. 'member' also has to have a different name, and this leads to verbosity in long programs.

A more fundamental difficulty is the passing of functions as data and results, and of incorporating them in data structures. Pascal simply does not allow the latter, partly because of the difficulty of knowing the scope of a variable which is not local to a function definition. Once functions can be stored in data structures, and passed around freely at run time, it becomes very difficult to establish a context from which to take values for their non-local variables. However, in functional languages, where there is referential transparency, this problem disappears since the non-local takes the value it had when the function was defined, and this cannot subsequently be altered.

Nevertheless there is still the problem of giving a type description for a function like maplist, where we must allow a very wide range of function types for the first parameter, provided only that they conform to the type of item in the list used as the second parameter. To overcome this Milner (1978) developed a theory of parametrised types or 'polymorphic types'. These have been incorporated into several languages, including ML (Milner 1978). We shall consider examples in the HOPE language (Burstall *et al.* 1981). Thus in HOPE notation the type of 'maplist' is

   (alpha → beta) # list(alpha) → list(beta)

This notation describes a function from two arguments (# denotes the cartesian product of their types) on to a result of type list of beta. The first argument must be a function from items of type alpha producing results of type beta, and the second argument must be a list of items of type alpha. In this definition alpha and beta are *type variables,* that is, they stand for data types which may be unknown till run time. Thus when we apply e.g. maplist(square,[1,3,5]), we are using maplist as a function of type

   (integer → integer) # list(integer) → list(integer)

However, if we apply e.g. maplist(odd,[1,3,5]) then we are using it as a function of type

$$(\text{integer} \to \text{bool}) \,\#\, \text{list(integer)} \to \text{list(bool)}$$

Using definitions such as these, it is possible to do most type checking at compile time, and to compile in run-time tests only where necessary.

Every function defined in HOPE must have a type declaration. For example we can define the type of the KRC function composition operator ('.') as:

$$(\text{beta} \to \text{gamma}) \,\#\, (\text{alpha} \to \text{beta}) \to (\text{alpha} \to \text{gamma})$$

5.10.1 Abstract data types in HOPE

The primitive types provided are booleans, integers, characters and linear lists. New data types can be introduced in HOPE by declaring a collection of primitive functions that work on the new data type. Usually these will be the constructors and selectors of the type, any constants of the type, and maybe some crucial predicates. The idea is to make it possible for implementations to change the representation of the type by changing only the implementation of the primitive functions, since all other functions are defined in terms of these. For example we might define the type boolean by defining

```
Constants   :— true,false  :boolean
Functions   :— and,or    :boolean # boolean → boolean
              not      :boolean → boolean
```

The chosen representations of false and true might be zero and one, or else the null list and everything else etc. In each case the detailed implementations of the primitive functions will be different but equivalent. The user will not need to know any of this.

In the case of lists the functions are:

```
Constants :  nil   :   list(alpha)
Functions :  cons  :   alpha # list(alpha) → alpha
             car   :   list(alpha) → alpha
             cdr   :   list(alpha → list(alpha)
Predicates:  null  :   list(alpha) → boolean
```

In HOPE we do not need to declare explicit selector functions 'car' and 'cdr', since the components of a list can be found by pattern matching, as in KRC and Prolog. In fact 'car' would be defined by the equation

$$car(cons(x,y)) \Leftarrow x$$

If we wished to define a tree data type we could introduce it via

```
Constants : empty :   tree(alpha)
Constructors: tip  :   alpha → tree(alpha)
              node :   tree(alpha) # tree(alpha) → tree(alpha)
Predicates   istip :   tree(alpha) → boolean
```

In HOPE syntax we write the declaration as:

$$\text{data tree(alpha)} = \text{empty} ++ \text{tip(alpha)} ++ \text{node(tree(alpha)} \# \text{tree(alpha))}$$

where ++ separates the alternative ways of constructing trees.

We can start to make new trees from tips or empty trees, joined as two-component nodes. These nodes can then be components of other nodes and so on. If we want to traverse a tree and check whether we have hit a node or a tip, then we apply 'istip'. This predicate is in fact not primitive. It can be defined in terms of 'tip' and 'node' by:

dec istip : tree(alpha) → boolean
——— istip(tip(x)) ⇐ true
——— istip(node(x,y)) ⇐ false
——— istip(empty) ⇐ false

We note that this definition of istip includes a number of alternatives, much as in KRC. The definitions are required for each case of the data structure as given in the 'data' declaration for 'tree', separated by '++' signs. The language requires that the cases should be disjoint and that the function definition should be exhaustive, covering all cases. A polymorphic type checking algorithm (Milner 1978) can then be applied to give strong type checks at compile time, whilst still allowing great generality of type declarations.

5.10.2 Types in FQL

When we come to consider abstract data types for databases in Chapter 10, we shall see that each new entity (such as 'instructor') has a number of functions defined on it, and that the types of the function results are given. The FQL language associates types with all its entities and functions, and checks at compile time that operations like ↑DEPT are applied to entities of the right type. It also includes provision for defining derived functions, whose types are declared in terms of the entity types present in the database, and in terms of streams of tuples of such entities. For example, a function to find the average salary of instructors in a department would be described as having type:

DEPARTMENT → INTEGER

A function to list the names of instructors in a department would be declared as:

EMPLIST : DEPARTMENT → *STRING
EMPLIST = ↑DEPT ○ *NAME

The system also has the ability, like ML, to infer the types of functions where these are not declared.

5.11 SUMMARY

We have studied one particular functional language, KRC, which makes extensive use of higher order functions and partial application. We have seen how functional programs can be implemented as collections of functions and constants, interconnected by combinators. Another important property of **KRC** is the ability to generate sets, and to work with infinite sets by the technique of lazy evaluation. Both these techniques are important in answering database queries, and are used by the FQL language, which also uses combinators.

We see that the ability to use data type information is important, as has been argued elsewhere (Hoare 1972, 1974). Principally the advantages are that it forces the programmer to think more carefully about his program, and to structure it more intelligently; and also it reduces the incidence of run time errors and incorrect programs. It also provides valuable information for program verification. In the case of databases a rich variety of data types is appearing and further research is needed to combine the generality of type descriptions, as in HOPE and ML, with the richness of type and sub-type hierarchies as described in the Functional Data Model and the Relational Model introduced in second half of this book.

6

The relational model

6.1 INTRODUCTION

The relational model was proposed by E. F. Codd in his seminal paper: 'A relational model of data for large shared data banks', published in 1970. This showed that a collection of tables, or relations, could be used to model the relationships between real world items, and to hold data about them. The form of a relation is deliberately chosen to be simple, yet, as we shall see, it is capable of capturing many of the relationships represented by the more complex data structures of Pascal and Cobol.

We shall start by examining the formal definition of a relation, and what is meant by the terms 'attribute' and 'primary key'. We then study the ways in which relations are used, and in particular the distinction between storing data about real world objects (entities), and about relationships between such objects. We then study various ways of 'normalising' relations, so that they can be broken into modular parts. Finally, we consider how these modular relations must relate together if they are to form a database, storing large volumes of consistent information.

In the next two chapters we shall see that, besides using relations as a data modelling tool, we can treat relations as sets and apply predicates to them so as to provide very powerful query languages. The real attractiveness of the relational model in practice has been that queries in these languages are expressed independently of the way in which relations are stored; thus the user is spared from many low level computational problems. They are thus truly 'high level' languages, and their invention has been as important to the development of database usage as was the invention of Algol 60 to the development of numeric computing.

6.2 GENERAL FEATURES OF RELATIONS IN A RELATIONAL DATABASE

There are various ways to approach the concept of a relation. We have already seen in Chapter 3 that a relation is defined mathematically as a set of tuples, and that this set is a subset of the cartesian product of a fixed number of domains. This tells us that every tuple must have the same number of attributes (components), and that the values of each attribute must be drawn from a certain domain. Further, since a set cannot have duplicate members, and we can only tell tuples apart by the values they contain, it follows that no two tuples can have identical values.

6.2.1 A relation considered as a file

Let us see the meaning of these restrictions in terms of the well known data-processing concept of a *file*.

A relation can be viewed as an abstraction of a certain restricted type of file. The file consists of a sequence of records, one for each tuple, and there must be no duplicate records. Next, all records must be of the same type; they must have the same number of fields with the corresponding fields in each record holding the same type of information. Figure 6.1(a) shows an example file. Figure 6.1(b) shows extra records that would be invalid because there were too many fields or fields in the wrong order, or of the wrong type, or duplicates of those present. The restrictions do in fact impose a certain discipline on a file, and make it easier to work with. In fact the restrictions on number, order and type are reminiscent of the rules for passing parameters to subroutines in a programming language, and are a well-recognised and useful discipline.

1978	Smith	5,900
1978	Jones	5,900
1978	Harris	6,300
	. . .	
1982	Smith	6,300

1978	Black	5,900	37
Green	1982	5,300	
27.5	Brown	A5	
1978	Smith	5900	

(a) Records in file.   (b) Records which cannot be added

Fig. 6.1 – An employee salary file, viewed as a relation.

6.2.2 Keys

The restriction on duplicates may seem awkward, but it becomes less so when we consider the notion of a 'key'. In data processing the 'key field' in each record contains a unique value by which the record can be identified. It might just be an ordinal number giving the position in the sequence (1,2,3,4, . . .) or it might be for example the social security number for a person. Usually in such a file we would want every record to represent a unique person, and we would not want two records for the same person.

In general this restriction suits files where we are keeping data on unique 'entities', such as towns, corporations, railway engines etc. However, the relational model allows us to use relations which show relationships between entities. For example we might have a relation 'LIVED', linking persons and towns they have lived in (Fig. 6.2). We see that there is no single key field, since any one person may live in several towns, and thus appear in several records. Likewise any one town may be lived in by several persons. Thus we generalise the notion of the 'key' to be one or more fields concatenated together. In this case it is the combination of name and town together which is unique, and which forms the key of the record. It is interesting because the record is 'all key'. Suppose we introduced an extra field, say the total number of years the person had lived in the town, to give the relation LIVED-IN (Name, Town, Years). Now the key of each record is still Name and Town, since the value of the extra field is fixed once we know the name and town. We cannot have two records with the same name and town, and a different total number of years in it! We say that the number of years is *functionally dependent* on the name and town; that is, we could imagine a function of the two values f(Name,Town) which would give us the number of years. In fact the relation LIVED-IN(Name,Town,Years) is a representation of such a function. Relations of this kind, consisting of a concatenated key and a few functionally dependent attributes, are quite common. The crucial point to grasp is that every relation must have a unique key, called the *primary key,* even if that key is the concatenation of all the attributes in a tuple, or all the fields in the record.

LIVED   LIVED-IN   PERSON

Name	Town
Brown	Aberdeen
Brown	Perth
Jones	Perth
Smith	Aberdeen
Smith	Oxford

Name	Town	Years
Brown	Aberdeen	15
Brown	Perth	5
Jones	Perth	20
Smith	Aberdeen	15
Smith	Oxford	5

Name	Age	Sex	Height
Brown	20	M	2.1
Jones	20	F	1.8
Smith	36	M	2.01

| Key | Key | Dependent attribute | Key | Dependent attributes |

Fig. 6.2 – Key fields for relations.

It is possible for a relation to have more than one potential primary key. For example it might have name and address and age, which forms an alternative concatenated key to social security number. These two choices are called *candidate keys.* One of these is then chosen as the primary key.

A relational database will contain several relations. Usually some of these will be *entity relations* (see section 6.4) which contain one tuple for each occurrence of an entity. Each tuple has a key attribute (or attributes) to identify the occurrence, together with other functionally dependent attributes describing properties of the entity (e.g. age, sex, height for a person). There will also be *relationship relations* which contain tuples with attributes that are the keys of other entities; e.g. LIVED-IN(Name,Town,Years) where the 'Name' occurs as the primary key of the relation PERSON(Name, Age, Sex, Height), as in Fig. 6.2. In such a case, where an attribute is the primary key of another entity, it is called a *foreign key*.

6.2.3 Value-based matching

A relational database, in order to be useful and consistent, should have a tuple in some relation with a matching primary key, for each occurrence of a foreign key in a tuple elsewhere. This is known as the constraint of *referential integrity*. Without this constraint, we could be in the position of having a foreign key which refers to an entity which we know nothing about; it is like having a cloakroom ticket, but not being able to find the cloak! Normally 'relationship relations' serve to link the database together through foreign keys so that we can pick up information from one relation, and use the values to locate relevant information from another relation. The operator that is used to do this is known as the 'join' operator, described in section 6.6. The crucial thing is that it uses value-matching. It is against the spirit of the relational model for a tuple to contain the 'address' of another tuple or any information on its position in the database. Thus, in Fig. 6.2, we see that the tuples ⟨Smith, Aberdeen, 15⟩ and ⟨Smith, Oxford, 5⟩, in the Lived-In relation, could be matched through the common value 'Smith' with the tuple ⟨Smith, 36, male, 2.01⟩ in the Person relation. It would be a mistake to, say, add an extra value '3' on the end of the Lived-In tuples to represent the fact that the tuple for Smith is the third from the start of the Person relation! The reason is that it confuses the relational model, which is independent of data storage and access considerations, with lower-level details. Models such as the CODASYL model do include such details, which cause great complication as we shall see later (Chapter 11). The beauty of the value-matching idea is that it keeps the structure simple, and allows us to study relationships between data items without concern for implementation details. In practice relational databases do have to have structures, such as indexes and B-trees, that keep track of the position of tuples, but these are details which are hidden from the user.

6.2.4 Normal form

Another restriction of the relational model is that the attribute values must be atomic, that is they cannot themselves be lists of values, or else names of whole relations standing for lists of values. The restriction means that a relation must be in *normal form* (see section 6.5). For example, we cannot extend tuples in the Person relation to contain a list of towns, e.g. ⟨Smith, 36, male, 2.01,

⟨Aberdeen, Oxford⟩⟩. The only way to hold such information is to expand it into two separate tuples, e.g.

⟨Smith, 36, male, 2.01, Aberdeen⟩,
⟨Smith, 36, male, 2.01, Oxford⟩

The precise way in which one should decompose information into various relations is the subject of study under the section on 'Normalisation', section 6.5. The subject of representing arrays of values is dealt with under 'Repeating groups' in Section 6.7.3.

6.2.5 Similarity to tables

Whenever we draw up an instance of a relation, all the 'records' are of the same type, and thus we tend to produce a table with the attribute names at the head of each column, and a row for each record or tuple. All values in a given column will be in the same domain. No two columns may have the same attribute name but two different columns may take values from the same domain (for example height and girth are both lengths measured in centimetres).

The definition of *domain* is left to the user. It is meant, rather like 'type' in programming languages, to stop one doing meaningless comparisons; for example one should not compare 'years' with 'numbers of goals', even though both use the same implementation type (integers).

We thus have the following correspondence:

Relation	File	Table
Tuple	Record	Row
Attribute name	Field name	Column number
Domain name	Field type	Column type

6.2.6 Relation definition – summary

To summarise the restrictions given above:

(i) No two tuples can be equal: each must have a different value for the primary key attribute(s), which must not include null values.

(ii) Every tuple must have the same number of attributes in the same order.

(iii) Values of each attribute must come from a fixed domain.

(iv) Attribute values must be atomic — they cannot themselves have components; relations cannot have other relations as components.

(v) If a relational database is to be consistent there must be certain extra constraints such as 'referential integrity'.

6.3 THE BINARY RELATIONAL MODEL

The problem of whether the data on any given attribute should be held in one relation or another is a vexed one. Some ideas are given in section 6.5 on 'normal forms'. One extreme idea is to decompose all relations into relations of two attributes. This has an interesting relationship to the functional model, as we shall see later, but it also has some drawbacks.

Consider the relation PERSON(Name, Age, Sex, Height). We can decompose this into a number of binary relations just by keeping the key (Name) with each one, as in Fig. 6.3. Thus we have three relations: PAGE(Name,Age), PHEIGHT (Name,Height), PSEX(Name,Sex). Since the second attribute is in each case functionally dependent on the first, these are just ways of storing the three functions Age(Name), Height(Name) and Sex(Name). There is, however, an important constraint. Since they all come from the decomposition of one relation, we expect matching tuples for the same key to occur in all three relations, and thus we expect the same total number of tuples in each relation.

PAGE

Name	Age
Brown	20
Jones	20
Smith	36

PHEIGHT

Name	Height
Brown	2.1
Jones	1.8
Smith	2.01

PSEX

Name	Sex
Brown	M
Jones	F
Smith	M

LNAME

T#	Name
137	Brown
216	Brown
104	Jones
121	Smith
122	Smith

LTOWN

T#	Town
137	Aberdeen
216	Perth
104	Perth
121	Aberdeen
122	Oxford

LYEAR

T#	Year
137	15
216	5
104	20
121	15
122	5

Fig. 6.3 – Binary decomposition of relations.

The decomposition becomes more awkward when we have a relationship relation such as LIVED-IN(Name, Town, Year). If we just had LIVED(Name, Year), then it would not have the full key. Because we do not have a single field for the key, we have to employ a trick to decompose the relation. We invent an extra field called the tuple identifier (TID) or surrogate key. We shall call it T#, and its values will be used to identify each tuple uniquely. Note that the use of the character # as part of an attribute usually means that the corresponding values are identifying numbers. They may be actual numbers used in the real world (e.g. part numbers used by a manufacturer) or they may only mean something to the computer, as in the case of T#. Now that we have such a field we can decompose the relation, as above, into LNAME(T#, Name), LTOWN(T#, Town) and LYEAR(T#, Year). However, this is rather artificial, since the problem is how to choose values for T#. We could choose them according to position in storage, or by concatenating the text strings for name and town, or by some random number generator that never gave repeated values. However, when we see the tables printed (Fig. 6.3), it all looks rather odd, since T# has no obvious physical significance. Thus most users prefer to see so-called 'n–ary' relations, where all related attributes are held together with the key.

6.4 THE ENTITY RELATIONSHIP MODEL

The discussion of the Binary Model shows that we have some feeling about what 'naturally' constitutes a relation, when we are keeping data on real world objects. The reason is that we want our relations to 'model' or abstract certain properties of real world objects. Chen (1976) proposed constraints on the choice of relations in his *entity-relationship model* which recognises two different classes of relations. This classification has been alluded to earlier. We have the notion of real-world entities, usually denoted by nouns: persons, places, things. An *entity relation* has data on all entities of the same type, and has one tuple per entity, including a key to identify the particular entity. All other fields should be functionally dependent on this key.

A *relationship relation* links the keys of two or more entity relations. It may also have attributes that are functionally dependent on this relationship. For example a classic instance is TAKES(Student,Course) describing the fact that a student takes a particular course. There would also be separate entity relationships giving data on the students and courses respectively, as in Fig. 6.4. Thus it would be wrong to have a relation TAKES(Student, Age, Course, Nunits) since Age depends only on Student, and should be in the STUDENTS entity relation. Similarly Nunits (number of units) depends only on the course, and should be in the COURSES relation. However, we might well have a relationship relation TAKES(Student,Course, Grade), as in Fig. 6.4, since here the Grade (i.e. exam mark) depends both on the Student and the Course. Thus Grade is an attribute of the relationship relation and not of the entity relations.

Entity
STUDENTS

Name	Age	Sex
Brown	20	M
Jones	20	F
Mckay	18	M

Key

Entity
COURSES

Course	Nunits
ComputingI	1
ComputingII	2
HistoryI	1

Key

Relationship
TAKES

Student	Course	Grade
Brown	ComputingI	A
Brown	ComputingII	B
Jones	ComputingI	C
Mckay	HistoryI	A

Key

Fig. 6.4 – Entity and relationship relations.

All this seems very obvious, but there are some cases which are not so clear. Take the case of modelling the colour of a car. Is it an attribute, an entity, or a relationship? The simplest case is to consider it as an attribute of an entity relation Car(Model#, Manufacturer, Year, Colour). Let us assume for simplicity that Model# (i.e. model number) is a key, some kind of international standard. We could instead have an entity for each colour, e.g. Colour(Colour#, Reflectance, Name) describing special properties of the colour, e.g. colour number 215 has reflectance 0.7 and is named 'dove grey'. We would then have a relationship Colourof(Model#, Colour#) to describe the alternative colours available for different models. This would certainly be a better representation if there was more than one colour used for each model, since in this case the Colour attribute used in the Car entity relation would no longer be functionally dependent.

Yet another possibility is to have a separate entity type for each colour listing the models of that colour, for example Blue(Model#), Red(Model#), Green(Model#), Black(Model#). . . . This might be useful if we wanted to partition colours into a small fixed number of classes, and we were only interested in questions of the type 'Print all Red models'. However, it makes it very hard to answer 'what is the colour of model X?', since we have no attribute whose value we can print! Instead, we can only answer yes or no to the question: 'Is Model X Red?'. The distinction is exactly similar to the choice of predicates in Predicate Calculus; should one have Colour(X,red) or Red(X)? The disadvantage of the second form is that, in the calculus, one cannot quantify over predicate names (such as Red), only over attribute values. Similarly, in the Relational Calculus, one cannot have relations that contain the names of other relations. Thus, if we want to return such a name in answer to a query, it is better to treat it as an attribute value, and not as a relation name. The important point is that there is no fixed method of deciding how to model objects, whether as entities or relations or attributes.

6.5 NORMALISATION

A lot of study has gone into the ways of decomposing relations, according to functional dependencies. We do not propose to go into this in detail here, since it is very well reviewed by Date (1981), who gives references to the original papers.

The two main ideas can be summarised as follows:

(i) Attributes should be dependent on the key, the whole key and nothing but the key. If not, then split the attributes off into a separate relation.
(ii) If you can split a relation into two or more relations with fewer columns, such that joining these together exactly reproduces the original relation, then do so.

Codd originally proposed a series of refinements from first normal form through second and third normal forms; others have proposed fourth and even fifth normal forms! Probably the best idea in practice is to use the Entity-

Relationship model to define relations which model the entities and the relationships between them, and then to check the relations to see that they cannot be split up further according to the ideas of normalisation.

We shall give some examples of the main types of normalisation:

(a) Partial dependency, e.g. Takes(Student, Age, Course, Nunits). Here Age is dependent only on part of the key (Student), instead of the whole key (Student,Course). It should be split off into the relation with Student.

(b) Transitive dependency e.g. Car(Model#, Manufacturer, Address, Year, Colour). Here Address depends actually on Manufacturer (it is the address of their Head Office), and only indirectly through this on the key (Model#). Thus Manufacturer should actually be kept with Address in a separate Entity relation, and a separate Relationship Relation should be created to link Manufacturer and Model#.

(c) Multi-valued dependency: Consider Sells(Manufacturer, Model#, Country), which is a relation with tuples saying that: Ford sells model 257 in Britain, Ford sells model 246 in Britain, Ford sells model 257 in Japan, and Ford sells model 246 in Japan. If each manufacturer sells all of its models in each country where it sells cars, then we really have two independent relations, namely Sells(Manufacturer, Model#) and Exports(Manufacturer, Country), since the list of models exported does not depend on the country (or vice versa). The key of the original relation was all three attributes but it can be reconstructed by joining the two other relations. However, if we think that in future this relationship might change, and that we might add data on a manufacturer who only exports certain models to some countries, then we had better keep the relation as it is.

(d) Unusual cases e.g. Takes(Student, Course, Teacher). A lot depends on the relationship between teacher and course. If each course has a specific teacher, then we should have separate (Student,Course) and (Course,Teacher) relations. If instead each Teacher only gives a specific course, but the same course may be taught simultaneously by alternative teachers, then the combination (Student,Teacher) is the primary key, and we should split the relation into separate (Student,Teacher) and (Teacher,Course) relations. However, suppose that in this case (Student,Course) is also a candidate key for the relation, which is possible if any one student only sees one of the alternative teachers for any given course. In this case the (Student,Teacher) and (Teacher,Course) relations are not truly independent and cannot be updated independently; for example we cannot add tuples pairing the same student with two teachers (⟨Smith,Mr.Hall⟩,⟨Smith,Mr.West⟩) if these two teachers appear in the other relation teaching the same course (⟨Mr.Hall, Maths⟩, ⟨Mr.West,Maths⟩). In this case it is probably better to leave the relation alone. This example shows how complex the question of functional dependencies can be. It should also be borne in mind that some functional dependencies may change with time; for example, at present, teachers may only teach one course, but future economic pressures may change this, so that knowing the teacher may no longer determine the course!

6.6 GENERALISED SET OPERATIONS ON TWO RELATIONS

Since a Relation is a set of tuples we can perform the classic operations of set theory on them, namely union and intersection. We shall be describing this in detail in Chapter 8. However, since we shall be looking at ways to decompose relations into smaller ones, it is useful to understand how to put these back together and make larger ones.

6.6.1 Relation composition by union

A relation can be split into two relations containing disjoint subsets of the original, just by selecting tuples on some basis and putting them into one or other relation. For example, we can separate persons into a relation containing persons under 25, and another containing persons of 25 and over. We can then use the union operation to put these two relations together and reproduce the original. In general, if there is some predicate P, then we have the equivalence:

   R = (R selected-on P) union (R selected-on not P)

If we take a number of subsets, and form relations which are not disjoint, then the operation of forming the union will, of course, have to remove any duplicate tuples, to ensure that the result is a set.

In the case of the union of two relations of different types, even with the same key fields, we cannot define a union because the resulting relation would contain tuples of mixed type. However, in the case of intersection we can define such a generalisation, and it turns out to be a very useful and fundamental operator called the 'join'.

6.6.2 Relation composition by join

Consider the case of two relations A(K1,K2) and B(K1,K2), where both have the same attributes K1 and K2, as in Fig. 6.5(a). Then the join of the two relations, which we write as 'A*B', is defined to produce the same result as an intersection; namely, a relationC(K1,K2) containing those tuples which occur both in A and B. The resulting relation may even be empty (this is allowable — like the empty set).

Now consider the case of Fig. 6.5(b), where B has an extra attribute, say 'B3'. Then the join of A(K1,K2) and B(K1,K2,B3) has attributes (K1,K2,B3), and contains just those tuples from B where the values of K1 and K2 match a tuple in A. In other words, we take the intersection but stick the 'B3' attribute back on, with values taken from the tuples in B. Note that if B3 is not functionally dependent on K1 and K2 then there may be several tuples from B matching a given tuple from A.

Now suppose that, as in Fig. 6.5(c), A also has extra attributes, say A3 and A4. We can generalise the join definition so that the result relation C(K1,K2,A3, A4,B3) contains extra attributes both from A and B. Where one tuple from A matches several from B, or otherwise, it is obvious how to do this. However, it may be that several from A match several from B, in which case we write down one tuple for each possible combination, all having the same key values for K1 and K2.

A(K1	K2)
Brown	20
Jones	20
Smith	36
Harris	39

B(K1	K2)
Jones	20
McKay	23
Harris	39

A*B(K1	K2)
Jones	20
Harris	39

Fig. 6.5(a) — Join as an intersection.

A(K1	K2)
Brown	20
Jones	20
Smith	36
Harris	39

B(K1	K2	B3)
Jones	20	2.1
Jones	20	2.2
McKay	23	1.8
Harris	39	1.9

A*B(K1	K2	B3)
Jones	20	2.1
Jones	20	2.2
Harris	39	1.9

Fig. 6.5(b) — Join as a generalised intersection.

A(K1	K2	A3	A4)
Brown	20	M	Perth
Jones	20	F	Perth
Jones	20	F	Oslo
Smith	36	M	Paris
Harris	39	M	Rome
Harris	39	M	Poole

B(K1	K2	B3)
Jones	20	2.1
Jones	20	2.2
McKay	23	1.8
Harris	39	1.9

A*B(K1	K2	A3	A4	B3)
Jones	20	F	Perth	2.1
Jones	20	F	Perth	2.2
Jones	20	F	Oslo	2.1
Jones	20	F	Oslo	2.2
Harris	39	M	Rome	1.9
Harris	39	M	Poole	1.9

Fig. 6.5(c) — Join as combined intersection and product.

A(A3	A4)
F	Perth
F	Paris
M	Oslo

B(B3)
2.1
2.2

A*B(A3	A4	B3)
F	Perth	2.1
F	Paris	2.1
M	Oslo	2.1
F	Perth	2.2
F	Paris	2.2
M	Oslo	2.2

Fig. 6.5(d) — Join as cartesian product.

Now suppose that, as in Fig. 6.5(d), A and B just consist of A(A3,A4) and B(B3), and that there are no matching attributes. In this case we just produce C(A3,A4,B3) which contains all combinations of the N tuples of A with the M tuples of B, giving N * M combinations in all. This is, of course, just the cartesian product of A and B.

6.6.3 Definition of join and equi-join

Thus the join operation behaves like a cartesian product when there are no common attributes, and like an intersection when all the attributes are common. In the case where only some attributes are in common, then we define it to be the result of taking the cartesian product of the two relations, removing those rows where the values of the common columns don't match, and then removing the redundant extra copy of the common columns. This definition reduces to intersection or pure cartesian product in the special cases already dealt with. If we don't remove the redundant columns we get an 'equi-join'. Many books describe the result with redundant columns removed as a *natural join* but we shall just call it a 'join'.

Let us look at an example of decomposing an un-normalised relation (Fig. 6.6) by projecting it into three separate relations which cannot be decomposed further. If we join A to B, and join the result to C, we shall get back the original relation. This is guaranteed by the functional dependencies of the attributes on the keys in this case. However, this is not always so. Even though the order of joining relations does not matter (join is associative and commutative since it is based on the cartesian product), it is possible to produce extra tuples after joining that were not in the original relation. Thus in Fig. 6.6(b) the original relation does not contain the tuple ⟨jones, 20, 2.2, F⟩, which arises as the result of taking the cartesian product of the tuples ⟨jones, 20⟩, ⟨jones, 2.2⟩ and ⟨jones, F⟩. Thus in decomposing a relation, one must be aware of the functional dependencies.

Sometimes it is inconvenient to lose tuples through the intersection property of a join. Codd (1979) has suggested an *outer join* which is a join followed by a union with those tuples of the first relation lost by intersection. Thus the result can be used to reconstruct the first relation, by projection. Unfortunately, the extra tuples have to contain null values for the attributes taken from the second relation. This is awkward for further processing (see 6.7.6).

Projections			Un-normalised relation			
A(K1 K2)	B(K1 K3)	C(K1 K4)	K1	K2	K3	K4
Jones 20	Jones 2.1	Jones F	Jones	20	2.1	F
Harris 39	Jones 2.2	Harris M	Jones	20	2.2	F
	Harris 1.9		Harris	39	1.9	M

Fig. 6.6(a) − Decomposition of a relation.

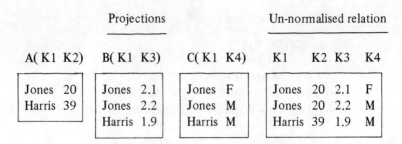

Fig. 6.6(b) − Projections which do not reconstruct the relation.

6.7 DIFFERENCES BETWEEN RELATIONS AND FILES IN PASCAL AND COBOL

So far we have emphasised the idea of a relation as an abstraction used in structuring data. The concept of a file of records occurs in programming languages, and it is interesting to compare relations with the kinds of structure that one can represent by files. We saw in the introduction that there was a correspondence between relations and simple files, but files in Pascal and Cobol can be more complex.

6.7.1 Domain information
First let us consider records in Cobol. An example definition is given in Fig. 6.7. First note that the PIC clauses convey type information, but that this relates to the implementation method for record storage rather than to the domain type used for comparisons. For example, COBOL allows one to compare two integers GRADYR and MARYR, even though they are stored with different pictures. Similar remarks apply to the types of record components in Pascal (integers and subranges).

6.7.2 Group fields
Next, note that records may contain other records as components, e.g. the group field for year, month and day, representing Birthdate, in Fig. 6.7. This is not allowed in a relation. One may instead create another relation Date(year, month,day,T#), and use the surrogate value T# to refer to a particular data tuple from the main relation, but it is awkward in this case. Nevertheless the join operator can be used to join on a group of fields, so for this purpose the fields will behave as a group even if not named as such.

6.7.3 Repeating groups
Another cause of difficulty is the 'repeating group', where the same field name has multiple occurrences referred to by number, as in an array. It is declared, as in Fig. 6.7 by the 'OCCURS 10 TIMES DEPENDING ON N' clause. A relation must instead have a fixed number of attributes, which must be addressed by attribute name, not by a calculated offset from some position in the record. One cannot ask for the Nth attribute of a relation, where the value of N is

(a) Cobol record type declaration

```
01  STUDENT.
    02  NAME                 PIC  X(6).
    02  HOMEORFOREIGN  PIC  9.
    02  NHINUMBER          PIC  X(8).                    ⎫
    02  PASSPORTNO REDEFINES NHINUMBER          ⎬  Variant
                                  PIC  X(8).             ⎭
    02  AGE                   PIC  9(3).
    02  GRADYR             PIC  9(4).
    02  MARYR               PIC  X(6).
    02  BDATE.
      03  BYEAR             PIC  9(4).                    ⎫
      03  BMONTH           PIC  X(3).                    ⎬  Group Field
      03  BDAY              PIC  9(2).                    ⎭
    02  N                     PIC  9(2) COMPUTATIONAL.
    02  VEHICLE OCCURS 10 TIMES                         ⎫
                  DEPENDING ON N.                          ⎬  Repeating Group
      03  VREG              PIC  X(7).                     ⎭
```

(b) Example record of this type

SMITH HZX/39/02 271979 19821960JAN12 3AAA561 ELN810 NRS851M

(c) Corresponding relational tuples

STUDENT

Name	Age	Gradyr	Maryr	Bdate
Smith	27	1979	1982	600112

STUD-VEHICLES

Name	No	Reg-no
Smith	1	AAA561
Smith	2	ELN810
Smith	3	NRS851M

HOMESTUDS

Name	Nhinumber
Smith	ZX/39/02

DATE

Year	Month	Day	Bdate
1960	Jan	12	600112

Fig. 6.7 – Representing Cobol records by relations.

obtained from some data item! The way of reducing this to normal form is to make a separate relation, where each occurrence of the repeated field is held as a separate tuple. All these tuples must be paired with the same foreign key value, which links them back to the tuple in the original relation (see Fig. 6.7). The join operation can then be used to put them back together if required. Thus, where the original Cobol record had N field occurrences, we represent it by N tuples with the same 'foreign key'. The number of occurrences may, of course, vary from record to record and correspondingly there will be varying numbers of tuples. It is also possible to include an extra attribute in the tuple, giving an ordinal number (1,2,3,. . .N) corresponding to the position of the repeated field in the original record, if this is significant (see STUD-VEHICLES in Fig. 6.7).

6.7.4 Variant records

The example in Fig. 6.7 shows how a REDEFINES statement may be used to provide an alternative field, or collection of fields, in place of some non-key fields. In this example we store either a National Health Insurance number (for home students), or else a passport number (for foreign students). Typically this is used where some attributes are not relevant to a certain class of entities. We cannot, of course, mix two different types of tuple in the same relation, but we can instead have two relations with different numbers of attributes but the same key fields. Unfortunately the operations of relational algebra make it slightly difficult to use such relations. It may be best to have three relations; one just listing the keys of all the records together with the fixed attributes, one listing some of these keys together with the first variant, and one listing the remaining keys together with the other variant. This idea is considered further in section 6.8.

6.7.5 Use of pointers in Pascal

Figure 6.8 shows an equivalent Pascal record declaration to the Cobol declaration given in Fig. 6.7. It has the same features, including records whose components are themselves records or arrays, and also records containing variants. These are dealt with just like the group fields, repeating groups and variant records discussed above. Pascal records may also contain references to other records through pointers, which allows one to construct tree structures and rings. Relations as abstract data structures do not use such constructs, for the reasons given earlier (value-based matching). Nevertheless such record structures are used as implementation structures, where the pointers are hidden from the user and used to speed up the search for matching records, or to share storage of common data.

However, it is possible to represent certain kinds of tree structure as relations. For example, the hierarchy of managers and employees in a firm can be represented either by a Pascal tree structure or else by a relation BOSS(Manager, Employee), as shown in Fig. 6.9. Here, a person who is a manager at one level can appear in another tuple as an employee of a higher level manager, and so on. Likewise, a tree of assemblies and sub-assemblies can be represented by the relation Component(Assembly, Part, Qty), where Qty is the quantity of a particular Part used in a particular Assembly, and the Part may itself appear as

```
type date = record
            year      :   1900. .2100;
            month     :   alpha;
            day       :   1. .31
          end(*date*);

      student = record
            name      :   alpha;
            age       :   0. .999;
         gradyr, maryr :  1900. .2100;
            bdate     :   date;
            n         :   0. .10;
            vehicle   :   array [1. .10] of
                          record vreg : alpha end;
      case    tag      : (home,foreign) of
                         home: (nhinumber   : alpha);
                         foreign : (passportno : integer)
               end(*student*);
```

Fig. 6.8 – Pascal record type description for Fig. 6.7.

an Assembly in other tuples. The problems of asking queries of such structures
by relational query languages are dealt with later. However, we note that, once
again, the relational method uses a common value to link one tuple to another;
in this case it is the Part number in one tuple, and the Assembly number in
another; it does not use pointers.

     In principle one can represent any tree or directed graph by a relation such
as Graph(Parent-Node, Child-Node, Arc-Property), where the start and finish
node numbers for each arc are listed, together with a property. This is, in fact, a
relationship relation, and one could have an extra entity relation giving information on the nodes.

6.7.6 Null values
Some tuples may have attributes with empty values containing a 'null' token.
The problem is to know what this means. Sometimes it means that the value
exists but has not been measured (e.g. the mass of a distant galaxy), but in
other cases it means that the measure is inapplicable (e.g. the social security
number of a galaxy)! It may also mean that the measure is generally applicable,
but not in this particular case (e.g. the size of the swimming pool may be left
blank for hotels without swimming pools).

     If we allow null values, then some alternative representations of repeating
groups and variant records become possible. For example, we can make space for
all possible attributes in every tuple, and put null values in the attributes not
used in a particular variant. Likewise we can invent ten attribute names for the ten
possible instances of a repeating group, and plant null values in the unused ones.

```
type Emprec  =  ↑ Bossrec;
     Bossrec  =     record
                        Name : alpha;
                        Next : ↑ Bossrec;
                        Emplist : Emprec;
                        end(*Bossrec*);
```

BOSS	
Manager	Employee
JR	Brown
JR	Smith
Smith	Jones
Smith	Harris

(a) Pascal type declaration

(b) Example tree as relation

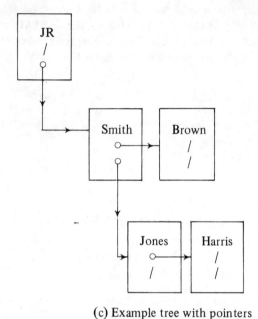

(c) Example tree with pointers

Fig. 6.9 — Tree structures as linked lists or relations.

In general, however, null values present problems. We must not allow the primary key of an entity to contain a null value, or we shall have the possibility of unknown entities which later turn out to be duplicates. Furthermore, many of the relational operations become undefined. Their definitions can be adjusted as described by Codd (1979) and Date (1981) but it is doubtful if this is worthwhile. The solution in a given case must be rather ad hoc, depending on what you wish to model.

6.8 SUB-TYPES AND TYPE HIERARCHIES

It was pointed out by Smith and Smith (1977) that a collection of relations forming a relational database are not really independent isolated tables, as they would appear to be, but that there is an implicity hierarchy amongst them. That is to say, some tables do not make sense without information from other tables. Thus we can arrange the tables in some sort of hierarchy, showing what depends on what. For example, relationship relations depend on entity relations, since they just contain keys or surrogates of tuples held in these relations.

There are two general methods of forming hierarchies: by aggregation of components, and by generalisation of sub-types.

Let us consider the 'World Cup' database (Appendix I), which describes the results over many years of an international soccer football competition. This will be used in most of the examples in the Chapters 7 and 8. If we take the relations YEARS, GROUPS, MATCHES, GAMES, STAD_ALLOC, GROUP_PLAC, TEAMS and VENUES, whose meaning is described below, then we can arrange them in a hierarchy as shown in Fig. 6.10.

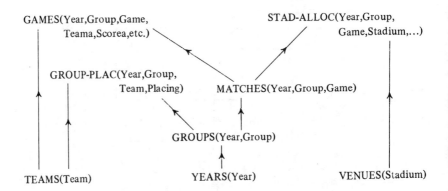

Fig. 6.10 – Component hierarchy in World Cup database.

6.8.1 Component hierarchy
Here YEARS is an entity relation describing years in which the World Cup football competition is played. VENUES is another entity relation describing the stadia used in the competition. GROUPS is an entity relation describing how groups of teams are formed for the competition; it contains Year as a foreign key, and thus depends on it. MATCHES is an entity relation describing individual games that occur in the competition groups. STAD_ALLOC is a relationship relation linking matches with stadia, and depends on information from both MATCHES and VENUES.

The hierarchy does not have to be a pure tree; it can be a net. We see that the GROUPS relation is used also by the GROUP_PLAC relation, which also depends on the TEAMS relation. The GROUP_PLAC relation shows, for each team in a competition group, their final placing in that group. Note that the same team can play in more than one group, and get a different placing in each. Finally, the GAMES relation shows the teams that play in each match and their scores. It thus depends on both TEAMS and MATCHES relations.

In this particular example, inspection of the tables in Appendix I shows that the **GROUPS** relation includes all years in the **YEARS** relation, and the **MATCHES** relation includes all groups in the **GROUPS** relation. There is one tuple in the **GAMES** relation for each tuple in the **MATCHES** relation, and it includes the same information. Thus these relations contain redundant information, and they are not used to answer the queries in Chapters 7 and 8. They would become non-redundant in two circumstances:

(i)   if they contained extra entity attribute information, for example if the **YEARS** relation included the name of the host country;
(ii) if some tuples were unrepresented in the higher relations, for example if all matches in a particular group were abandoned one year.

It must be emphasised that this diagram is showing dependencies of relations, and not of particular tuples. It shows a kind of 'meta-relationship', not between the data values themselves, but between the record types that hold them. In fact, when we come to discuss the **CODASYL** model, we shall see that this diagram is closely related to a 'Bachman diagram' showing relationships between record types.

Smith and Smith (1977) call this hierarchy a 'hierarchy by aggregation', which is the process of constructing records from fields as components. In each case a record type (or relation) is constructed by using foreign keys as components, which refer to record types (or relations) at lower levels. Thus one can talk of components of components of components, e.g. Year of Group of Game.

The main implication this has for relations is that of 'referential integrity'; namely, where a tuple occurs in a higher-level relation there should be matching tuple(s) present in lower level relations.

6.8.2 Sub-type hierarchy
The other type hierarchy is that of sub-types, each forming a subset of some higher type, and each with their own particular properties. The easiest example to understand is that of Persons shown below.

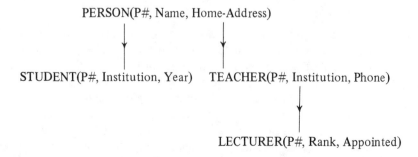

Here the **PERSON** relation lists data on people, giving their name and address and social-security identification number P#. A subset of these people will be teachers, with additional information on the Institution where they teach, and their phone extension. A subset of this set will be Lecturers at a University, and will have a particular rank (professor, senior lecturer etc.) and year of appointment. The point is that every Lecturer will also appear in the Teacher relation, and every Teacher will also appear in the Person relation (but not vice versa). A Lecturer thus has a Rank in virtue of being a Lecturer, belongs to an Institution in virtue of being a Teacher, and also has a Home Address in virtue of being a Person. Lecturers, Teachers and Persons are all entity relations, but they overlap, since they describe different roles of the same collection of entities. The crucial thing is that they all use the same Entity Identifier to identify occurrences of the same entity in different relations.

If we tried to make one big relation PERSON(P#, Name, Home Address, Institution, Phone, Rank, Appointdate) then it would include null values for attributes of non-lecturers and non-teachers. In Pascal we could construct a variant record with fixed information for persons and a tag field for a teacher variant, within which was a lecturer variant, but, as pointed out earlier, we cannot do this with the tuples of a relation.

The matter is further complicated by the possibility of alternative sub-types of PERSON. For example one might have Students and Teachers. However, there is then the question of whether Students and Teachers will always be disjoint, or should the two sub-types be allowed to overlap? For purposes of implementation it may be convenient to insist that a complete set of disjoint sub-types be declared, which are non-overlapping, and that every person falls into one of these sub-types. However, for the purposes of data modelling this is rather restrictive; for example a junior lecturer may still be completing a higher degree and thus registered as a student. A fuller discussion of this is given in Smith and Smith (1977).

The hierarchy of sub-types is formed by subsetting. Going down the hierarchy we have sub-types of sub-types of sub-types and so on. Going up the hierarchy we get increasingly general information. This hierarchy is closely related to an 'IS-A' hierarchy used in Artificial Intelligence to represent e.g. 'a Teacher is a Person', and in semantic nets (Mylopoulos *et al.* 1984).

6.9 SUMMARY

A collection of tables or relations can be used to model the relationships between real world items, and to hold data about them. Whilst the form of a relation is more restrictive than the data structures of Pascal and Cobol, yet it can capture many of the relationships represented in these more intricate structures.

There are many ways to decompose relations and join them together. The crucial operations for composing relations are the union and join operations, which are based on union and intersection in set theory. The join operation uses 'value-based matching'. The relational model deliberately does not specify how to implement the match efficiently, and it discourages one from using unnormalised forms containing lists or pointers. In fact this feature gives it much of its generality and power, and allows the definition of high-level languages based purely on set theory, as we shall see in the next chapter.

There is a considerable amount of theory about how to decompose a collection of relations into a more modular set; this is the process of normalis-ation. However, this process is not purely mechanical, and in order to model the real world it is necessary to define entities and relationships and to consider how the entities may be arranged in hierarchies by sub-type. Relationships will usually form a hierarchy too, through their components. Thus a collection of relations forming a consistent, cross-referenced database has a hidden structure, and must conform to a number of constraints. It must not be thought of as a collection of completely self-contained tables.

7

Calculus-based languages

7.1 INTRODUCTION

We have already seen the power of the Predicate Calculus as a query language, using examples of everyday queries. Following a proposal by E. F. Codd (1970), various specialised forms of it have been developed to work on relations; such a language is called a *Relational Calculus*.

We shall start by discussing QUEL, which is the language used in the INGRES database system (Stonebraker *et al*. 1976). The QUEL language was one of the earliest implementations of Codd's proposals and its style of query formulation is very close to his proposed predicate calculus notation. For contrast, we shall look at another proposed database language QBE (Query by Example); at first sight it looks very different, and appears to be based on interactive form filling. We shall see how it, too, is based on the calculus, but using a different type of variable to range over the relation. In addition we shall look at SQL, which can be regarded as an extension of QUEL with facilities for handling sets.

7.2 THE QUEL LANGUAGE OF INGRES AS A TUPLE-ORIENTED CALCULUS

QUEL uses the notion of a *Tuple Variable,* which can be instantiated to reference any tuple in a given relation. The attribute values for a particular tuple are obtained from the tuple variable by using a record selector notation, very similar to that of Pascal. For example, if the variable S ranges over the STAD_ALLOC relation of the World Cup database tabulated in Appendix I, then the five attributes of each tuple are given by S.Year, S.Group, S.Game, S.Statium and S.Date respectively. We shall use the World Cup database for examples throughout this chapter.

A query, for example, as to which games in 1978 took place in Cordoba stadium, would be written in QUEL as:

> RANGE OF S IS STAD_ALLOC
> RETRIEVE (S.Group, S.Game)
> WHERE S.Year = 1978 AND S.Stadium = 'Cordoba'

Note that we need both the Group and the Game number within the Group in order to identify the game; so we ask for the retrieval of these two attributes from each selected tuple. The idea is that S is instantiated with each tuple of the STAD_ALLOC relation in turn. For those tuples which satisfy the selection conditions on the Year and Stadium fields, we print the Group and Game fields.

If we were to formulate the query in predicate calculus notation, as used in Chapter 2, it would be:

$$(\exists X,Y)\,(S \in STAD\_ALLOC) \wedge X = S.Group \wedge Y = S.Game \wedge$$
$$S.Year = 1978 \wedge S.Stadium = \text{'Cordoba'}$$

Here we use the existential quantifier to enquire if there exist values X and Y, such that X is the Group and Y is the Game number of some tuple S. A suitable interpreter, such as the Prolog interpreter, could be made to enumerate pairs of values of X and Y for which it is true. For example if we represented STAD_ALLOC as a collection of unit clauses in Prolog, each containing one tuple, then we could write the query as:

> query(X,Y) :—
>   stadalloc(S), S = rec(Year,Group,Game,Stadium,Date),
>   X = Group, Y = Game, Year = 1978, Stadium = 'Cordoba'.

For example, if the clauses for STAD_ALLOC were as follows, then the results would be (A,2) and (A,3):

> stadalloc(rec(1978, 'A' 1, 'Rosario', '2-Jun')).
> stadalloc(rec(1978, 'A' 2, 'Cordoba', '2-Jun')).
> stadalloc(rec(1978, 'A' 3, 'Cordoba', '3-Jun')).
> etc.

Note that, in the Prolog version, 'Year', 'Group' etc. are just local variables, which take on the desired values by pattern matching with the tuple constructed by 'rec'. Their actual names do not matter, but we have chosen them to bring out the similarity in the form of query.

7.3 SYNTAX OF QUEL

In general, queries in QUEL take the form

> RANGE OF ⟨var⟩ IS ⟨rel⟩
> {RANGE OF ⟨var⟩ IS ⟨rel⟩}
> RETRIEVE [INTO ⟨rel⟩]
> (⟨rel⟩.⟨var⟩ {,⟨rel⟩.⟨var⟩ })
> WHERE ⟨pred⟩

(Curly brackets denote repetition, and square brackets enclose optional items.)

Predicates are boolean expressions involving comparisions of attribute values, thus:

⟨pred⟩   ::= ⟨pred⟩ AND ⟨comp⟩ |
             ⟨pred⟩ OR   ⟨comp⟩ |
             NOT (⟨pred⟩) | ⟨comp⟩
⟨comp⟩   ::= ⟨val⟩ ⟨compop⟩ ⟨val⟩
⟨compop⟩ ::= = | ⌐= | > | ⩽ | < | ⩾
⟨val⟩   ::= ⟨rel⟩.⟨var⟩ | ⟨constant⟩

We notice that, in general, only tuple variables or constants may appear in the selection conditions given by ⟨comp⟩; e.g. we cannot say 'WHERE 3 * S.Game > 2 + S.Year'. This is done deliberately, since it is easier to work directly with the values stored in the database than with derived data, which has to be computed from stored values. More recent versions of INGRES do in fact allow the use of arbitrary expressions, but we shall keep this constraint, since it is more illustrative of Codd's original relational calculus.

7.3.1 Two-variable queries

Let us now look at queries involving two or more tuple variables. We can extract tuples from one relation, depending on values in another relation. Suppose we want information on the stadia used by the group in which Poland came first:

RANGE OF SA IS STAD_ALLOC
RANGE OF GP IS GROUP_PLAC
RETRIEVE INTO Res (SA.Stadium)
WHERE GP.Placing = 1 AND GP.Team = 'Poland'
    AND GP.Year = SA.Year AND GP.Group = SA.Group

Notice that the last line of the query looks for tuples from the GROUP_PLAC relation which have a match with tuples from the STAD_ALLOC relation over the Year and Group attributes. If we look at an extract from the two relations we shall see how this works

STAD_ALLOC

Year	Group	Game	Stadium
1978	1	1	Buenos Aires
1978	2	1	Buenos Aires
1978	2	2	Rosario
1978	2	3	Cordoba
1978	2	4	Rosario
1978	2	5	Cordoba
1978	2	6	Rosario
1982	1	.	. . .
. . . .	.	.	.

GROUP_PLAC

Year	Group	Placing	Team
1978	2	1	Poland
1978	4	3	Scotland
1978	B	1	Argentina
1978	F	1	Argentina

Res

Stadium
Buenos Aires
Rosario
Cordoba

We see that one tuple from the GROUP_PLAC relation satisfies the selection conditions on Placing and Team, and that six tuples from STAD_ALLOC have the same values of Year and Group as it does. From these tuples, there are six values for the stadium, but several of these are the same. Since we only want the distinct values, we use the key word 'INTO Res' to say that we want the result tuples to be built up into a result relation named 'Res', which, since it is a set, will not have duplicates. This gives the result shown.

If the test had used the condition 'Team = "Scotland"', then no tuple in GROUP_PLAC would have matched it, and consequently no tuples from STAD_ALLOC would be selected. The result would be a null relation, corresponding to the empty set.

If instead, the test had used the condition 'Team = "Argentina"', then two tuples in GROUP_PLAC would have matched it, (groups B and F in 1978); consequently eight tuples would be selected from STAD_ALLOC (six for group B and two for group F).

When we come to consider the 'join' operation of relational algebra, we shall find that it is defined to perform exactly the same matching process as this.

Suppose we had asked the question with 'Team = "Argentina"', then we could have asked to see each stadium paired with the name of the team that came first in that group; this requires us to make up new tuples containing values from two different relations. The query would be:

    RETRIEVE INTO RES (SA.Stadium, GP.Team)
    WHERE GP.Placing = 1 AND GP.Team = 'Argentina'
    AND   GP.Year = SA.Year AND GP.Group = SA.Group

The result would be

STAD_ALLOC

Year	Group	Game	Stadium
1978	B	1	Rosario
1978	B	2	Mendoza
1978	B	3	Rosario
1978	B	4	Mendoza
1978	B	5	Mendoza
1978	B	6	Rosario
1978	F	1	Buenos Aires
1978	F	2	Buenos Aires

GROUP_PLAC

Year	Group	Placing	Team
1978	1	2	Argentina
1978	B	1	Argentina
1978	F	1	Argentina

RES

Stadium	Team
Rosario	Argentina
Mendoza	Argentina
Buenos Aires	Argentina

7.3.2 Problems of negation and quantification

All variables in QUEL are implicitly existentially quantified. Thus the last query would be written in Predicate Calculus as

$$(\exists X, Y)\,(\exists SA, GP)\ (SA \in STAD\_ALLOC) \wedge (GP \in GROUP\_PLAC) \wedge$$
$$X = SA.Stadium \wedge Y = GP.Team \wedge$$
$$GP.Placing = 1 \wedge GP.Team = \text{'Argentina'} \wedge$$
$$GP.Year = SA.Year \wedge GP.Group = SA.Group$$

In other words we are asking 'Does there exist an X and a Y and an SA and a GP such that . . .?' and 'For each such combination of X, Y list the values'.

Notice that the quantifiers are always at the front, and that we cannot produce the effect of Universal Quantification, since we cannot put a NOT before the existential quantifier. For example, if we want to find those groups where none of the matches were played in Buenos Aires, then it would be wrong to say:

RETRIEVE INTO Res (SA.Group) WHERE
NOT (SA.Stadium = 'Buenos Aires')

The reason is that this query will retrieve those groups where any single match was not played at Buenos Aires, instead of retrieving those where no match at all was played at Buenos Aires. In predicate notation we wish to write:

$$(\exists G)\ \text{not}\,((\exists SA)\ SA.Stadium = \text{Buenos Aires} \wedge SA.Group = G)$$

i.e.

$$(\exists G)\,(\forall SA)\ SA.Stadium \neq \text{Buenos Aires} \vee \text{not}(SA.Group = G)$$

i.e.

$$(\exists G)\,(\forall SA)\ (SA.Group = G) \rightarrow (SA.Stadium \neq \text{Buenos Aires})$$

We cannot obtain this directly in QUEL. We can achieve it, in a roundabout way, by using extended facilities as follows:

RANGE OF SA is STAD_ALLOC
RANGE OF GP is GROUP_PLAC
RETRIEVE INTO RES (GP.Group)
WHERE COUNT (SA.Game
          WHERE SA.Group = GP.Group
          AND SA.Stadium = 'Buenos Aires') = 0

This says that, for each value of GP.Group, we wish to form the set of values of SA.Game for those tuples in the *same group,* such that the stadium is Buenos Aires. If the count of members in the set is nil, then we wish to select that value of GP.Group, but not otherwise. We are using here the definition given in Chapter 2, which says that we can check 'not$(\exists x)P(x)$' by checking that the extension of P is null, and here we are forming the extension and counting its members. We shall consider the use of aggregation functions like COUNT further when we look at SQL and QBE.

7.4 SQL AND OTHER LANGUAGES

We have seen that QUEL provides a means of formulating queries involving the comparison and the retrieval of items from parts of tuples, selected from one or more relations. It lacks the full power of the Predicate Calculus, since it only uses Existential Quantifiers.

Before QUEL, Codd (1970) made a theoretical proposal for a language ALPHA which was based on tuple variables. This was never implemented, but it provided the inspiration for QUEL. It was also important theoretically, since it established an equivalence between relational calculus and relational algebra, which we shall explore further in Chapter 9.

At about the same time, a team at the IBM research centre developed SQL (Chamberlin *et al.* 1976) which has become a widely used language for querying relational databases. Simple queries in SQL are very like those in QUEL, but we can also write more complex ones which involve the formation of intermediate sets (i.e. relations). It is possible to use set union and difference operations on these sets, which gives the effect of universal quantification, and also some of the features of relational algebra. We shall now look at some examples.

7.4.1 Simple queries in SQL

The initial query we studied in QUEL would be written in SQL as

        SELECT Group, Game
        FROM STAD_ALLOC
        WHERE Year = 1978 AND Stadium = 'Cordoba'

The main difference is the use of SELECT in place of RETRIEVE, and the use of attribute names like 'Year', which are not prefixed by a tuple variable. However such a variable is understood to exist, and to refer to the relation in the FROM clause.

When we come to the two variable query we considered earlier for QUEL, we again see a close similarity:

        SELECT UNIQUE Stadium
        FROM STAD_ALLOC, GROUP_PLAC
        WHERE Placing = 1 AND Team = 'Poland'
            AND STAD_ALLOC.Year = GROUP_PLAC.Year
            AND STAD_ALLOC.Group = GROUP_PLAC.Group

We see that we have to give the tuple variable names in the last two lines, since the name 'Year' is ambiguous (it occurs in both relations), unlike 'Placing', for example, which occurs only in one relation.

We also note the use of UNIQUE, in place of 'INTO Res' in QUEL, as a means of requesting the removal of duplicates on output.

An alternative means of writing this query in SQL is the use of a *nested sub-query,* which effectively generates an unnamed intermediate relation:

        SELECT UNIQUE Stadium
        FROM STAD_ALLOC
        WHERE ⟪Year, Group⟫ IN (SELECT Year, Group
                            FROM GROUP_PLAC
                            WHERE Placing = 1 AND Team = 'Poland')

The indented portion of the query denotes a relation containing desired years and groups. The outer WHERE clause requests tuples with (Year,Group) values that occur IN the intermediate relation (IN is the usual set membership operator). We could get the same effect in relational calculus by naming the result of a sub-query. This is easily done in Prolog, e.g. we name the intermediate 'firstPlac', thus:

        query(Stad) :—
            stadalloc(S),
            S = rec(Year,Group,Game,Stad,Date),
            firstPlac(Year,Group).

        firstPlac(Y,G) :—
            groupplac(R),
            R = recg(Y,G,Team,Placing),
            Placing = 1, Team = 'Poland'.

The use of nested queries extends to a variety of examples, as shown in Date (1981). This method of using nested queries does not work, however, where we wish to extract values from both relations; thus if we wish to get the stadium values paired with the team values, then we have to go back to the original method like QUEL:

        SELECT UNIQUE Stadium, Team
        FROM STAD_ALLOC, GROUP_PLAC
        WHERE Placing = 1 AND Team = 'Poland'
        AND STAD_ALLOC.Year = GROUP_PLAC.Year
        AND STAD_ALLOC.Group = GROUP_PLAC.Group

7.4.2 Quantified queries in SQL

When we apply the IN operation in SQL, we are implicitly using an existential quantifier. Thus when we say 'WHERE X IN P', it means '$\exists x\, P(x)$'.

We can also use the NOT IN operation, which gives us the effect of a Universal Quantifier. Thus to ask for groups where no game is played in Buenos Aires (as considered earlier) we can say:

        SELECT UNIQUE Group
        FROM GROUP_PLAC
        WHERE 'Buenos Aires' NOT IN
            (SELECT Stadium
            FROM STAD_ALLOC
            WHERE Group = GROUP_PLAC.Group)

We can also use the method of INGRES given above, but instead of using COUNT to test that the number of tuples in sub-query is zero, we test that the relation is empty, using the NOT EXISTS predicate.

    SELECT UNIQUE Group
    FROM GROUP_PLAC
    WHERE NOT EXISTS (SELECT Game
                      FROM STAD_ALLOC
                      WHERE Group = GROUP_PLAC.Group
                      AND Stadium = 'Buenos Aires')

7.4.3 Two variables in the same relation

We can ask queries in QUEL where two tuple variables range over the same
relation. Thus suppose we want to know about all other teams that played in
the same group as Holland:

    RANGE S1 IS GROUP_PLAC
    RANGE S2 IS GROUP_PLAC
    RETRIEVE S1.Team INTO RES
    WHERE S1.Team ⌐= 'Holland' AND S2.Team = 'Holland'
    AND S1.Year = S2.Year AND S1.Group = S2.Group

Here the S2 variable is locating tuples concerning Holland, and the S1 variable
is then ranging over all tuples, looking for matching ones with the same group
(excluding the original tuple, which will match itself).

In SQL we can do the same, but the difficulty is how to distinguish the
names of the two tuple variables. SQL normally tries to guess the tuple variable
by context but in this case the user has to provide a name 'S2' for the second
tuple variable. The name is declared following the relation name, but separated
only by a space, so that it is taken to refer to the same relation. Thus we have:

    SELECT UNIQUE S1.Team
    FROM GROUP_PLAC S1, GROUP_PLAC S2
    WHERE S1.Team ⌐= 'Holland' AND S2.Team = 'Holland'
    AND S1.Year = S2.Year AND S1.Group = S2.Group

We can also formulate this query using a nested sub-query thus:

    SELECT UNIQUE Team
    FROM GROUP_PLAC
    WHERE Team ⌐= 'Holland'
    AND 《(Group, Year)》 IN (SELECT Group,Year
                            FROM S2
                            WHERE Team = 'Holland')

7.4.4 Syntax of SQL with nested sub-queries

A nested sub-query denotes a set of tuples or an unnamed relation, which has
been dynamically created, and may be of a different type from any of the
stored relations. Since it is unnamed, it can only be used at the place where it
appears in the sub-query; it cannot be referenced by name from some other
part of the query.

Syntactically a sub-query takes the same form as the main query, namely

SELECT [UNIQUE] ⟨varlist⟩ FROM ⟨rel-list⟩ WHERE ⟨pred⟩

Here ⟨varlist⟩ is one or more attribute values, which are taken from tuples referenced by tuple variables ranging over the relations in ⟨rel-list⟩. The tuples are selected by the predicate in ⟨pred⟩. As we shall see, it is also possible to write expressions inside ⟨varlist⟩, besides simple attribute values. A full syntax of a common version of SQL is given in Appendix IV. A number of manufacturers provide variations on this, with different trade names. Note that SQL as described in Date (1981) can only apply IN to a sub-query with a single column name in ⟨varlist⟩. To get over this we use ⟨⟨. . .⟩⟩ as in RASQL (Appendix IV).

The operations that may be applied to a sub-query S are based on those which one could apply to a set i.e.

S1 UNION S	Set union
X IN S	Set membership
X NOT IN S	Complement of set membership
EXISTS S	S is non-null
NOT EXISTS S	S is null
COUNT(S)	No. of members in S

The following apply only where S is a set of integers:

SUM(S)	Total of S
MAX(S), MIN(S)	Largest and smallest integers in S
AVG(S)	SUM(S)/COUNT(S)

The operations IN, NOT IN, EXISTS and NOT EXISTS are predicates and may be combined together with others using AND, OR and NOT in the WHERE clause.

The operations COUNT, SUM, MAX, MIN and AVG are known as *grouping functions* or *built-in functions*; they are described in greater detail in section 7.8. They are applied to sets and deliver numeric results, which can be compared with other numbers or used in expressions, e.g.

N = COUNT(S)
2 * AVG(S) > 0.6

It is the ability to talk about sets, and to apply set operations and functions to sets, that distinguishes SQL from simple QUEL. Both languages use tuple variables and calculus expressions to select values. However, the set operations of SQL make it very much more like relational algebra which, as we shall see, works entirely in terms of sets. We shall conclude this study of SQL by looking at the use of two classic set operations.

7.4.5   UNION and SET DIFFERENCE in SQL
The operation UNION is the usual operation for adding sets. Suppose we wanted

all groups that included Scotland or played some matches in Rosario, then we could write it as:

```
(SELECT UNIQUE Group
 FROM GROUP_PLAC
 WHERE Team = 'Scotland')
 UNION
(SELECT UNIQUE Group
 FROM STAD_ALLOC
 WHERE Stadium = 'Rosario')
```

Some dialects of SQL allow one to use the MINUS operation to take the difference of two sets. Thus if we want a list of those groups where none of the games were played in Cordoba, then we could write

```
(SELECT UNIQUE Group
 FROM STAD_ALLOC)
 MINUS
(SELECT UNIQUE Group
 FROM STAD_ALLOC
 WHERE Stadium = 'Cordoba')
```

Here we effectively make a list of all groups, and then make a 'bad list' containing all groups where any game is in Cordoba. By removing those on the bad list we get the desired result.

The same result can be obtained by using the NOT EXISTS function, thus:

```
SELECT UNIQUE Group
FROM STAD_ALLOC SA
WHERE NOT EXISTS
        (SELECT Year, Group, Game
         FROM SA
         WHERE STAD_ALLOC.Year = Year
         AND STAD_ALLOC.Group = Group
         AND Stadium = 'Cordoba')
```

This is a nice example of the duality between set extensions and their characteristic functions (predicates), discussed in Chapter 2. The first example is of the form $(P - Q)$ and the second is of the form $(P(x)$ and not $Q(x))$.

7.5 QBE : QUERY-BY-EXAMPLE

Query-by-Example was developed at IBM's Yorktown Heights Research Center by M. Zloof, rougly concurrently with the development of SQL. The classic paper on it appeared in (Zloof 1977). Since then it has been refined into an IBM product QBE (IBM Corporation 1979), and it has also been used as the basis of a forms-based 'System for Business Automation' (Zloof and De Jong 1977).

The user of QBE does not write out his query using an elaborate nested syntax as for SQL. Instead he is presented with a screen on which he can throw up a template representing relational tuples. By filling in *example elements* in these tuples he gives examples of tuples to be retrieved, and the corresponding actual tuples are selected. For example, a query about stadia used by the group in which Poland came first would take the form:

STAD_ALLOC

Year	Group	Game	Stadium	Date
1978	A		P.Rosario	

GROUP_PLAC

Year	Group	Placing	Team
1978	A	1	Poland

Here we ask for tuples in the **STAD_ALLOC** relation where the Group value (underlined **A**) matches that from tuples in the **GROUP_PLAC** relation with Year = 1978, Placing = 1 and Team = Poland. The 'P.' under Stadium marks it as the value to be printed and an example element value 'Rosario' is given.

The use of underlines under 'A' and 'Rosario' shows that they are example elements, whose values are plausible, but should be replaced by the correct values when the results are printed. They are distinguished thus from actual constant values, such as '1' and 'Poland', which are not underlined. The frame and the headings for the queries are printed by the computer; the user just fills in the boxes. Boxes of no interest (e.g. Game, Date) are left blank.

7.5.1 QBE as a domain-oriented calculus

The example elements used in the templates are, of course, just existentially quantified variables. The user is supposed to be unaware of this, but, interestingly, people soon realise that the actual name means nothing and they choose short names. Also it is only necessary to place an underline before the first letter instead of under the whole name, so that people pretty quickly start using example elements like '_X' and '_Y'.

The significant difference from QUEL and SQL is that the values of the variables range over a particular attribute domain, e.g. the set of all possible stadia or of all possible groups, instead of over all tuples. Thus it is called a *domain-oriented calculus* in contrast to a 'tuple-oriented' one (Pirotte 1978).

We could write the query under discussion in a domain-oriented calculus as:

$$(\exists S: \text{Stadia}) (\exists A:\text{Groups}) (\exists X:\text{Games}) (\exists D:\text{Dates})$$
$$\text{STAD\_ALLOC}(1978,A,X,S,D) \wedge \text{GROUP\_PLAC}(1978,A,1,\text{'Poland'})$$

Here STAD_ALLOC and GROUP_PLAC are used as predicates which are true if tuples with the given argument values exist in the corresponding relations. More formally we could write this as, for example,

member($\langle$1978,A,X,S,D$\rangle$, STAD_ALLOC)

In Prolog, if we store STAD_ALLOC and GROUP_PLAC as unit clauses with five and four arguments respectively, instead of using a single tuple as argument, which suits a tuple-oriented calculus, then we can write the query as

STAD_ALLOC(1978,A,X,S,D), GROUP_PLAC(1978,A,1,'Poland'),
write(S).

The only snag with this is that it does not eliminate duplicates. To do this, we would have to use some of the techniques discussed in Chapter 4. QBE, by contrast, always eliminates duplicates, unless this is countermanded by the 'ALL' keyword (see below).

We are not constrained in QBE to equality tests. Suppose we wish to know: 'Which teams were placed higher than Poland in Group 2?'

GROUP_PLAC

Year	Group	Placing	Team
1978	2	_N1	Poland
1978	2	< _N1	P._X

In Prolog notation this query would read thus:

?– GROUP_PLAC(1978,2,N1,'Poland'), GROUP_PLAC(1978,2,N2,X),
(N2 < N1), write(X).

7.5.2 Correspondence between QBE and Prolog

In general, queries in QBE translate very easily into Prolog. Each row in a relation template translates into an atom, whose predicate symbol is the relation name, and whose arguments are the example elements (variables) and constants, reading in order across the row. Blank columns are replaced by nameless Prolog variables (_). We take the conjunction of the atoms, for each row that is linked to the others, together with extra predicates to express comparisons (e.g. $N2 < N1$), and predicates which express the tests in the Condition Box (see 7.6). The correspondence between Prolog variables and QBE example elements is exact, since both are existentially quantified over domains.

7.6 EXAMPLES FROM QBE COMPARED TO SQL

In general, we can easily form any query of the basic SQL form

SELECT F1, F2, . . . FROM R1, R2, . . . WHERE (F1 $\langle$comp$\rangle$ F2)
AND (F3 $\langle$comp$\rangle$ F4) AND. . .

We simply put a 'P.' under each selected field F1, F2, etc., in the templates for relations R1, R2, etc., and we put example elements under the fields that occur in the WHERE clause on the right of a comparison operator ⟨comp⟩. We then put, under any field that is on the left of ⟨comp⟩, an expression for the comparison, using the example element. For example, 'F1 > F2' is done by placing '_X' under F2, and the expression '>_X' under F1. However, if the comparison is equality, then we leave out the '=' sign, as with '_A' in our first example.

Problems arise where we have several conditions referring to the same field, since there is only room to put one condition under any attribute name. If we use more than one row, then it is taken as referring to an independent tuple variable ranging over the same relation, as in the example about teams placed higher than Poland. Whether the condition on the second row is 'AND-ed' or 'OR-ed' with the condition in the first row depends on the use of example elements, which can be rather confusing for the beginner.

Consider the following:

GROUP_PLAC

Year	Group	Team	Placing
1978		P._T	1
1978		_T	2

GROUP_PLAC

Year	Group	Team	Placing
1978		P._T	1
1978		P._S	2

The left-hand template asks for teams which were first in one group and second in another. The right-hand template asks for teams which were first in some group and then asks an independent query, using a different domain variable _S, about teams which were second in any group; the overall effect is to ask for the union of the two sets of teams and thus to ask for teams which were first in a group *or* second in a group.

Later versions of QBE introduced a separate *Condition Box* into which the user could write combinations of conditions, which thus allows one to write any condition that could appear in the WHERE clause of SQL. Thus, 'List teams which were first or second in any group between 1960 and 1982':

GROUP_PLAC   Condition

Year	Group	Team	Placing
_Y		P.	_N

Condition
_Y ⩾ 1960 and ⩽ 1982
_N = 1 or 2

If a variable is missed out before a comparison operation, it is assumed to refer to the variable at the start of the condition, or the variable last mentioned. Thus in normal calculus notation we would write the second condition as '(N=1) or (N=2)'

7.7 USE OF OUTPUT RELATIONS, SNAPSHOTS AND VIEWS

All the queries we have considered so far in QBE have generated result values from tuples of a single relation. The tuples of other relations have been used only in selection conditions. However, we may wish to extract information from more than one relation, and we may also want to compute values not stored in the database: the so-called 'derived fields'. In order to do this we need a separate template for the result relation. The user has facilities to create such a template. The values in this template are expressions made up from domain variables defined in the existing templates. The user is allowed to make up his own attribute names for the columns; they need not be the same as the columns in other relations from which values were extracted. For example, suppose we want to list the goal differences for games played in group 2, together with the stadia in which they were played:

STAD_ALLOC

Year	Group	Game	Stadium	Date
_Y	2	_G	_S	

GAMES

Year	Group	Game	TeamA	ScoreA	TeamB	ScoreB
_Y	2	_G		_SA		_SB

RESULT

Stad	Gdiff
P._S	P._SA−_SB

·Here the Stad value is taken from Stadium in STAD_ALLOC, and the Gdiff value is computed from the two fields ScoreA and ScoreB in the GAMES relation. The tuples are linked by the condition that the tuples should refer to the same Year(_Y), and Group(2) and Game(_G).

In Prolog notation we could write the query as:

    ?− STAD_ALLOC(Y,2,G,S,_), GAMES(Y,2,G,_,SA,_,SB),
    GD is (SA − SB), write([S, GD]).

7.7.1 Snapshots and views
We can use the result relation of one query as an input relation in another query. This is called forming a 'snapshot'. Instead of just printing the result,

we arrange to store it as a relation in temporary storage and to use it subsequently, with other relations, to answer another query.

This facility is very important for the practical use of query languages. It is a way of providing a *view* of the data to certain types of user. These are people who do not require to see the whole database, and who like to view it as though it just contained certain derived relations rather than the basic ones. For example they might like game and stadium information merged together into a single relation, with average scores included. Subsequent queries would be in terms of this and other relations.

SQL has powerful facilities for defining and naming such views, and for storing and editing view definitions. For example, one can define a view of the QBE relation just discussed as:

DEFINE VIEW STADIF(STAD, GDIFF) AS
  SELECT Stadium, ScoreA − ScoreB
  FROM GAMES, STAD_ALLOC
  WHERE GAMES.Year = STAD_ALLOC.Year
    AND GAMES.Group = 2 AND STAD_ALLOC.Group = 2
    AND GAMES.Game = STAD_ALLOC.Game

A subsequent query could then be, for example,

SELECT STAD
FROM STADIF
WHERE GDIFF > 3

The main difference between a view and a snapshot is that a view is a more general concept. It might be implemented by using the view definition as a kind of macro; the query on the view is macro-expanded and re-arranged so that it just refers to the basic relations. The advantage of this approach is that, if the basic relations are updated, one does not have to update all the stored copies of the snapshots, nor does one have to provide storage space for them. Fuller descriptions of the view definitions in SQL and QBE are given in Date (1981) and in manufacturer's literature.

7.8 THE GROUP_BY OPERATION IN SQL AND QBE

We have already seen the use of functions like COUNT, MIN and MAX applied to sets. These are variously called *built-in* functions in SQL or *aggregation* functions in QUEL or *grouping* functions in Relational Algebra (Gray 1981). The characteristic of these functions is that they allow the computation of values over sets of tuples. Now it is possible to ask for the result of an aggregation function as the single answer to a query, as in, for example, SELECT MAX(ScoreA) FROM GAMES . . .', which selects a single number giving the highest score obtained by the 'A' team in any game. However, it is often interesting to partition a relation into subsets, which are identified by having the same common value for some attribute, and then to tabulate the value of the grouping function for each subset beside the common attribute value. For example, suppose we want the highest scores in each group, and the average, then we could write the query in SQL thus:

> SELECT Year, Group, MAX(ScoreA), MAX(ScoreB), AVG((ScoreA
>   + ScoreB)/2)
> FROM GAMES
> GROUP BY Year, Group

The 'GROUP BY' clause specifies how to form the subsets of tuples over which the values of MAX() and AVG() are to be calculated. The resulting relation might look like:

Year	GROUP	MAX(ScoreA)	MAX(ScoreB)	AVG((ScoreA + ScoreB)/2)
1978	1	3	2	1.50
1978	2	3	6	1.25
1978	3	1	2	0.67
1978	4	4	2	1.58
1978	A	3	5	1.58
1978	B	3	6	1.33
1978	F	1	3	1.75
1982	1			
. . .	. . .	. . .	. . .	

Thus there are 6 tuples in GAMES with Year = 1978 and Group = 1. From these tuples the average score is 1.5, and the highest score was 3 for the A team and 2 for the B team. There are only two tuples with Year = 1978 and Group = F and the highest scores were 1 and 3.

It is possible to impose selections on the results of the Group-By operation so that we only see some of the tuples in the result. There are two ways of doing this in SQL. One way is to form the result of Group-By into a view and then to ask a query which selects tuples from this view. The other way is to use a HAVING clause after GROUP BY. This contains a selection predicate which refers to the attributes of the grouped relation, not the original relation.

For example, if we want the average scores of those groups in 1978 which have high maxima, then we could write it as:

> SELECT Group, AVG((ScoreA + ScoreB)/2)
> FROM GAMES
> WHERE Year=1978
> GROUP BY Group
> HAVING (MAX(ScoreA)>5) OR (MAX(ScoreB)>5)

The HAVING clause is very like the WHERE clause. The distinction is that the WHERE clause first refines the contents of each subset while the HAVING clause selects whole subsets depending on their aggregate properties.

In QBE we can also use the Group-By operator, usually in conjunction with an Output Relation. Thus we would write the original query given above as

GAMES

Year	Group	Game	TeamA	ScoreA	TeamB	ScoreB
_Y	_G			_SA		_SB

RESULT

Yr	Gp	MaxA	MaxB
P.G._Y	P.G._G	P.MAX.ALL._SA	P.MAX.ALL._SB

Average
P.AVG.ALL.((_SA+_SB)*0.5)

Here the syntax seems awkward. We define the columns for use in grouping by use of the G prefix. Where there is more than one, we can indicate the sort order of the result by use of '.AO(1)' and '.AO(2)' under the appropriate positions. If we wanted it sorted by Year within Group, thus clustering the Year values together for each Group, then we would put 'G.AO(2)._Y' under 'Yr' and 'G.AO(1)._G' under 'Gp'. The use of MAX and AVG under the other columns, which are newly created, is fairly obvious.

We can deal with a HAVING clause in QBE by using the Condition Box to hold the condition on the aggregate values, thus:

CONDITIONS
(MAX.ALL._SA) > 5.OR. (MAX.ALL._SB) > 5

The use of '.All.' following MAX and MIN is required in order to stop QBE suppressing duplicates before the grouping operation. However, there is one case where we do not want this to happen. It may be that we want to apply the COUNT operation (CNT) to the result of Group-By, and we want to count the number of distinct Stadia played in by Scotland, grouped by Year. Then we can formulate it:

STAD_ALLOC

Year	Group	Game	Stadium	Date
P.G._Y	_Gp	_GA	P.CNT.UNQ._S	

GAMES

Year	Group	Game	TeamA	ScoreA	TeamB	ScoreB
_Y	_Gp	_GA	_TA		_TB	

CONDITIONS
_TA = Scotland | _TB = Scotland

Note that in this case we are aggregating over an existing field instead of over a derived value (like _SA + _SB) and so we do not need to introduce an output relation template.

The use of the Group-By operation is difficult to formulate in calculus notation because it requires one to describe a set of values satisfying a predicate and then to apply functions to the set, whereas the basic style of calculus is to ask queries about individual elements. It is much easier to specify queries on sets in a functional language, such as relational algebra, or in a language with set constructs like KRC.

In Prolog the specification of the predicate defining the set of year and stadium values is very similar to QBE, thus:

```
stadpred(_Y,_S) :—
        STAD_ALLOC(_Y,_GP,_GA,_S,_),
        GAME((_Y,_GP,_GA,_TA,_,_TB,_),
        (_TA = 'Scotland'; _TB='Scotland').
```

However, as explained in Chapter 4, one has then to write a number of recursive functions to form subsets and eliminate duplicates, in the absence of built-in facilities to do this.

In conclusion, both SQL and QBE have very similar facilities for using GROUP BY, which forms derived results by applying an aggregation function chosen from (CNT,SUM,MAX,MIN,AVG) to subsets of tuples clustered by values of certain attributes. The semantics of the Group-By operator become much clearer when we study it in relational algebra, so we will postpone further discussion till then. Relations formed by GROUP BY can be made into views (SQL) or snapshots (QBE) and fed back for use in subsequent queries. In the case of later versions of QUEL used with INGRES, snapshots are formed using the INTO clause, and aggregation functions are applied in a fashion similar to SQL.

7.9 SUMMARY

The languages QUEL, SQL and QBE all provide powerful high-level query facilities for use with relational databases. They are based on the relational calculus and the method of query formulation is largely independent of the implementation of the database. QUEL and SQL are based on a tuple-oriented calculus, where the variables represent individual tuples. QBE is based on a domain-oriented calculus where the example elements represent attribute values; it is thus very close to Prolog in style. All the languages now include functions that work over sets of values but SQL has the most powerful facilities in this respect. Complicated queries are formulated by breaking them down in stages and defining the intermediate results as views or snapshots.

8

Relational algebra: an applicative language

8.1 INTRODUCTION

We have seen how to ask queries in calculus notation, both tuple-based and domain-based. We shall now study a very different notation which has equivalent power — Relational Algebra. It is based not on calculus but on function application and the evaluation of algebraic expressions. We know that we can define a number of operations on real numbers (addition, multiplication, etc.), and use them to write down algebraic expressions (e.g. 2*x+y), together with rules for simplifying them; similarly we can define operations on relations (union,join,select,and others listed below) and write down expressions in relational algebra (e.g. GAMES*GROUP_PLAC), together with rules for simplifying them. We shall introduce a notation (ASTRID) for a full relational algebra which also includes the ordinary algebraic expressions on integers. We shall see how to write queries in the ASTRID language, just by thinking in terms of clerical operations on tables that produce new tables, until we have a table containing the desired result. We shall write down many of the queries that we have formulated in calculus notation on the 'World Cup' database. Then, in the next chapter, we shall go on to consider algorithms for converting queries from calculus to algebraic form and vice versa.

The basic operations of relational algebra were first suggested by Codd (1970). He also established that queries formulated using his calculus 'DSL-ALPHA' could be formulated in algebra and vice versa (Codd 1972); in consequence he called both languages *relationally complete*.

However, ASTRID includes extra operations, principally Extend and Group-By, which were not in Codd's algebra, and which allow the computation of derived data. Similar operations, like the built-in functions of SQL and QBE, have been added to the calculus-based languages to give them similar powers, as we saw in Chapter 7.

8.2 THE FOUR BASIC ALGEBRAIC OPERATIONS

In this section we consider four operations on relations considered as tables of rows and columns. The results of the operations are illustrated in Fig. 8.1, which uses the relations of the World Cup database given in Appendix I. Two of the operations, Selection and Projection, take just one relation and produce modified versions of a single table. The two other operations — Union and Join — are dyadic and were introduced in Chapter 6.

8.2.1 Selection

GROUP_PLAC selected_on [Year=1978 and Group="2"]

Selection (Fig. 8.1a) reduces the number of rows in a table, and can be thought of as cutting a table across horizontally with scissors, and thus removing any unwanted tuples which have been placed together below the cut. Formally speaking, we write it, using actual square brackets, thus:

R selected_on [⟨pred⟩]   {ASTRID syntax}
R [⟨attno⟩ ⟨comp⟩ ⟨attno⟩]   {Codd's syntax}

Here ⟨pred⟩ is a boolean expression, acting as a predicate, which can contain comparisons between attribute values and other attribute values in the same tuple, or else constants. Only those rows satisfying ⟨pred⟩ are kept. ASTRID allows very general boolean expressions, with 'and', 'or' and 'not' inside ⟨pred⟩, but Codd's original algebra only allowed simple comparisons. In the literature the use of general predicates is often referred to as 'Selection', in order to distinguish it from the simpler 'Restriction' operation, but we shall use these terms interchangeably.

8.2.2 Projection

STAD_ALLOC projected_to Year, Group, Stadium

Projection (Fig. 8.1b) reduces the number of columns in a table; it can be thought of as cutting it down vertically. The name derives from the notion of projecting a number of points from a space of n dimensions into one of fewer dimensions, and thus with fewer components, e.g. projecting a set of points in the X,Y plane into a set of points lying along the X axis. Unfortunately, the projected values of such 'points' may coincide; this happens when we have projected away a column which was part of the key, and consequently the remaining parts of two shortened tuples may be identical. Then we have to remove duplicate tuples and thus reduce the number of rows. However, if at least one candidate key is left intact for all rows, then there will be no duplicates to remove.

Year	Group	Team	Placing
1978	2	Poland	1
1978	2	W.Germany	2
1978	2	Tunisia	3
1978	2	Mexico	4

Fig. 8.1(a) – Selection.

Year	Group	Stadium
1978	1	Buenos Aires
1978	1	Mar Del Plata
1978	2	Buenos Aires
1978	2	Rosario
1978	2	Cordoba
1978	3	Velez
1978	3	Mar Del Plata
1978	4	Cordoba
1978	4	Mendoza
1978	A	Cordoba
1978	A	Buenos Aires
1978	B	Rosario
1978	B	Mendoza
1978	F	Buenos Aires

Fig. 8.1(b) – Projection.

Year	Group	Team	Placing
1978	1	Italy	1
1978	2	Mexico	4
1978	2	Poland	1
1978	2	Tunisia	3
1978	2	W.Germany	2
1978	3	Austria	1
1978	4	Peru	1
1978	A	Holland	1
1978	B	Argentina	1
1978	F	Argentina	1

Fig. 8.1(c) – Union.

Year	Group	Team	Placing	Stadium
1978	2	Poland	1	Buenos Aires
1978	2	Poland	1	Rosario
1978	2	Poland	1	Cordoba
1978	2	W.Germany	2	Buenos Aires
1978	2	W.Germany	2	Rosario
1978	2	W.Germany	2	Cordoba
1978	2	Tunisia	3	Buenos Aires
1978	2	Tunisia	3	Rosario
1978	2	Tunisia	3	Cordoba
1978	2	Mexico	4	Buenos Aires
1978	2	Mexico	4	Rosario
1978	2	Mexico	4	Cordoba

Fig. 8.1(d) – Join.

Formally we write the operation as:

R projected_to ⟨attname⟩ {,⟨attname⟩}   {ASTRID syntax}
R [⟨attno⟩ {,⟨attno⟩}]   {Codd's syntax}

where the list of ⟨attname⟩s denotes names of columns to be kept; Codd's syntax uses column numbers ⟨attno⟩ instead. The ⟨attname⟩ values must of course be names of attributes of R.

8.2.3 Union

GROUP_PLAC selected_on [Year=1978 and Group="2"] union
GROUP_PLAC selected_on [Year=1978 and Placing<2]

The Union operation (Fig. 8.1c) is dyadic; it takes the rows of two tables and puts them one after another to form one long table. This is, however, only possible if the two tables are of the same type, i.e. they have the same column names and column types. We then say they are 'union compatible'. Any duplicate tuples must of course be removed from the result relation.

We write the operation as 'R1 union R2', and it behaves exactly like the operation of set union. As remarked in Chapter 6, it is complementary to restriction, in that we can recreate a relation from the union of two complementary restrictions.

8.2.4 Join

GROUP_PLAC selected_on [Year=1978 and Group="2"] joined_to
STAD_ALLOC projected_to Year, Group, Stadium

The join operation (Figs. 8.1(d), 6.5) is dyadic; it is defined for any two tables. If the two tables have no column names in common it behaves as a cartesian product, and concatenates each row of the first table with every row of the second table in turn. If the two tables have identical column names, it behaves as a set intersection operation and produces a table of those rows which occur in both tables (this may even be empty, like the null set). If the tables have some columns in common, then it produces a table with all the column names from the first table together with any extra column names from the second one. Rows are selected from the first table, and extra values are concatenated on from rows in the second table which have matching values in the common columns, as explained at the end of Chapter 6. To some extent Join is complementary to Projection; if one projects a relation into a number of relations, each retaining the prime key, then the Join of these relations will reconstruct the original relation, provided that every column of the original relation appears in at least one of the projections.

In the formation of queries, the join operation is crucial to any query involving more than one relation. Typically a query is formulated by joining together several tables, then selecting desired rows and finally projecting to desired columns for printing. The union operation is uncommon in practice, since it can often be rewritten by using an 'or' inside a selection operation, as discussed in Chapter 2.

8.2.5 Degree and cardinality
We can tabulate formulae for the Degree (no. of columns) and Cardinality (no. of rows) of tables resulting from the basic operations acting on relations A and B, giving upper and lower limits where appropriate. Let the cardinalities of A and B be AR and BR respectively and the corresponding degrees AD and BD. Then we have:

Args	Operation	Cardinality		Degree	
		max	min	max	min
A	Select	AR	0	AD	AD
A	Project	AR	1	AD	1
A,B	Union	AR+BR	max(AR,BR)	AD	AD(=BD)
A,B	Join	AR*BR	0	AD+BD	max(AD,BD)
A	Extend	AR	AR	AD+n	AD+n
A	Group_By	AR	1	AD+n	n

These formulae follow straightforwardly from the definitions of the operators given above, except for Extend and Group-By, which are used to derive 'n' extra fields; they are described in later sections but included here for completeness. The function 'max' gives the greatest of its two arguments. We are assuming that the cardinalities, AR and BR, are non-zero and that the degree of relations is always non-zero; (it is possible to define the behaviour of relations with zero degree but it is not easy for users to understand this or make use of it).

8.3 CORRESPONDENCE WITH DATA PROCESSING OPERATIONS ON SERIAL FILES

Since a relation can be represented as a file of records, it is interesting to consider the implementation of relational operations using this representation, to see how this corresponds to the method used in commercial data processing based on tapes. The correspondence is of interest, since it may show us whether the algebra is powerful enough to compute results on real data used in commerce. The operations and their results are shown in Fig. 8.2.

Input Files:

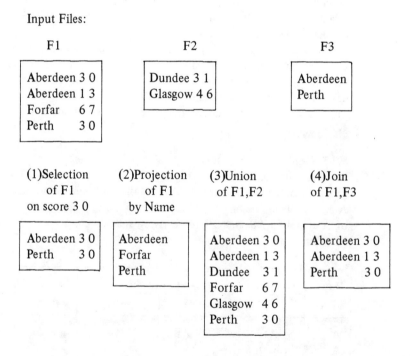

Fig. 8.2 – Relational operations on files of records.

The selection operation corresponds closely with programs that extract records from files and print them. However, the selection conditions can only pertain to individual records; e.g. we cannot select a record because it has a value matching or exceeding that in a preceding record. In fact it is almost impossible to model the behaviour of a finite state automaton which keeps changing its state with each record, and thus altering the selection criteria for the next record.

The projection operation also corresponds with an extraction program, but one that only prints particular fields from each record. The removal of duplicates is commonly achieved by using the fact that the records are sorted on the desired field, and by skipping past records until the field changes. In commercial practice the projection operation is usually combined with a selection operation in a single pass through a file.

The union operation is shown in Fig. 8.2 and corresponds to the well known 'file merge' or 'append' operation. If the files are known to be disjoint, and order is unimportant, then the operation of copying one file onto the end of another (append) suffices. However, it is more usual to keep the files in order by primary key, and to use the classic merge algorithm to read from each file in turn, depending on which has the lowest key, and thus to write out the new file in order of prime key.

The join operation in Fig. 8.2 corresponds most closely to 'selective extraction', where a list of keys is provided as records in a Transaction File, and the corresponding records in the Master File are to be extracted or written to an output file. The keys in the transaction file may just match a foreign key in the Master File, or else part of the primary key, in which case several Master records may be extracted for each Transaction record. In this way we are using the Join as a generalised Intersection. However, it is unusual to use the 'Cartesian Product' property of join, where N Transaction records match M Master records and (N x M) records are written out. This only occurs where, for each record on the Master, a pass is made through the whole Transaction File (or at least through the N matching records), a process which is bound to be slow and usually avoided.

8.4 COMBINING THE BASIC OPERATIONS

The basic operations can be composed just by putting them one after another in an expression. The expression is evaluated left to right, except that modifier operations (taking one relation) have a higher precedence than dyadic operations (like join on two relations), and are thus done before them. (See Syntax in Appendix II.) For example, to list all the groups in which Scotland played in 1978, we have:

> GROUP_PLAC selected_on [Year=1978 and Team="Scotland"]
>   projected_to Group

To get the stadium used by the groups we write:

> (GROUP_PLAC selected_on [Year=1978 and Team="Scotland"]
>   projected_to Group
>   joined_to STAD_ALLOC selected_on [Year=1978])
> projected_to Stadium

In order to see the meaning of this query, let us name each intermediate result, and write it in stages, which is allowed in ASTRID. The syntax requires one to put the name of each intermediate relation on the left of a ':=' symbol. However, this should be read as a definition statement, rather in the manner of 'Let X=', and not as an assignment statement. Relation names come into scope once they are introduced and can be used anywhere in subsequent expressions.

SCOTPLAC:= GROUP_PLAC selected_on[Year=1978 and Team="Scotland"]
SCOTGROUPS:= SCOTPLAC projected_to Group
STAD78:= STAD_ALLOC selected_on[Year=1978]
SCOTSTAD78:= SCOTGROUPS joined_to STAD78
SCOTSTADS:= SCOTSTAD78 projected_to Stadium

Output SCOTSTADS

We see here how each line defines a new table in terms of existing ones, until finally we define the result table SCOTSTADS and order it to be printed. This form is more comprehensible to beginners, but it can always be transformed into a single algebraic expression by substituting for the intermediate relation names. Thus it is based on building up expressions by function application without assignment. It is actually permissible to re-use a relation name, e.g. by writing

R := R projected_to Group

In this case subsequent references to R reference the new meaning of R and not its old value. Since there are no loops or jumps backward in the algebra, this convention is unambiguous. We are just re-using a name, and not destroying the original value of R.

8.5 COMPARISON OF ALGEBRA AND CALCULUS

The principal advantage of the algebra is that it is *closed* under the relational operations. That is to say, each operation on a relation produces a new relation which has exactly the same status as the original one, in that all the operations of the algebra are potentially applicable to it (subject only to semantic restraints). No operation produces an object which lies outside the scope of the algebra. In calculus-based languages, by contrast, certain difficult queries have to be formulated by asking sub-queries and storing the results either as Views or Snapshots, as discussed in Chapter 7. The language for formulating these Views is to some extent 'outside' that of the calculus. However, in the case of algebra, we do not need any extra constructs to describe the making of Views, since the notion of using intermediate relations is already there, and thus queries of arbitary complexity can be built up, some running to as many as twenty-five lines! The crucial thing is that the user can give each intermediate result a *name* to remember it by, if he chooses; by contrast, calculus notation tends to produce complex nested expressions which are unnamed, and it is thus harder to read and understand.

Books on the calculus usually claim it is more 'non-procedural' than relational algebra, because it just describes the result in terms of a collection of predicates, whilst the algebra gives a succession of operations to be applied to produce the desired result. However, relational algebra has the property of 'referential transparency' (discussed in Chapter 5), which allows one to make substitutions and to rewrite the operations in many equivalent forms; thus the description is more flexible than it looks. In practice, when transforming queries, it seems just as easy, if not easier, to work with algebraic rather than calculus notation. This is an advantage shared with the functional programming languages discussed in Chapter 5.

8.5.1 Relational algebra as an applicative language

We have seen that ASTRID relational algebra has an applicative syntax using infix operations. We have also seen how we can substitute expressions for named intermediate relations: this is allowable because the language has refer- ential transparency. Because of this property, we can substitute equivalent expressions for existing ones without altering the value of the result; this is very important in optimisation, as shown in the next chapter.

For example, we can rewrite:

(GROUP_PLAC joined_to STAD_ALLOC) selected_on[Year=1978]

as

(GROUP_PLAC selected_on[Year=1978]) joined_to
(STAD_ALLOC selected_on[Year=1978])

This allows us to do the selection before the join, and thus to reduce the size of the tables to be joined, which will usually speed up the operation.

The syntax using infix operators should not conceal the fact that we are applying functions. In case anyone doubts this, let us rewrite the algebraic expression above in prefix notation:

join(select(GROUP_PLAC,eq(Year,1978)), select(STAD_ALLOC,eq(Year,1978)))

8.6 THE ASTRID LANGUAGE : SYNTAX FOR A GENERALISED ALGEBRA

An early implementation of Codd's proposals using relational algebra was carried out as part of the PRTV project (Todd 1976). The ASTRID project (Gray and Bell 1979) was strongly influenced by this and included a full relational algebra, which has been in use for a number of years at various sites. The full syntax of the algebra is given in Appendix II.

8.6.1 Cardinal (two-relation) operators
The list of dyadic operations, which are all of type

Relation × Relation → Relation

is:

Operator	Mnemonic form	Meaning
*	joined_to	{Join}
+	union	{Union}
−	without	{Set Difference}
**	produced_with	{Cartesian Product}
.	intersect_with	{Intersection}
/	divided_by	{Division}

Each operator can be used in the infix position, either in the short form (left column) or mnemonic form (centre column). The cartesian product operator is not technically necessary, since it is a special case of Join. However, by providing a separate operator for it, we are enabled to print a warning message whenever a normal join is used between two relations with no common columns, since this is commonly caused by a mis-spelt column name. If the user really wants this construct then he can use '**', which only prints a warning if its arguments do have column names in common. Thus it allows extra semantic checks. Similarly the intersection operation behaves exactly as a join, but first checks that its two argument relations are of the same type. The division operator is described later.

8.6.2 Modifier (single-relation) operators

These operators take only one relation, plus an extra argument telling how to modify it and produce a relation as a result. They are:

Operator	Mnemonic Form	Meaning
;[ ]	selected_on [⟨boolexp⟩]	{Selection}
;−[ ]	limited_by [⟨boolexp⟩]	{Select & Project}
%	projected_to ⟨attnamelist⟩	{Projection}
%−	discarding ⟨attnamelist⟩	{Projection}
%+[ ]	extend_by [⟨assignlist⟩]	{Extension}
%[:]	group_by [⟨attnamelist⟩ creating ⟨assignlist⟩]	{Group By}
%. . .	renaming ⟨renamelist⟩	{Change of Col. Names}

where

⟨attnamelist⟩ ::= ⟨attname⟩ | ⟨attname⟩, ⟨attnamelist⟩
⟨assignlist⟩   ::= ⟨assitem⟩ | ⟨assitem⟩, ⟨assignlist⟩
⟨assitem⟩   ::= ⟨newattname⟩ := ⟨exp⟩
⟨renamelist⟩   ::= ⟨renameitem⟩ | ⟨renameitem⟩, ⟨renamelist⟩
⟨renameitem⟩   ::= ⟨attname⟩ as ⟨newattname⟩
⟨newattname⟩   ::= ⟨attname⟩
⟨exp⟩   ::= ⟨constant⟩ | ⟨attname⟩ | ⟨bool exp⟩ | ⟨string exp⟩
                   | ⟨real exp⟩ | ⟨integer exp⟩

We have already seen Selection and Projection. The Discarding operation does a projection but it takes the list of names to be removed instead of those to be kept, which can be more convenient. The Extend_By and Group_By operations are explained below. They generate extra columns for relations, with new column names given by ⟨newattname⟩. The Rename operation is needed to change column names prior to Join as explained below. The full syntax for ⟨exp⟩ is given in the appendix and allows the computation of arithmetic, boolean or string expressions, which was not present in Codd's algebra.

8.7 USE OF JOIN WITH RENAME

All operations on relations produce new relations. In the case of Selection,

Projection, Union and Difference, the new relation has the same column names as the old, or else a subset of them. In the case of Extend and Group_By, the names of the new columns are supplied by the user and it is an error if they duplicate existing ones. However, a problem arises with the join operation. By our definition the join takes place by matching pairs of values in columns with the same name. However, we might wish the join to take place on columns with different names or else we might not want a join to take place on two columns which happen to have the same name. If we do perform a join in the latter case then we get a relation with an extra column which has the same name as an existing one; this is ambiguous and cannot be permitted. The way round both these problems is to use the Rename operation to change the offending column name before carrying out the join.

The most usual form of this problem is where we are joining a relation to itself. For example, suppose we have a relation MANAGES(Boss#, Emp#). If we want to know the manager of the manager of Employee E145 then we write:

R := MANAGES selected_on[Emp# = E145] projected_to Boss#
R := R renaming Boss# as Emp#
Ans := (MANAGES joined_to R) projected_to Boss#

The results and intermediate answers are illustrated in Fig. 8.3.

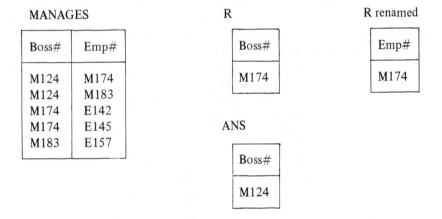

Fig. 8.3 – Use of Rename combined with Join.

The first line produces a relation of one column named Boss#, which has one tuple giving the immediate boss of employee E145. We now rename it so that the one column is named Emp#. We then join this to MANAGES so as to select the tuple in which the Boss appears as an employee of his superior, and then project the employee number of his superior. If we had not done the rename, we would have picked up the tuple(s) in which the boss appears as boss, and projected them to give his own Employee number!

The change of column name actually corresponds to a change of '*role*' by the person concerned. This can happen where values for the same entity appear under more than one column name, usually acting as different sub-types in the two cases (see end of Chapter 6).

Codd's original syntax just used column numbers and did not have explicit column names. Thus it had no need to change names but instead it needed to know which were the common columns. In consequence the join operator took, as an extra argument, a list of pairs of column numbers, rather like the join predicates used in relational calculus. Thus in his syntax we would write:

$$MANAGES\ [\ 1=1\ ]\ R\ \ \{MANAGES.Boss\# = R.Emp\#\}$$
or else $\quad MANAGES\ [\ 2=1\ ]\ R\ \ \{MANAGES.Emp\# = R.Emp\#\}$

The first version joins column 1 of MANAGES (Boss#) to column 1 of R (Emp#). The second version joins column 2 of MANAGES to column 1 of R, which is what we want. The corresponding predicate in QUEL syntax is shown in curly brackets. The snag with this scheme is that we have to keep remembering what each column number represents, which gets confusing after a number of joins and projections, so that it is harder to use than ASTRID.

8.7.1 The theta-join operation of Codd

In his original paper Codd defined the *equi-join* to be just like the natural join but without elimination of duplicate copies of common columns. Thus it is just a subset of the cartesian product of the two relations, with rows selected so that they contain the same values for the common columns. Codd generalised this definition to allow a *theta-join*, where the comparison operator 'theta' between the common columns was not restricted to equality but could instead be any of the six comparison operators $(=, <, >, \leqslant, \geqslant, \neq)$. However, since this can always be modelled by a cartesian product followed by a selection, very little use has been made of it in practice, though it is of some theoretical interest when we consider equivalences with relational calculus in the next chapter.

8.7.2 Traversing trees in relational algebra

By using combinations of join and rename we can find the ancestors or descendants, to a given depth, of any node in a hierarchy, for example the Employee-Manager hierarchy discussed in 6.7.5. Roughly speaking, we need an extra join for each extra level of depth. However, this relies on knowing the depth at the time of forming the query. It we wish instead to explore the tree to its tips (at an unknown depth) then we cannot write the query either in ASTRID or in Codd's relational algebra. Thus, although they are both 'relationally complete', the *completeness* does not extend to this class of query! What is needed in general is the ability to incorporate a 'while loop' in relational algebra, or to write recursive functions, as in KRC and FQL. There have also been proposals for a *transitive closure* operation, which repeatedly expands a relation, for example by adding new descendants of tuples, until no more can be found. This is discussed by Merret (1984), but there is no general agreement on such an operator.

8.8 EXAMPLE QUERIES IN ASTRID COMPARED TO QBE

We shall now see how to formulate many of the queries we looked at in QBE and SQL by using ASTRID. Some of these queries will need extra facilities and be dealt with in later sections of this chapter.

Query 1
'List games in 1978 which took place in Cordoba.'

>   STAD_ALLOC
>   selected_on [Stadium = "Cordoba" and Year = 1978]
>   projected_to Group, Game

This is typical SELECT . . FROM . . WHERE . . query on a single relation. In ASTRID it is effectively rewritten in the order FROM . . WHERE . . SELECT . ., with Project carrying out the job of SELECT (which makes a selection of fields and not of tuples). We do not have to say UNIQUE since ASTRID automatically eliminates duplicates.

Query 2
'List Stadia used in those Group(s) in which Poland came first.'

>   (GROUP_PLAC joined to STAD_ALLOC)
>   selected_on [Placing=1 and Team="Poland"]
>   projected_to Stadium

Again this is very like FROM . . WHERE . . SELECT . ., with the Join in the first line taking the place of 'FROM GROUP_PLAC, STAD_ALLOC' in SQL.

Query 3
'List stadia used by each group together with the team that came first in that group.'

>   (GROUP_PLAC selected_on [Placing = 1] joined_to STAD_ALLOC)
>   projected_to Stadium, Team

Here we have moved the selection inside the join in order to improve efficiency, as explained later. This can be done either by the user or else by a computer program automatically rewriting it. Note that the attributes in the projection list come from more than one relation, but this does not require any change in the form of the query.

Query 4
'List the other teams that played in the same group(s) as Holland.'

>   HGROUPS:=GROUP_PLAC selected_on [Team="Holland"]
>   projected_to Group,Year
>   RES:=(HGROUPS joined_to GROUP_PLAC)
>   selected_on [Team<>"Holland"] projected_to Team

Here we have an example of joining a projection of a relation back onto the original relation. Note that we do not have to use a synonym for GROUP_PLAC, as in SQL, since the join operation automatically matches columns with the same name, and thus eliminates the need to write join predicates. We never need to write, for example, 'GROUP_PLAC.Year' (as in SQL), since it is always clear from the context which relation the attribute 'Year' applies to; often it is an unnamed intermediate relation.

Query 5
'List teams in Group 2 which were placed higher than Poland.'

HPLACES:=GROUP_PLAC selected_on [Team="Poland" and Group=2]
projected_to Placing, Group, Year
renaming Placing as Hplace
RES:=(HPLACES joined_to GROUP_PLAC) selected_on [Placing <
Hplace] projected_to Team

This query requires the use of the theta-join which was defined earlier, so instead we use a join followed by a selection. We first generate a table of one row only, which contains the placing for Poland. We then rename it, to stop the join operation matching the Placing values with those in GROUP_PLAC. The join will select tuples with the same Year and Group and then concatenate the value of Hplace onto each one. The selection operation can now work on each tuple, comparing Placing with Hplace and selecting the desired tuples for projection to final results. The crucial thing to note is that, even though we know that the placing of Poland is a unique integer, we cannot name this integer and pass it across, for example as some kind of parameter. Instead we have to bundle it up as a relation and join it on.

This is an important feature of relational algebra. We can name relations and name relation attributes, but we cannot name individual values, as one can for example in QBE. This is because the result of each operation can only be a *relation* and not for example an integer, because of the closure property referred to earlier. Functions such as addition and subtraction can be used on integers, but only within a single tuple; one cannot add a value from one tuple to that from another without first joining the two tuples into one.

Query 6
'List teams placed first or second in any year between 1960 and 1982.'

GROUP_PLAC selected_on [Year≥1960 and Year ≤1982 and
(Placing=1 or Placing=2)]
projected_to Team

Note that we can cope with a general boolean selection expression, without using a condition box as in QBE.

8.9 THE EXTEND OPERATION AND DERIVED FIELDS

Suppose we wish to compute some derived information from fields in a tuple; for example, to work out an employee's net pay from (SALARY − TAX). We can do this by using the *extend* operation, which allows us to define a new relation containing extra columns whose values are derived from those of the preceding columns. Thus these extra values are functionally dependent on the key of the old relation, which thus becomes the key of the new relation.

The syntax of the operatior was given earlier as:

⟨relation⟩ := ⟨relation⟩ extend_by [⟨assign_list⟩]
⟨assign_list⟩ ::= ⟨attname⟩ := ⟨exp⟩ | ⟨attname⟩ := ⟨exp⟩, ⟨assign_list⟩

For example:

PSAL := EMPS extend_by [Deducs := Tax+Insurance]
                       extend_by [Netpay := Salary−Deducs]

The results of this query are shown in Fig. 8.4.

EMPS

EMPS extend_by [Deducs:=Tax+Ins] %−Ins
extend_by [Netpay:=Salary−Deducs]

Name	Salary	Dept	Tax	Ins
Smith	1500	A	400	130
Brown	1600	A	450	140
Jones	1600	B	320	140

Name	Salary	Dept	Tax	Deducs	Netpay
Smith	1500	A	400	530	970
Brown	1600	A	450	590	1010
Jones	1600	B	320	460	1140

EMPS group_by [Dept creating Number:=count(), Totsal:=sum(Salary)]

Dept	Number	Totsal
A	2	3100
B	1	1600

Fig. 8.4 − Derivation of new columns using Extend and Group_By.

The result is a relation with all the columns of **EMPS** plus two extra columns (Netpay and Deducs), which calculate the net pay and deductions respectively, for each employee record. If we think of it as a clerical operation on a table printed as a line printer listing, then it corresponds to writing extra columns down the right-hand side and filling them in using values from earlier in the row.

We can now formulate a query considered earlier:

Query 7
'List goal differences for games played in group 2, together with the stadia used.'

> (STAD_ALLOC joined_to GAMES) selected_on [Group=2]
>   extend_by [Gdiff:=if ScoreA > ScoreB
>   then ScoreA − ScoreB else ScoreB − ScoreA]
>   projected_to Stadium, Gdiff

Note that we must carry out the extend operation before the projection, because otherwise we will lose the fields ScoreA and ScoreB required for calculation! The expression which is used to calculate the value of the goal difference is a conditional expression, as used in the lambda calculus examples in Chapter 3. It can, however, be used only in the context of an Extend_By clause. The predicate following 'if' is any boolean expression which is written in terms of attributes of the current tuple and constants. Both 'then' and 'else' clauses must be given, and they must both compute expressions of the same type (real, integer, boolean, string).

In general, this operation allows us to compute any value that could appear as an expression in the SELECT line of an SQL query; in fact it is more general because of the possibility of conditional expressions. Its real power comes in multi-line queries, since the derived values can be used in joins and selections later on.

8.10 THE GROUP_BY OPERATION AS AN EXTENDED PROJECTION

The extend_by operation only allows us to compute values from other values in the same row. We need the dual of this operation, which will enable us, for example, to total up the values in a column. This is provided by the *group_by* operation. The operation behaves as a projection combined with extension (Gray 1981). It first partitions the values in given columns into subsets, based on their all having the same value for the attributes in the projection list. It then projects the relation to these attributes, but for each row in the result it computes a derived value by applying a built-in function to the corresponding subset, and then puts this value in an extra column as with the extend_by operation.

For example see Fig. 8.4, in which we have a relation 'EMPS (Name, Salary, Dept, Tax, Insurance)', as used above, and where 'Dept' is a foreign key giving the department of the employee. Then we can produce a table giving the number of employees in each department and the total salary bill for the department thus:

> EMPS group_by [Dept
>   creating Number:=count( ), Totsal:= sum(Salary)]

If we had just projected the EMPS relation to 'Dept' instead, then we would have got a list of departments with duplicates removed. The result of Group_By in this case is also a list of departments, and has the same number of tuples as the projection, but instead of just removing duplicates it computes a derived value from the specified column in each set of duplicates. Here 'Totsal' is computed by using 'sum' to add the values in the salary column, and 'Number' is computed by using 'count' to count how many there are.

The built-in functions include those of SQL and QBE (COUNT, SUM, MAX, MIN) together with two boolean functions ANY and ALL. If an average is required it can be computed by dividing the result of SUM by that of COUNT. The functions SUM, MAX and MIN are defined for a set of arithmetic values and give the total, largest value and smallest value respectively. ANY and ALL are defined over a set of boolean values and give the 'or' of the values and the 'and' of the values respectively. They are used in forming quantified queries, as explained later. Interestingly, if 'true' is considered greater than 'false', then ANY and ALL correspond to MAX and MIN respectively. Thus ANY is true if any of the values are true, and ALL is true if all the values are true. Let us now see how to formulate those queries which we have written in SQL using built-in functions.

Query 8
'List groups where no game is played in Buenos Aires.'

SAE   := STAD_ALLOC extend_by[InBA:=(Stadium="Buenos_Aires")]
GPS   := SAE group_by[Group creating Anyin:=any(InBA)]
BAGPS := SAE selected_on[not Anyin]
                     projected_to Group

The results of this query are shown in Fig. 8.5. Here we create an extra column InBA which contains 'true' if the game is played in Buenos Aires. We group the results by competition group and form the column 'Anyin', which is true if any game in that group has a value true for 'InBA', i.e. if any game in the competition group was played in Buenos Aires. The relation just contains tuples with columns for Group and Anyin, and we select those for which Anyin is false. Finally the column for Anyin is removed by projecting to Group. This form of the query is rather long-winded and it is possible to shorten it thus:

    STAD_ALLOC group_by[Group
                  creating Anyin:=any(Stadium="Buenos Aires")]
            limited_by[not Anyin]

Here we have allowed the built-in function 'any' to take an expression as its parameter. The function *limited by* acts like a selection, but also discards the values of any attribute names that are used in the selection expression, thus saving an extra projection.

It is interesting to note that the built-in functions never get applied to empty subsets, because the implicit projection operation in Group_By will always produce one tuple for each projected attribute value in the original relation. In consequence we cannot formulate the preceding query as:

    STAD_ALLOC selected_on[Stadium="Buenos Aires"]
              group_by[Group creating Ct:=count()]
              limited_by[Ct=0]

SAE

Year	Group	Game	Stadium	Date	InBA
1978	1	1	Buenos Aires	2_Jun	t
.	.	.	. . .	.	.
1978	A	6	Buenos Aires	21_Jun	t
1978	B	1	Rosario	14_Jun	f
1978	B	2	Mendoza	14_Jun	f
1978	B	3	Rosario	18_Jun	f
1978	B	4	Mendoza	18_Jun	f
1978	B	5	Mendoza	21_Jun	f
1978	B	6	Rosario	21_Jun	f
1978	F	1	Buenos Aires	24_Jun	t
1978	F	2	Buenos Aires	25_Jun	t

GPS

Group	Anyin
1	t
2	t
3	f
4	f
A	t
B	f
F	t

BAGPS

Group
3
4
B

Fig. 8.5 — Illustration of group-by operation.

The last selection condition can never be satisfied, since if the count were zero then the corresponding Group value would simply not be present in **STAD_ ALLOC** after the selection, and thus there would be no tuple for Group_By to work on! Hence, instead of actually doing the selection and losing the tuple, we mark it with the boolean value 'false' for 'InBA', and then use the function 'any' in place of 'count'.

Query 9
'List groups and average scores for games played in 1978 where the highest score in the group was over 5.'

GAMES group_by[Group creating Ma:=max(ScoreA), Mb:=max(ScoreB),
                        Av:=sum((ScoreA+ScoreB)/2)/count()]
        limited_by[Ma>5 or Mb>5]

We note here the use of 'limited_by' to perform the function of the HAVING clause in SQL, selecting values of max(ScoreA) and max(ScoreB) computed in the group_by clause. It seems neater and less ambiguous to do this. One disadvantage of the SQL method is that built-in functions can appear in both the SELECT clause and the HAVING clause; thus, if there is more than one group_by clause, it is not immediately apparent to which grouping operation the built-in functions refer.

Query 10
'List the year and the number of different stadia played in by Scotland in that year.'

(STAD_ALLOC joined to GAMES)
selected_on[TeamA="Scotland" or TeamB="Scotland"]
projected_to Year, Stadium
group_by[Year creating Nstad:= count()]

The main thing to note about this query is the use of projection to remove duplicate values of stadium before the group_by operation, since otherwise the count would include the same stadium several times. This is achieved in QBE by the built-in function CNT.UNQ.

8.11 THE GENERALISED DIFFERENCE OPERATION AND UNIVERSAL QUANTIFICATION

We saw in Fig. 8.1 how to use the union operation and the intersection (join) operation in relational algebra. The other classic operation on two sets is the difference operation, which finds those elements which are in the first set but not in the second. In ASTRID we write the operator as 'without' and we can use it to write an alternative form of query 8:
'List groups where no game is played in Buenos Aires.'

STAD_ALLOC projected_to Group
without
(STAD_ALLOC selected_on[Stadium="Buenos Aires"]
                        projected_to Group)

A very similar formulation is used in SQL. We first form a list of all groups and then remove those on the list of 'bad' groups. Note that, because the projection removes duplicates, any game played in Buenos Aires which occurs in the group will be enough to include that group on the 'bad list'. Thus the projection is performing a similar role to Group_By discussed earlier. We shall see rules for rewriting such queries in the form using Group_By in the next chapter.

In order to list those groups where *all* games are played in Buenos Aires, we just change the comparison from 'Stadium=' to 'Stadium <>' in the above query. Effectively we are using the calculus rule for negating quantifiers which was given in Chapter 7, section 7.3.2:

($\exists$ group)($\forall$ game) STAD_ALLOC(year,group,game,stad) → stad="Buenos Aires"
     equals

($\exists$ group) ~($\exists$ game) STAD_ALLOC(year,group,game,stad) $\land$
                              stad<>"Buenos Aires"

In other words, the set of groups where, for all games, the stadium is Buenos Aires is equivalent to the complement of the set of groups where at least one game is played in another stadium. We are using the 'without' operation to perform the set complement, having first established the 'universe' as the set of all groups in the competition, which is formed by projecting the entire STAD_ ALLOC relation to Group.

This observation shows how a set difference can be used to express universal quantification. It is not always this easy and sometimes we must form the difference of a difference, as we shall see in Chapter 9. In ASTRID we can use either set difference or the boolean grouping function 'all' to express such queries. Often the formulation using 'all' is more obvious:
'List those groups where all games are in Buenos Aires.'

          STAD_ALLOC group_by [Group
                      creating Allin:=all(Stadium="Buenos Aires")]
                      limited_by [Allin]

8.12 FORMING COMPLEX MULTI-LINE QUERIES

Suppose we want to ask a really complicated query. The advantage of relational algebra is that we do not have to define views; instead we just keep adding extra lines to the query. In practice it seems that people start with simple queries of the 'SELECT .. FROM .. WHERE' variety, but that as they get more experienced they get more ambitious and they try to modify the query and add further lines; this is very easily done in relational algebra. Consider the example below.

Query 11
'List those teams who scored at least two goals in Cordoba but failed to score this many goals in any other stadium.'

          ALLGAMES   := GAMES extend_by [Team:=TeamA, Score:=ScoreA]
                      union
                      GAMES extend_by [Team:=TeamB, Score:=ScoreB]

CORTEAMS   := (ALLGAMES joined_to STAD_ALLOC)
                           selected_on [Stadium="Cordoba" and Score⩾2]
                           projected_to Team
GOODSCS   := (ALLGAMES joined_to STAD_ALLOC)
                           selected_on [Stadium<>"Cordoba"]
                           group_by [Team creating Sm:=max(Score)]
                           limited_by [Sm⩾2]
ANSWER   := CORTEAMS − GOODSCS

We start by forming **ALLGAMES**, which contains two tuples for each game. This is necessary because we are considering each team's behaviour independently and we may want to consider *both* teams on the basis of only *one* tuple in **GAMES**. Thus in **ALLGAMES** we treat each game as giving us two almost independent facts. It turns out that a lot of queries on this database start this way. Thus it might be better to give the user a view in which it appeared that **ALLGAMES** was stored directly; we can do this just by prepending the definition of **ALLGAMES** to his query.

We then form the set **CORTEAMS**, of those teams which scored more than two goals when playing in Cordoba. We then form a list of those teams whose highest score in any stadium outside Cordoba was 2 or better, and then we take the difference.

There are many ways of writing this query in **ASTRID** and we will consider the use of rewrite rules to do this automatically in the next chapter. Here we will just show one alternative using Group_By:

ANSWER := (ALLGAMES joined_to STAD_ALLOC)
                      group_by [Team creating
                                   Cor:=any(Stadium="Cordoba" and Score⩾2),
                                   Gsc:=any(Stadium<>"Cordoba" and Score⩾2)]
                      limited_by [Cor and not Gsc]

8.13 SUMMARY

Relational algebra works on sets of tuples and produces sets as results. It is thus closed under its operations. The ASTRID language, which includes both extend and group_by operations, can be used to express any query formulated in SQL; this is not true of Codd's original algebra. Universal quantification can be expressed by using the built-in function ALL with Group_By, or else by using the set difference operation. The optional naming of intermediate relations makes the language easy to use for large queries and provides the facilities of a view definition.

The important property of referential transparency makes for ease of query manipulation and optimisation. We shall be exploring this in the next chapter.

9

Query transformation in algebra and calculus

9.1 INTRODUCTION

On the surface, the algebraic and calculus methods of forming queries look very different. In this chapter we shall explore these differences and look at various ways of converting queries from one representation to another. One reason for doing this is that it allows us to *optimise* a query, by rewriting it in a form suitable for efficient computation. We are familiar with this concept from the techniques used in 'optimising' compilers, which re-order expressions in a long statement and remove redundant computations. However, this can only save microseconds, but in the case of a complicated database query it may reduce the number of accesses to secondary storage by an order of magnitude, which makes a very big difference.

9.1.1 Motives for query transformation

It is perfectly possible to take four hours to evaluate a query one way, but only five minutes to do it another way. Typically this is because the first method examines almost every record in the database and attempts to match them with other records, only to find that a subsequent operation selects only a few records out of all the results computed. The faster method will probably try to select a small number of candidate records very early on and process only these. The two different methods are usually based on a simplistic way of executing the query as written, and it is usually not at all obvious to the person writing the query that his formulation of it is inefficient. Furthermore, it is the job of a good system to save the user from worrying about efficiency, and to let him write a query in a way that seems natural to him.

One of the big advantages of writing a complex query entirely in relational algebra or calculus form, as against letting the user write a Fortran program with embedded database manipulation commands, is that it allows the system to do global optimisations on the whole query, and to change the entire strategy for its evaluation. Most optimising compilers can only do small local optimisations, because they cannot 'understand' the action of a group of statements. If they did, they would almost certainly decide to rewrite them completely; for example a group of statements might constitute a very poor algorithm for inverting a matrix, which should be replaced. By contrast, a relational algebra optimiser can work on an expression representing the entire query and completely change its form and order of evaluation. This advantage comes partly because relational algebra is an applicative language, as discussed in Chapter 5. It also arises because the query is formulated in terms of the abstract notion of a relation, and the user does not specify lower level operations such as sorting and indexing, which would be hard to undo. This is an advantage of working with the relational model. However, the consequence of allowing the user freedom from worry about efficiency is that the system must be capable of transforming queries into reasonably efficient forms, which is why the equivalences given later on are important.

9.1.2 Advantages of query translation for users
Another important reason for making transformations is because of the growing use of *distributed databases*. A user in one part of the country who is familiar with one database query language, say QUEL, may wish to access a remote database which uses a different language, say ASTRID. Rather than have the user learn a new language, it is desirable for the system to translate the query into the target language automatically, and we shall look at algorithms to do this. In the case where the user wishes to ask a query of several databases which are held separately but are to be treated as one database, these transformations are even more necessary. Projects using this technique include the MULTIBASE project (Smith, Bernstein *et al.* 1981) and the PROTEUS project (Stocker *et al.* 1984).

Even where a user is working on a single database, it is an advantage to provide several query languages, so that he can choose one that suits his purpose, and also to save learning a new language. Once again, it is an advantage to implement one general query language as efficiently as possible, and to translate other languages into this, rather than to implement each one independently. In most relational systems to date the general query language has used the operations of relational algebra.

9.1.3 Outline of chapter
In this chapter we start by looking at how to translate expressions from the algebraic form into calculus or Prolog, which is comparatively straightforward. We then explore the wide range of techniques available for transforming and optimising expressions in relational algebra, largely based on the work of Hall, Hitchcock and Todd (1975), and Smith and Chang (1975). We then consider how to translate queries expressed in relational calculus form in Query-by-Example into relational algebra. We conclude by examining in detail Codd's algorithm

(1972) for converting an arbitrary quantified query in relational calculus into relational algebra, particularly **ASTRID R.A.**

9.2 CONVERSION FROM RELATIONAL ALGEBRA TO CALCULUS

We shall consider the rules for translating from relational algebra to calculus. These are not often used in practice, since most relational database systems execute relational commands such as Join, and the problem is to translate calculus expressions into this form in order to execute them. However, we shall give here a list of algebraic expressions and the corresponding set expressions in calculus notation. Based on this, it is fairly straightforward to write a translator. The translation is based on the correspondence between the extension of a set and its predicate which was tabulated in Chapter 2. We shall also use this correspondence to justify some of the optimisations of relational algebra expressions given in the next section.

Our rules produce what Ullman (1980) calls a *safe* calculus expression, that is one which denotes a subset of a finite domain formed from the cartesian product of stored relations (possibly repeated). This is in contrast to an 'unsafe' expression, including terms like ($\sim t \in R$) which simply specify that a tuple t is *not* in some relation R, and so its possible values are unknown and taken from a potentially infinite domain. Ullman shows that the class of 'safe' expressions is exactly those relations computable in relational algebra.

9.2.1 Correspondence of algebraic operations and set expressions

For each type of algebraic operation we shall write down an example together with an equivalent calculus expression. We assume that stored relations are denoted by R1(x,y,z,. .), R2(a,b,c,. .), etc. in the algebra and by the corresponding predicates P1(t), P2(t) etc. in the calculus, where t is a tuple variable.

Each calculus expression is written in the form '{tp | P}', which denotes the set of those tuples 'tp' satisfying P. The notation '⟨x,y,z⟩' denotes a tuple with three component values, while 't++r' denotes a tuple made by concatenating tuple r onto the end of tuple t. The notation 't––r' denotes a tuple t, shortened by removing the attributes in tuple r. We use the concise form (%. .) of the ASTRID rename operation in some examples so that (x,y) become the common columns for a join, and so that both relations have the same columns (x,y,z) for the union and difference operations.

(1) Selection

R1;[f(x) and (g(y) or h(z))] $\{t \mid P1(t) \land f(t.x) \land (g(t.y) \lor h(t.z))\}$

(2) Projection

R1 projected_to x,y $\{\langle t,x,t.y\rangle \mid P1(t)\}$

(3) Cartesian product

R1 ** R2 $\{t++r \mid P1(t) \land P2(r)\}$

(4) Join

R1 * (R2 %. . a→x,b→y) $\{t++r-\langle r.a,r.b\rangle \mid P1(t) \land P2(r) \land$
$(t.x = r.a) \land (t.y = r.b)\}$

(5) Union
R1 + (R2 %. . a→x,b→y,c→z)   { t | P1(t) ∨ P2(t) }

(6) Difference
R1 − (R2 %. . a→x,b→y,c→z)   { t | P1(t) ∧ ˜P2(t) }

(7) Extend
R1 extend_by [e:=f(x,y,z)]   { t++ ⟨f(t.x,t.y,t.z)⟩ | P1(t) }

(8) Group_By
R1 group_by [x,y : e:=gf(z)]   { ⟨t.x,t.y,e⟩ | P1(t) ∧
                                     e = gf({ r.z | P1(r) ∧ r.x =t.x ∧ r.y = t.y}) }

We can also write pieces of Prolog to define the same results in a domain-oriented calculus. For simplicity we assume relations R1(x,y,z) and R2(a,b,c). If R1 and R2 have extra attributes, then the Prolog definitions will need extra parameters, but the changes are fairly obvious.

(1) Selection
R1 ;[f(x) and (g(y) or h(z))]   Res(X,Y,Z) :−
                                     R1(X,Y,Z), f(X), g(Y).
                                   Res(X,Y,Z) :−
                                     R1(X,Y,Z), f(X), h(Z).

(2) Projection
R1 projected_to x,y   Res(X,Y) :− R1(X,Y,Z).

(3) Cartesian product
R1 ** R2   Res(X,Y,Z,A,B,C) :− R1(X,Y,Z), R2(A,B,C).

(4) Join on common columns
R1 * (R2 %. . a→x,b→y)   Res(X,Y,Z,C) :− R1(X,Y,Z), R2(X,Y,C).

(5) Union
R1 + (R2 %. . a→x,b→y,c→z)   Res(X,Y,Z) :− R1(X,Y,Z).
                                 Res(X,Y,Z) :− R2(X,Y,Z), not R1(X,Y,Z).

(6) Difference
R1 − (R2 %.. a→x,b→y,c→z)   Res(X,Y,Z) :− R1(X,Y,Z), not R2(X,Y,Z).

(7) Extend
R1 extend_by [e:=f(x,y,z)]   Res(X,Y,Z,f(X,Y,Z)) :−R1(X,Y,Z).

(8) Group_By
R1 group_by [x,y : e:=gf(x)]   Res(X,Y,R) :− setof(Z, R1(X,Y,Z), S),
                                     apply(gf, S, R).

We note the remarkable ease with which the algebraic operations are expressed in Prolog. However, there is a problem about removing duplicates. All the Prolog clauses will work if used with particular values of X, Y and Z, to test if a given tuple is a member of the result of the operation. However, if they are used to generate results, then the definitions for projection and join are capable of generating the same tuple more than once. This could be overcome by using the 'setof' operation, as defined by Warren (1981a), and given in Chapter 4. This operation has to be used to express Group_By, and we have invented a predicate 'apply such that apply(gf, S,R) is true if R is the result of applying a grouping function gf (e.g. sum) over the set of values in S.

9.3 OPTIMISING ALGEBRAIC EXPRESSIONS – RE-ORDERING OPERATIONS

Some of the most significant improvements in query formulation are made simply by changing the order of operations. Thus by moving selection operations so that they take place *before* instead of after joins, we can often answer the query faster. This is because operations such as join and cartesian product act as *generators,* producing large amounts of tuples; thus if we can make some selections early we can reduce the amount generated. This is an example of a general principle of computation; one should always use problem-specific information to control and reduce the output of a generator at source instead of waiting till later to test the output and reject it.

9.3.1 Moving selections through joins
The important equivalence that we rely on is as follows.

Let $A(a1, a2, \ldots am)$ and $B(b1, b2, \ldots bn)$ be two relations with attributes a1 to am and b1 to bn respectively. Let P be a predicate involving only the attributes of A, then:

$$(A \text{ joined\_to } B) \text{ selected\_on } [P] \\ = (A \text{ selected\_on } [P]) \text{ joined\_to } B \tag{E1}$$

The proof of this is based on the commutativity of 'and'. If we write the equivalent formula in calculus notation using $JP(r1,r2)$ to represent a join predicate involving terms such as $(r1.a1=r2.b3)$, where r1 and r2 are tuple variables (Chapter 7), then we see this immediately:

$$(\exists r1,r2) ((r1 \in A) \land (r2 \in B) \land JP(r1,r2)) \land P(r1) \\ = (\exists r1,r2) ((r1 \in A) \land P(r1)) \land (r2 \in B) \land JP(r1,r2)$$

For a practical example on the World Cup database consider:

$$(STAD\_ALLOC * GROUP\_PLAC) \text{ selected\_on } [\text{ Stadium}=\text{``Cordoba''} \\ \text{and Year}=1978]$$

rewritten as

$$(STAD\_ALLOC \text{ selected\_on } [\text{ Stadium}=\text{``Cordoba'' and Year}=1978]) \\ * GROUP\_PLAC$$

The result of this is to reduce the number of tuples considered for the join down from 40×40 to 5×40 in the year 1978. This example also shows that one could make the selection [Year=1978] also on GROUP_PLAC, thus:

(STAD_ALLOC selected_on[Stadium="Cordoba" and Year=1978]) *
(GROUP_PLAC selected_on[Year=1978])

Thus we can generalise the equivalence if we separate the selection predicate P into the conjunction of four terms: PA referring only to A, PB referring only to B, PC referring only to the common columns of A and B, and PR which includes anything that cannot be included in PA, PB or PC. Any of PA,PB,PC or PR may be empty, corresponding to the constant 'true' (i.e. no selection). Then we have that:

(A*B) selected_on[PA and PB and PC and PR]
= ((A selected_on[PA and PC]) * (B selected_on[PB and PC]))   (E2)
    selected_on[PR]

9.3.2 Combining multiple selections
Another useful equivalence is:

(A selected_on[P]) selected_on[Q]
= (A selected_on[P and Q])
= (A selected_on[P]) intersect (A selected_on[Q])   (E3)
= (A selected_on[P]) joined_to (A selected_on[Q])

The proof of the first two lines follows from the definition of 'and', since those tuples of A which are selected to satisfy P and are then selected to satisfy Q must be just those which satisfy both P and Q. The next line follows from the equivalence between the intersection of two sets and the conjunction of their characteristic functions, discussed in Chapter 2. The last line follows because both relations are of the same type, so the join behaves as an intersection.

The various forms may be converted onto that in the second line which uses 'and'. The advantage is that this can be computed in one pass through the relation A. Also, if A is itself the result of a join, then we can separate and recombine parts of P and Q to pass through this join as explained above.

Unfortunately, not all selections are equally easy to perform, so that in practice it pays to group 'fast selections' together, and to move them through joins, and not to combine them with 'slow selections' on large relations. Fast selections are those which are done using some kind of direct access technique, such as indexing or hashing, where the time for the selection depends mainly on the number of tuples selected, and not on the size of the whole relation. Thus it is limited to equality selections on specific columns. Other selections will require a sequential pass through the whole relation, and will be much slower. In consequence, it will not pay to pass a slow selection through a join which is acting as an intersection and which uses a fast selection technique to retrieve relatively few tuples. Thus, while our equivalences E1, E2 and E3 are generally useful, we need to know about the speed of the different selections before deciding how to combine them and re-order them.

It is possible to simplify a selection from [P and Q] to [P] in the case where P selects a subset of Q, e.g. if P is (a1=5) and Q is (a1<7). If we think of P and Q as set extensions instead of predicates then we rely on the fact that if P is a subset of Q then the intersection of P and Q is just P.

9.3.3 Combining selections and projections

Selection operations can be moved through projections to take place earlier. This is particularly valuable where there are special facilities to apply a selection direct to a stored relation (e.g. via an index or special hardware) which would be inhibited by the projection. It is also useful where the projection requires removal of duplicates by sorting, and the selection significantly reduces the number of tuples to be sorted. It is unusual to move a selection in the other direction (after a projection); in fact this is illegal if the projection removes an attribute involved in the selection.

In general if we have a relation of 'm' attributes A(a1,. .am) which is projected to 'n' attributes ap1,. .apn and we have a predicate P which only involves the projected attributes then:

$$(A \text{ projected\_to } ap1,ap2,. .apn) \text{ selected\_on}[P] \qquad \text{(E4)}$$
$$= (A \text{ selected\_on}[P]) \text{ projected\_to } ap1,ap2,. .apn$$

Several projection operations may be replaced just by the last one thus:

$$(A \text{ projected\_to } a1,. . .) \text{ projected\_to } ap1,ap2,. .apn \qquad \text{(E5)}$$
$$= A \text{ projected\_to } ap1,ap2,. .apn$$

Combining these two rules we can see that for example

$$\text{STAD\_ALLOC projected\_to Year,Stadium selected\_on[Stadium=}$$
$$\text{"Cordoba"] projected\_to Year}$$
$$= \text{STAD\_ALLOC selected\_on[Stadium="Cordoba"] projected\_to Year}$$

9.3.4 Moving projections through joins

Projection operations may be moved inside joins with two possible advantages.

(a) If the projection leaves the key intact, which means it can be done cheaply, then it reduces the size of tuples to be stored (and possibly sorted) for the join operation.

(b) Even if the projection involves removing duplicates, it may be possible to do this efficiently, e.g. via an index on the projected column(s); then if many duplicates are removed, the join will be quicker because the relation is much smaller.

Alternatively it may be useful to move projections outside joins so that they do not inhibit the join of two stored relations by indexes or special hardware facilities. Which order is chosen in practice depends on costing the operation and choosing the cheapest overall plan (Todd and Verhofstad, 1978; Selinger *et al.,* 1979).

The rule is as follows. Let relation A have a set al= (a1,. .an) of 'n' attributes. Similarly let relation B have the set bl=(b1,. .bm). Let the set of common attribute names be cl which is given by (al intersect bl). Let the list of projected attributes be pl=pl1,. .plr. Then:

$$(A * B) \text{ projected\_to pl} \tag{E6}$$
$$= ((A \text{ projected\_to al}') * (B \text{ projected\_to bl}')) \text{ projected\_to pl}$$

where the sets of attributes in the projection lists al', bl' are

$$al' = (al \text{ intersect pl}) \text{ union cl}$$
$$bl' = (bl \text{ intersect pl}) \text{ union cl}$$

The reason the rule is complicated is that we must not project away any of the common columns (cl) before the join, since this will inhibit carrying out the join matching on these columns. Thus the new projection lists al' and bl' are formed by removing attributes not in the target list pl, and then adding back those in cl by the union operation. The final projection to pl is retained in case it removes some of the common columns cl. If however cl is a subset of pl then this projection has no effect. For example if al is the attribute list of A then:

A projected_to al = A

If we wish to move projections out through joins then we have:

$$(A \text{ projected\_to pl}) * B = (A * B) \text{ projected\_to pl}' \tag{E7}$$

where pl' = pl union bl, provided that ((al − pl) intersect bl) = 0 {empty}.

The provision is necessary in case some of those attributes of A that were projected away, namely (al − pl), had common names with the attributes bl of B, and so would be taken as extra columns for the join. If this is so, we must rename them to avoid the clash thus:

$$(A \text{ projected\_to pl}) * B \tag{E8}$$
$$= ((A \text{ renaming r1 as xr1,. . rn as xrn}) * B) \text{ projected\_to pl}'$$

where pl' = pl union bl, and the list r1,. .rn = ((al − pl) intersect bl).

As an example of this consider

(STAD_ALLOC selected_on [Stadium="Rosario"] projected_to Year)
* GAMES
= (STAD_ALLOC selected_on [Stadium="Rosario"] renaming Group as X,
Game as Y
*GAMES) projected_to Year,Group,Game,TeamA,ScoreA,TeamB,ScoreB

9.4 OPTIMISING UNION AND DIFFERENCE OPERATIONS

9.4.1 Moving selections

A form of the distribution law holds for moving selections through union(+) and difference(−) operations.

$(A + B)$ selected_on$[P] = (A$ selected_on$[P]) + (B$ selected_on$[P])$ (E9)
$(A - B)$ selected_on$[P] = (A$ selected_on$[P]) - (B$ selected_on$[P])$

A similar result holds for intersection, which is just a special case of that established earlier for the join operation. If we write down equivalent expressions in the tuple-oriented predicate calculus, we see that the first result follows at once from the distribution law (Chapter 1), whilst the second follows similarly after using De Morgan's law.

$$\{ t \mid ((t{\in}A) \lor (t{\in}B)) \land P(t) \}$$
$$= \{ t \mid ((t{\in}A) \land P(t)) \lor ((t{\in}B) \land P(t)) \}$$

$$\{ t \mid ((t{\in}A) \land P(t)) \land {\sim}((t{\in}B) \land P(t)) \}$$
$$= \{ t \mid ((t{\in}A) \land {\sim}(t{\in}B)) \land P(t) \}$$

9.4.2 Moving projections
We can distribute projections through union and difference thus:

$(A + B)$ projected_to pl $= (A$ projected_to pl$) + (B$ projected_to pl$)$

$$(E10)$$

$(A - B)$ projected_to pl $= (A$ projected_to pl$) - (B$ projected_to pl$)$
provided that pl includes the key fields of A (and hence of B)

The first rule can be proved by a similar method to that for selection just given. We show that the existence of any given tuple in the left-hand relation implies its existence in the right-hand relation and vice versa. Let the tuple be (t) after projection, resulting from a tuple which is the concatenation t++r of t with the discarded fields r.

$$\{ t \mid (\exists r)(t{+}{+}r{\in}A) \lor (t{+}{+}r{\in}B) \}$$
$$= \{ t \mid ((\exists r)(t{+}{+}r{\in}A)) \lor ((\exists r') t{+}{+}r'{\in}B) \}$$

In the case of difference we replace $(\lor)$ by $(\land {\sim})$, and then the equivalence only holds if t++r is the same as t++r'. This can be guaranteed if t includes the key fields, since then no two tuples with the same value of t can have different values of r and r'. A similar result holds for intersection, which is just a special case of join.

9.4.3 Combinations of selections and projections
We get interesting results if the two relations A and B in the preceding example are formed by using different selection conditions on the same relation. We have:

A selected_on$[P1]$ projected_to pl + A selected_on$[P2]$ projected_to pl
$=$ A selected_on$[P1$ or $P2]$ projected_to pl   (E11)

The corresponding calculus expressions are:

$$\{ t \mid ((\exists r)(t{+}{+}r{\in}A) \land P1(t{+}{+}r)) \lor ((\exists r')(t{+}{+}r'{\in}A) \land P2(t{+}{+}r')) \}$$
$$\{ t \mid (\exists r)(t{+}{+}r{\in}A) \land (P1(t{+}{+}r) \lor P2(t{+}{+}r)) \}$$

Just as above, we can get similar results for join(intersection) and difference, provided that the primary key is left intact by projection. We shall use the short forms ';' for selection and '%' for projection.

$$A;[P1] \%pl - A;[P2] \%pl = A;[P1 \text{ and not } P2] \%pl \qquad (E12)$$
$$A;[P1] \%pl * A;[P2] \%pl = A;[P1 \text{ and } P2] \%pl$$

9.4.4 Implementation of transformations

We can arrange to mechanise the transformations by the method of 'Rewrite Rules', as described by Bundy (1981). This is a technique used by artificial intelligence programs whereby a pattern matcher repeatedly seeks a match between part of an expression and some template containing variables. The part is replaced by a new expression containing the appropriate instances of the variables found by matching. Usually matching continues until no further change can be made to the expression, usually because it has been simplified into a canonical form. In order for the method to work it is important not to allow rewrite rules that go round in circles, for example allowing A*B to be rewritten as B*A, and then as A*B, and so on.

It is very easy and convenient to express our relational algebra equivalences as rules in Prolog as shown by Gray and Moffat (1983). Here we are using Prolog as a list processing language to manipulate expressions, and not directly to answer queries. As an example consider the Prolog rules:

rewrite(sel(R1, and(P1,P2)), sel(sel(R1,P1), P2)).

rewrite(intersect(sel(R1,X1), sel(R2,X2)),
                    sel(sel(R1,X1),X2)) :– equal(R1,R2).

The two rules implements parts of equivalence E3 given earlier. We are using 'sel', 'intersect' etc., as record constructors to make a tree which is to be matched with a sub-expression in the query. In the second rule the goal 'equal' is used to test if the expressions R1 and R2 denote the same relation; for example R1 might be A*B, and R2 might be B*A, and we do not wish to rewrite these the other way round for the reason just given.

9.5 TRANSFORMING EXPRESSIONS INVOLVING GROUP_BY

We can use the group_by operation to write a more general version of equivalence E12, where projection removes part of the primary key.

A;[P1] %pl − A;[P2] %pl
= A group_by[pl creating Ap1 := any(P1), Ap2 := any(P2)]   (E13)
    limited_by[Ap1 and not Ap2]

A;[P1] %pl * A;[P2] %pl
= A group_by[pl creating Ap1 := any(P1), Ap2 = any(P2)]
    limited_by[Ap1 and Ap2]

The group_by operation enables us to consider each cluster of tuples that gives rise to a given result tuple, with the projected attributes (pl). If any tuple in the cluster satisfies the selection predicate P1 then a corresponding projected tuple will appear in the result of 'A;[P1] %pl'. We argue similarly for a tuple satisfying P2, but note that the qualifying tuple does not have to be the same one in the cluster. Thus instead of using 'P1 and not P2' in our selection, as we do when the primary key is left intact, we use 'any(P1) and not any(P2)' grouped over the cluster. This allows us to see two different qualifying tuples from the same cluster. The use of limited_by instead of selected_on enables us to remove the unwanted extra attributes Ap1 and Ap2.

As an example consider the query:

POLE_GPS := GROUP_PLAC ;[Team="Poland"] %Year,Group
ARG_GPS := GROUP_PLAC ;[Team="Argentina" and Placing<3]
        %Year,Group
ANSWER := POLE_GPS − ARG_GPS

The equivalent form is:

GROUPS := GROUP_PLAC group by [Year,Group creating
        Pole := any(Team="Poland"),
        Arg := any(Team="Argentina" and Placing<3)]
ANSWER := GROUPS limited_by [Pole and not Arg]

The intermediate results for this query for 1978 are:

POLE_GPS

Year	Group
1978	2
1978	B

ARG_GPS

Year	Group
1978	1
1978	B
1978	F

GROUPS

Year	Group	Pole	Arg
1978	1	f	t
1978	2	t	f
1978	3	f	f
1978	4	f	f
1978	A	f	f
1978	B	t	t
1978	F	f	t

ANSWER

Year	Group
1978	2

9.5.1 General equivalences with 'any' and 'all'

The use of the grouping functions 'any' and 'all' corresponds closely to the use of quantifiers in a domain-oriented calculus. We can see this if we write down four equivalences which define it (Gray and Bell 1979):

A group_by [pl : Ep:=any(P)] limited_by [Ep]   = A;[P] %pl   (E14)
A group_by [pl : Ep:=any(P)] limited_by [not Ep] = A%pl − A;[P] %pl   (E15)
A group_by [pl : Ap:=all(P)] limited_by [Ap]   = A%pl−A;[not P] %pl (E16)
A group_by [pl : Ap:=all(P)] limited_by [not Ap] = A;[not P] %pl   (E17)

Equivalence E14 follows directly from the definition of projection, since group_by is a generalised projection. It says that for each cluster of tuples with the same values for the attributes in pl, then if any of them satisfy the selection P, a corresponding tuple will appear in the projection of those tuples of A satisfying P.

Equivalence E15 is a special case of E13 given earlier, with $P1 = true = Ap1$ and $Ep = Ap2$. The other two equivalences follow from substitution in the first two using a version of the rule for negating quantifiers given in Chapter 2.

$$\text{not all (not P) = any(P)}$$

Thus we see that existential queries can be formed using 'any', or by projection following selection. Universal queries can be formed using 'all', or by a difference of projections.

9.6 THE DIVIDE OPERATION AND ITS EQUIVALENCES

Codd (1972) introduced the divide operator as part of his algorithm for converting from calculus to algebra, which we shall shortly examine. The divide operator(/) is essentially an inverse of join in the same way that arithmetical division is the inverse of multiplication. It is defined in such a way that for any two relations $A(a1,..an)$ and $B(b1,..bm)$ then

$$(A ** B) / B = A$$

In general if a relation $C(a1,..an,b1,..bm)$ is divided by a relation $B(b1,..bm)$, whose attribute names are all included in C, then the result $R = (C / B)$ has attributes $(a1,..an)$, i.e. those of C with the attributes of B removed. For each tuple t in R we have that:

$$(\forall t'') (t'' \in B) \rightarrow (\exists t') (t' \in C) \wedge t' = t ++ t''$$

In other words each tuple t in the result R must occur in C concatenated in turn with every possible tuple t'' from B, as in the cartesian product of B and R. However, C may also contain other tuples incorporating t. Thus in general:

$$B ** (C / B) \leqslant C$$

This is just like integer division, where we discard the remainder. If we call this operator 'div', as in Pascal, then we have similarly:

$$(a * b) \text{ div } b = a \quad b * (c \text{ div } b) \leqslant c$$

9.6.1 Equivalence with group_by

We can carry out the division operation using group_by as follows. Let us take the case of dividing a relation $C(a,b)$ of two attributes by a relation $B(b)$ to produce $R(a)$. Then we first rename $B(b)$ as $B(b')$, and form the cartesian product

C(a,b)*B(b′), since this allows us to compare the values of b and b′ in groups of tuples with the same value of a. Thus we have:

>R := C / B
>>rewritten as
>R := C ** (B renaming b as b′)   (E18)
>>group_by[a,b′ creating Eb := any(b=b′)]
>>group_by[a   creating Ab := all(Eb)]
>>limited_by[Ab]

The second group_by implements the universal quantifier in the definition of division given above in calculus notation. It checks that for every tuple value b′ in B there is at least one matching sub-tuple 'b' paired with 'a' in C.

The definition looks expensive to implement, but this is not necessarily so if the values of B can be stored in memory in sorted order, and the relation C is sorted by values of b within a. Then we just need space for an extra domain Eb alongside b′, which is initialised to false, and is marked true whenever a matching value of 'b' is found. Thus we need only one pass through C; at the end of each group of tuples with the same value of 'a' we form the value of Ab from Eb and decide whether or not to output the value of 'a'. The fact that it needs only a single pass with suitably sorted relations was noted by Pecherer (1975).

In the case where 'a' and 'b' are multiple attributes a1,. .an and b1,. .bm, the equivalence (E18) can easily be generalised, with the modification that '(b=b′)' is replaced by '(b1=b1′) and . . . (bm=bm′)'.

If we look at expression (E18) we see that we are selecting a tuple, based on the properties of a whole group of tuples associated with it. The property is calculated using group_by. In this case we select tuples where the associated group of tuples is a *superset* of the tuples in the divisor B. We could instead require it to be a subset, or that the two groups should not intersect. Merrett (1984) has a proposed a 'sigma join' which includes all these variants, as a generalisation of division. However, it appears that this too can be expressed in terms of group_by, using boolean grouping functions.

9.6.2 Equivalent to double difference

Codd (1972) quotes the following equivalences between division and repeated application of set difference (given here in **ASTRID** notation):

>C/B = C%al − (C%al**B − C)%al   (E19)
>where al = result attribute list = (attributes of C − attributes of B)

We shall now prove this, starting from the form using group_by, in order to show the use of some of the equivalences given earlier.

>First we rename B(b) as B(b′)
>Let C1 = C**B
>and C2 = C1 group_by[al,b′ : Eb:=any(b=b′)]

Now, by (E15),

C2 selected_on[not Eb] %al,b′

= C1%al,b′ − C1 selected_on[b=b′] %al,b′

= C1%al,b′ − (C′*B) {by defn of join, where C′(al,b′) renames C(al,b)}

Now, by our equivalence between divide and group_by, (E18)

C/B = C2 group_by[al : Ab :=all(Eb)] limited_by[Ab]

     = C2%al − C2 selected_on[not Eb]%al   {by (E16)}

     = C2%al − (C1%al,b′ − C′*B)%al   {from above}

     = (C**B)%al − ((C**B)%al,b′ − C′*B)%al

     = C%al − (C%al**B − C′*B)%al   {moving projns through join}

Now let C3 = C%al**B

and so C3%b′ = B

and so C3 − C′*B = C3 − C′*(C3%b′) = C3 − C′

This last result follows from a theorem of De Moivre:

$$X − Y*(X\%t) = X − Y$$

The justification for the theorem is that the join is acting as an intersection and can only reject tuples in Y that have no match with tuples in X. These tuples can have no effect on the difference operation and so the join can be dropped.

Thus we have proved that

C/B = C%al − (C3 − C′*B)%al

     = C%al − (C3 − C′)%al

     = C%al − (C%al**B − C)%al   {by renaming b′ as b throughout}

which is the desired equivalence.

This shows that the divide operation can be expressed in terms of difference and projection. Thus any query involving universal quantification can always be expressed using difference and projection, or else by using group_by and 'all', which is often the easiest in practice.

9.7 OTHER USEFUL EQUIVALENCES FROM SET THEORY

For completeness we list a number of useful equivalences. The first three we have used earlier and are obvious from the definitions of the operators involved. The remainder are taken from classical set theory.

A selected_on[P] + A selected_on[not P] = A   (E20)

(A ** B) %al = A   (E21)

A group_by[al : x1:=. .etc] %al = A%al   (E22)

A * A = A   A + A = A   (E23)

A * (B+C) = A*B + A*C   A* (B−C) = A*B − A*C   (E24)

A + A*B = A   {if attributes of B are all in A}   (E25)

A − A*B = A−B   {if attributes of B are all in A}

A * (A+B) = A   {B and A have same attributes}   (E26)

A * (A−B) = A−B {B and A have same attributes}   (E27)

9.8 THE PRTV OPTIMISATION ALGORITHM

Much early work on systematic optimisation of relational algebra expressions was done by Hall *et al.* (1975) and Todd and Verhofstad (1978), working on the 'Peterlee Relational Test Vehicle' called PRTV. They evolved a systematic method of applying transformations as follows:

(i)   Move selections to be performed as early as possible.
(ii) Move projections out, to be performed as late as possible.
(iii) Combine selections and projections applying to the same relation.
(iv) Combine selections and projections with union and difference, so as to use a 'one pass' method where possible. Also do general simplifications.
(v)   Move projections in and evaluate the costs (usually sort costs) of moving them down to various depths, allowing for the improvements to joins resulting from working on smaller numbers of shorter sorted tuples. Sometimes a projection can be done very efficiently on a stored relation just by using values from a sorted index on the desired column. In general such calculations are not easy; approximations and guesses have to be made, because of the unknown distribution of key values, and simple heuristics have to be used to cut down the search for combinations, as discussed by Selinger *et al.* (1979).
(vi) Reconsider forming compound selections (iii and iv).
(vii) Spot common sub-expressions and arrange to evaluate them once only and store the values.

This method makes good use of the equivalences we have studied. Our equivalence for group_by would be used under (iv). The order of applying transformations is chosen so that earlier transformations assist later ones and do not inhibit them. The main problem comes with stage (vii), which could be done earlier but at the risk of inhibiting some important optimisations. For example, several different expressions may include selections and projections on some large cartesian product of relations. If we store this product as a common sub-expression, then we take up a lot of space, and we inhibit the use of selections that could have reduced its size and computational cost. Thus it is probably best to leave this step till last.

9.9 TRANSLATION FROM QBE TO RELATIONAL ALGEBRA

Later in this chapter we shall see how to translate from a full tuple-oriented relational calculus, including any combination of quantifiers, to relational algebra. We shall first treat a simpler problem, that of translating from a domain-oriented calculus QBE, including a single group_by function. The reason it is simpler is that QBE only allows existential quantifiers: every 'example element' is existentially quantified. Further, in most cases complex queries must be formed by storing the intermediate results as snapshots, so the complexity of a query in any one snapshot is limited.

9.9.1 Selections on a single relation

Before describing the general method let us look at some simple examples and their translation.

GROUP_PLAC

Year	Group	Team	Placing	CONDITION
_Y>1977	"A"	P._T	>1983–_Y	_T="Italy" or "Peru"

This query is rather unrealistic, but it shows the four types of selection on a single relation:

(a) An equality selection on a constant (Group = 'A');
(b) A selection using a comparison (Year > 1977)
(c) A selection involving another field in the same record (Placing >1983−Year) (i.e. is the placing better in later years!).
(d) A selection involving a combination of comparisons (Team = "Italy' or Team = 'Peru').

The final result takes the conjunction of these selections and then projects to fields containing 'P.' giving:

> GROUP_PLAC selected_on [Year>1977 and Group="A" and
> (Team="Italy" or Team="Peru") and Placing>1983−Year]
> projected_to Team

9.9.2 Equi-joins and self-joins

Consider the query: 'list the years in which Holland was placed first in some group, and played some game in that group in Rosario, and also played another game in that same year in another group in Cordoba'.

GROUP_PLAC

Year	Group	Team	Placing
P._Y	_G	Holland	1

STAD_ALLOC

Year	Group	Game	Stadium	Date
_Y	_G		Rosario	
_Y	¬_G		Cordoba	

We have here two joins: (a) a natural join between GROUP_PLAC and STAD_ALLOC on Year and Group; (b) a natural join of STAD_ALLOC to itself on Year. This translates into algebraic notation as:

> ((GROUP_PLAC selected_on [Team="Holland" and Placing=1] *
> STAD_ALLOC selected_on [Stadium="Rosario"]) *
> STAD_ALLOC selected_on [Stadium="Cordoba"]
>   renaming Group as XGroup, Date as XDate,
>   Game as XGame, Stadium as XStadium)
> selected_on [Group <> XGroup]
> projected_to Year

The things to notice about this are: (i) we have to rename some columns of STAD_ALLOC in order to prevent a join on it; (ii) the selection on (Group <> XGroup) can only take place outside the join; it is in fact a kind of self-theta-join!

9.9.3 Extension and group_by

'List results for teams which came first or second in their group, giving the number of games played and the average score.'

GAMES

Year	Group	Game	Teama	Scorea	Teamb	Scoreb	CONDITION
_Y	_G	_A	_T1	_SA	_T2	_SB	_T=_T1 or _T2

GROUP_PLAC

Year	Group	Team	Placing
_Y	_G	_T	<3

OUTPUT

Year	CompGroup	Team	Interval	AvScore	NGames
G._Y	G._G	G._T	_Y−1970	avg.((_SA+_SB)/2)	cnt._A

Translated into algebraic form this gives:

> (GROUP_PLAC selected_on [Placing<3] * GAMES)
> selected_on [Team=Teama or Team=Teamb]
> group_by [Year,Group,Team : NGames:=count(),
>   AvScore:=sum((Scorea+Scoreb)/2)/count()]
> extend_by [Interval:=Year−1970]
> renaming Group as CompGroup

The links (_Y, _G) are used to join the relations and the selections are applied as early as possible. Then the group_by operation is applied, followed by the extend_by operation to compute a derived field. The rename operation comes last, to make the names match those in the output table. There is no final projection, since this is effectively done by group_by.

9.9.4 General algorithm

Having studied specific examples, we can now formulate a general translation algorithm from QBE to ASTRID notation. The only new feature is that it introduces extra projections before the joins. These projections preserve the primary key: their main purpose is to project away unwanted columns so as to avoid renaming them in case of accidental joins.

The stages are as follows:

(i)   For each relation template used in the query, write down its name together with a selection operation using a conjunction of terms. Write down a term for every attribute which is compared with a constant or another attribute of the same relation. Also write down a term for any entry in the condition box which does not involve other relations.

(ii)   For each relation from (i), after the selection (if any), write a projection operation to discard any non-key columns which do not contain example elements or print commands.

(iii)   Form joins between the relations resulting from steps (i) and (ii) as follow. Find two relations linked by common example elements. Insert rename operations, if necessary, so that the columns linked by a common example element have the same name, and no other pairs of columns have the same name. Then write down the join of these relations. Now find another relation that has an example element in common with one of the joined relations and join it on, renaming columns if necessary. Repeat until no more relations can be joined on.

(iv)   Let R be the joined result formed at the end of step (iii). If there are any other relations left, then they must be joined on by a theta-join. Look for a relation that has an example element related to one in R by a condition other than equality. Join this to R by a cartesian product. Repeat this process until no more relations are left, using cartesian product or equi-join as required.

(v)   Find all columns which are related by inequalities to attributes of other relations. Write down a selection operation using a conjunction of terms, one for each inequality predicate appearing in the templates. Also add on a term for any selection in the 'condition box' not dealt with under (i).

(vi)   If there is no output table then add a final operation projecting to those columns containing print commands (P.).

(viii) If there is an output table containing group_by commands, then add a group_by operation projecting to the columns being grouped on. These columns start with 'G.'; for their column names use the column names above the corresponding example elements in the relation templates. The attribute list of the group_by operation must create an attribute with the column name for each column in the output table which includes a grouping function (sum, cnt etc. . .).

(ix)   If there are any columns in the output table not containing 'G.' or grouping functions, but containing arithmetic expressions, then add on an extend_by operation creating a new attribute whose value is given by the expression.

(x)   Finally add a rename operation to change the attribute names of columns to those given in the output table, if they are different, and finish with a projection to these names.

9.10 CODD'S ALGORITHM FOR CONVERTING RELATIONAL CALCULUS TO ALGEBRA

This algorithm (Codd 1972) is for calculus expressions in a language called Alpha. We first describe how to form *range-separable WFFs* (Well Formed Formulae) which specify the range of values for each variable. We then form the cartesian product of all these ranges, reduce it by means of selection, and then use projection and division to implement the quantifiers. The resulting expression is not very practical for direct evaluation; however, it may be converted into a better form by the PRTV method. The original paper did not, in fact, propose the algorithm for practical use. It was given in order to show that any relation denoted by a calculus expression could also be denoted by an equivalent algebraic expression, and thus the two languages were equivalent in expressive power.

9.10.1 WFF in Alpha

We start with *tuple variables* r1,r2,.. which range over relations. The j'th relation Rj is represented by a unary predicate Pj, such that Pj(ri) is true if the value of the i'th tuple variable is present in the j'th relation, i.e. ri∈Rj. Note that tuple variables are not bound to specific relations. A term such as Pj(ri) is called a *range term.*

We next introduce the comparison operators $(=, <, >, \geqslant, \leqslant, <>)$, as predicates with two arguments, and use them to form *join terms.* One argument of each join term will be a *tuple component* which we write as ri[N], where N is an integer constant giving the column number in the tuple which holds the desired attribute value. N must be positive, non-zero and within the degree of relation. The other argument of the join term must be another tuple component or a constant. Those terms with two tuple components we have previously called join predicates and those terms including constants we have called selection predicates. Thus for example $(r2[1] = r3[2])$ and $(r2[2] < r3[5])$ are both join terms. Note that, as in simple versions of QUEL, we cannot have arithmetic expressions like $(2*r1[1] < 3+r2[2])$.

A *WFF* is formed out of join terms and range terms using the operations '∧', '∨', '~', together with the quantifiers '(∃ri)' and '(∀ri)', where ri is a range variable. We wish to consider a special class of WFF which are *range-separable.* These are of the form

$$U1 \wedge U2 \wedge \ldots Un \wedge W$$

Here W and each Ui are WFFs and there must be at least one Ui (i.e. n>0), but W may be empty. Each Ui refers to a different range variable and consists only of range terms without quantifiers. W may contain both Join terms and range terms. If it contains quantifiers then they must be *coupled* to a range term, that is they must be of the form '(∃ri)(Pj(ri) ∧ W)' or else '(∀ri)(Pj(ri)→W)', which follows the style adopted in Chapter 2. Lastly, every tuple variable in W must have its range given either by a Ui or else by a quantifier.

Two other conditions are imposed on the Ui. Firstly, if the same range variable is used with two different predicates, as in P2(r1) and P3(r1), then of course the corresponding relations must be of the same type. Secondly, no Ui may start with a negation, although the combination '$\wedge$ ~' is permissible within a Ui. This means that the range must be given explicitly, and not just as 'any value not in. . .'.

9.10.2 Conversion of range-separable WFFs

Stage 1

We first use the method in Chapter 2 to convert W to normal form, with the quantifiers at the front. We also renumber the Ui so that the tuple variables ri are arranged in ascending order, i.e. U2 refers to r2 and so on. Thus the query is of the form:

$$\text{tl} : U1 \wedge U2 \wedge \ldots Up \wedge (Q1\ Q2 \ldots Qq)\ W$$

Here tl is the list of tuple components required in the answer, there are 'p' range variables governed by range terms in the Ui and there are 'q' further variables, numbered from p+1 up to p+q, which are governed by the quantifiers Q1 to Qq. W contains only join terms.

Stage 2

From the Ui and Qi, form the cartesian product S of the set extensions which give the tuple variable ranges. Inside each Ui, replace Pj(ri) by the relation Rj, replace '$\vee$' by union, '$\wedge$' by intersection and '$\wedge$ ~' by difference. For each Qi coupled to a range term Pk(ri) write down the relation Rk. Thus for:

$$P2(r1) \wedge (P1(r2) \vee P2(r2)) \wedge (P1(r3) \wedge {^\sim} P2(r3)) \wedge (\exists r4)\ (P3(r4) \wedge W)$$

the corresponding product of range is

$$S = R2\ ** \ (R1 + R2)\ ** \ (R1 - R2)\ ** \ R3$$

Stage 3

For each join term in W (range terms can only be in Qi or Ui) apply to S the appropriate selection, connecting them with '$\wedge$', '$\vee$' or '~' as appropriate, e.g. S := S selected_on[r1[2]<4 or r3[1]>6 and . . .]. In the case where the join term refers to two tuple components '(r1[2]<r2[2])', the combination of the selection with the cartesian product over the tuple ranges effectively forms a theta-join as explained in Chapter 7.

Stage 4

For each quantifier Qi (i=1 to q) apply either projection or division to S, working from inside out as follows. Let the column list for *ri* be *bl,* and the corresponding relation, taken from the range term coupled to the quantifier, be Rk. then:

If Qi is ($\exists$ri) (Pk(ri) $\wedge$ W) then S := S discarding bl
If Qi is ($\forall$ri) (Pk(ri) $\rightarrow$ W) then S := S / Rk

Stage 5
Finally project to the target list tl thus:

S := S projected_to tl

9.11 IMPROVED VERSION OF CODD'S ALGORITHM USING GROUP_BY

We can adapt Codd's algorithm to use group_by, for a more straightforward translation into ASTRID as follows.

Stage 1
Instead of moving all the join terms down from inside the quantifiers, where possible leave them associated with the appropriate range-coupled quantifier. Thus each Qi now has the form:

$$(\exists ri) \, (Pk(ri) \wedge Wi \wedge W)$$
or $$(\forall ri) \, (Pk(ri) \wedge Wi \rightarrow W)$$

Here Wi is a WFF containing join terms which refer only to ri and earlier range variables. Wi may of course be empty (the constant true).

Stage 3
Instead of doing selections for all the join terms, separate W into $(V \wedge WR)$, where V contains only join terms referencing the unquantified variables r1 to rp (V may be empty). Let PV be the boolean expression selecting tuples for V and PW be the corresponding expression for WR. Then:

S := S selected_on[PV] extend_by[Fl:=PW]

Here we are doing the selection for V but delaying the selection for terms involving quantifiers. We use the extra attribute Fl to hold the truth or falsehood of a selection condition, for use by the next quantifier. The selection takes place at Stage 4.

Stage 4
At this stage, instead of using projection and division we use group_by, as follows. Let 'al' be the attribute list of S just after removing the attributes of relation Ri, then:

If Qi = $(\exists ri)$ $(Pk(ri) \wedge Wi \wedge W)$
        then S := S group_by[al creating Fl:=any(Wi and Fl)]
If Qi = $(\forall ri)$ $(Pk(ri) \wedge Wi \rightarrow W)$
        then S := S group_by[al creating Fl:=all(not Wi or Fl)]

Finally, after dealing with all the Qi from q to 1 in sequence,

S := S limited_by[Fl]

Here Fl is used as a kind of working variable to compute the net boolean selection condition implied by all the quantifiers. It was initialised at Stage 3, but the actual selection is delayed until the net effect is known. There is actually a value of Fl associated with each tuple that is left following the projections done by the group_by operations; only those tuples with a true value for Fl will be kept. Note that statements like 'Fl:=all(Fl)' allow us to calculate the new attribute Fl from the value of the old one, which is removed by the projection.

Stage 4A

We now substitute for S to form one long expression, and then use the rules for moving selections through projections together with the following two equivalences:

$$S \text{ group\_by} [\text{ al} : \text{Fl}:=\text{any(Wi and Fl)}] \text{ selected\_on} [\text{Fl}]$$
$$= S \text{ selected\_on} [\text{Wi}] \text{ selected\_on} [\text{Fl}] \text{ projected\_to al, Fl}$$
$$S \text{ group\_by} [\text{ al} : \text{Fl}:=\text{all(not Wi or Fl)}] \text{ selected\_on} [\text{Fl}]$$
$$= S \text{ selected\_on} [\text{Wi}] \text{ group\_by} [\text{ al} : \text{Fl}:=\text{all(Fl)}] \text{ selected\_on} [\text{Fl}]$$

The first equivalence follows because we are only interested in cases where both Wi and Fl are true, and this can only be true for tuples where Wi is true. We then replace the group_by using (E14). The second equivalence follows similarly, because again we are only interested in those tuples where Wi is true, in order to verify (Wi → Fl).

After passing the selections through group_by we can then combine them with the cartesian product of range sets, in order to give equi-joins where possible. Finally we project to the target list (Stage 5); this projection can be combined with those resulting from group_by and used to turn equi-joins into natural joins by eliminating duplicate columns.

9.11.1 Validity of the algorithm

The proof is based on two lemmas which are based on those originally used by Codd. The first lemma is related to (E14) and the second to (E18).

Let RC be the cartesian product of one or more relations not involving Ri. Let 'al' be the attribute list of RC. Let Pred be any predicate involving join terms which only reference Ri or the relations in RC.

$$\text{Let } T = (RC ** Ri) \text{ extend\_by} [\text{Fl} := \text{Pred}] \text{ limited\_by} [\text{Fl}]$$
$$\text{Then } T = \text{the set } \{t\text{++}r \mid t \in RC \wedge r \in Ri \wedge \text{Pred}\}$$

Lemma 1

$$T \text{ projected\_to al}$$
$$= (RC ** Ri) \text{ group\_by} [\text{al} : \text{Fl}:=\text{any(Pred)}] \text{ limited\_by } [\text{Fl}]$$
$$= \text{the set } \{t \mid t \in RC \wedge (\exists r) \text{ Pi}(r) \wedge \text{Pred}\}$$

Lemma 2

$$T / Ri$$
$$= (RC ** Ri) \text{ group\_by} [\text{al} : \text{Fl}:=\text{all(Pred)}] \text{ limited\_by } [\text{Fl}]$$
$$= \text{the set } \{t \mid t \in RC \wedge (\forall r) \text{ Pi}(r) \rightarrow \text{Pred}\}$$

These two lemmas establish that the new version of Stage 4 will give the same version of Codd's in the case where there is only one quantifier. For the case of nested quantifiers we rely on the fact that each newly formed result from lemmas 1 or 2 is of the form

$$(RC' ** R(i-1)) \text{ extend\_by } [Fl := Pred'] \text{ limited\_by } [Fl]$$

where RC' only involves relations from 1 to i–2. Thus we can just feed Fl through in place of Pred at each stage, as done in the algorithm.

9.11.2 An example of the algorithm

Consider the query on the World Cup database:

'List the names of teams together with the years in which they came first in some group and also played all their matches in at least one group in Buenos Aires'.

Calculus form :=
Let R1 = GROUP_PLAC, R2 = GAMES and R3 = STAD_ALLOC
(r1.Year, r1.Team) : P1(r1) $\wedge$ (r1.placing=1) $\wedge$
   ($\exists$r2) P1(r2) $\wedge$ (r2.year=r1.year) $\wedge$
      ($\forall$r3) P2(r3) $\wedge$ (r3.year=r2.year) $\wedge$ (r3.group=r2.group) $\wedge$
      (r3.teama=r1.team $\vee$ r3.teamb=r1.team) $\rightarrow$
         ($\exists$ r4) P3(r4) $\wedge$ (r4.year=r3.year) $\wedge$ (r4.group=r3.group) $\wedge$
         (r4.game=r3.game) $\wedge$ (r4.stad="Buenos Aires")

After applying the algorithm and simplifying we get:

S := (GROUP_PLAC renaming Group as XGroup selected_on [Placing=1] *
    GROUP_PLAC renaming Team as R2Team, Placing as R2Placing *
    GAMES selected_on [Teama=Team or Teamb=Team] *
    STAD_ALLOC)
    extend_by [Fl:=true]
    group_by [Year,Team,Group,Game creating
         Fl:=any(Stadium="Buenos Aires" and Fl)]
    group_by [Year,Team,Group creating Fl:=all(Fl)]
    selected_on [Fl]
    projected_to Year,Team

9.12 SUMMARY

We have seen how to translate both tuple- and domain-oriented calculus expressions into relational algebra and vice versa. This is very useful for allowing users to express queries in their usual query language, for execution on a remote database system using a different language. It also serves to establish the close similarity in expressive power of the two formalisms. Codd called them both 'relationally complete' on this account, and we have shown that this still holds when we include the group_by and extend operations in both formalisms.

We have seen a wide range of ways of optimising expressions in relational algebra. Undoubtedly a number of these optimisations could also be done in the calculus form, as shown by Warren (1981b), but he does not consider the group_by operations, or those needing the 'setof' construct. The application of relational algebra operations can be done by using the 'rewrite rule' technique, as used in simplifying ordinary algebraic expressions, and it can be implemented in Prolog. However, there is a further problem, which we shall consider in Chapter 12. This is the problem of how the relations are actually represented in computer storage. Depending on how this is done, some rewrite rules may not improve the computation, particularly those involved in moving projections. In order to understand this we shall describe the CODASYL database system, which is commonly used to store large databases, in Chapter 11, preceded by an examination of the Functional Model in Chapter 10, which enables us to understand the abstract basis for the CODASYL model.

10

The functional data model

We have already discussed the Functional Query Language (FQL), developed by Buneman for database use. FQL is based on the application of functions to streams of entities. At about the same time Shipman (1979), working at MIT and CCA, developed the Functional Data Model. Like FQL, it has the notion of entities, and of functions from entities to entities, but it is formulated in terms of sets rather than streams. Queries are written in the 'Daplex' language, in a style based on predicate calculus rather than applicative programming. Nevertheless, it depends on the composition of functions producing sets as results, which is just like function composition in FQL. The significant contribution of the functional model is that it combines the *computational* power of applicative programming with the *data definition* and abstraction facilities provided by the standard database languages.

The ideas of Shipman are based on the artificial intelligence notion of a *semantic net* (see Fig. 10.1). This is a structure which is used to represent associations between objects. For each object of a given type, there is a corresponding collection of functions which are applicable to it; some of these provide simple values, but the results of others are found by following 'arcs' in the net, which connect the object to other objects of various types. Functions can be applied in turn to these objects, thus exploring a network of associations. Usually the network is represented as a list structure with many pointers. The essential difference from relations is that, instead of a set of explicit data values (tuples), we have a set of nameless objects whose properties may be given either as data values or as pointers to other objects. The properties can be obtained only through function application, and if the results point to other objects, then further functions must be applied, thus resulting in a composition of functions.

The language Daplex is very general and much more high level than FQL, and so far only one or two implementations have been made (Atkinson and Kulkarni 1983). The ideas of Shipman were taken on by CCA and a subset of Daplex embedded in ADA, called Adaplex, has been designed (Smith, Fox and Landers 1981). This is being implemented. At the same time a project 'Multibase' was started to access heterogeneous distributed databases, possibly by using Adaplex as the common language (Smith *et al.* 1981). This uses the ability of the functional model to map the same abstract data definition onto both CODASYL and relational databases.

In this chapter we start by exploring the various types of functions available on entities, and we see how to represent both binary relationships and many–many relationships in terms of functions, leading up to a description of a full schema. We then look at the composition rule for functions, which plays the same crucial role in this model that the join operation plays in the relational model. With this in mind, we study the syntax for queries and updates in Adaplex and Daplex. Next we see how to set up a relational database which corresponds to a given functional schema, and also how to represent an existing relational database in terms of functions. This study will enable us to appreciate the similarity in power of the functional and relational models, despite their very different methods of query formulation. We conclude by summarising the key ideas of the model, particularly its relationship to the programming language concept of 'Abstract Data Types'.

10.1 BASIC NOTIONS – ENTITIES AND FUNCTIONS

The notion of a function is basic in mathematics. For example we are familiar with trigonometric functions such as $sin(x)$, or two-argument functions such as $max(x, y)$. Functions may take objects of one type, e.g. two real numbers, and produce a result of another type, e.g. boolean. Similarly, a function subprogram in Algol 68, or PL/I, or Pascal, can take arguments which are complex data structures, and may return references to a structure as the result. The functional model generalises the idea that the result is functionally dependent on the arguments, but it does not specify the precise representation of the arguments or results, only their types.

The functional model works on two classes of item – entities and scalar values. Scalar values are single atomic values (like integers, reals, booleans and strings) which have a literal representation on the printed page (e.g. '1', '2.7', 'true', 'Aberdeen City').

An entity is some form of token identifying a unique object in the database and usually representing a unique object in the universe. You cannot print this token; you can only print scalar functions of it! For example if the entity represents a person, you could apply the scalar-valued functions Name( ), Age( ) and Sex( ) to it, and print the person's name, age or sex. (Similarly, in Pascal, the standard 'write' routine can be applied to the atomic components of a record, but not to the record as a whole.)

It is possible for two different person entities to have the same name, age and sex. The model can still distinguish them, unlike the relational model, if these were the only attributes stored. Thus an entity is something you can point at and distinguish from other entities, without recourse to comparisons of attribute values. In Fig. 10.1(a) the rectangular boxes represent an entity type, of which there may be many instances, and the arrows show the possible functions.

Functions defined over entities may return scalar values, entities or sets of entities. Thus the functions may be *multi-valued,* since they return sets rather than single instances. Mathematically a multi-valued function is equivalent to a binary relation, and similarities exist with the binary relational models described in Chapter 6, which are discussed further below. Multi-valued functions are shown in Fig. 10.1(a) with a double arrow.

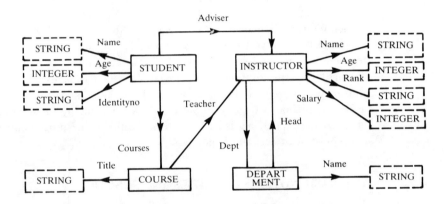

Fig. 10.1(a) – Daplex schema diagram for University database.

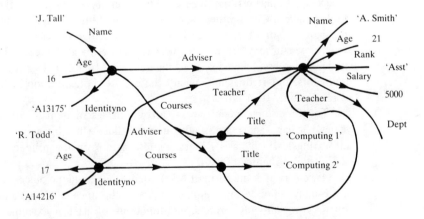

Fig. 10.1(b) – Portion of semantic net for University database.

10.1.1 Classes of functions
There are three classes of functions on entities as illustrated in Fig. 10.1(a), taken from Shipman's paper, which represents a University database.

(a) Scalar-valued

For example Name(Student) delivers a string, and Salary(Instructor) delivers an integer. In Fig. 10.1 these are represented as arrows terminating on dashed rectangles, which represent scalar value types. Scalar values, unlike entities, are directly printable and correspond to the usual basic types used in programming languages.

(b) Single-valued

For example Head(Department) denotes a unique entity representing the head of a university department. Likewise Teacher(Course) denotes a unique person. The arrow terminates on an entity and the actual value must be a unique instance of that entity type.

(c) Multi-valued

For example Courses(Student) denotes a set of courses (0,1 or more) which are being taken by a student. The arrow terminates on an entity but it is double-headed ($\longrightarrow\!\!\!>$) to show that the actual value is a set of instances of that entity type.

10.1.2 Corresponding with binary relations

There is an obvious correspondence between the scalar-valued and single-valued functions given above, and binary relations with attributes (Stud#, Name) and (Dept#, Head), where # denotes an identifying number.

For the correspondence with multi-valued functions, consider a number of example tuples from the binary relation (Stud#,Course#) shown below, which shows the courses taken by students in a given year; the corresponding mappings from Student Entity to set of Courses is shown on the right. Here we use the #number as a token for the entity.

Binary Relational View   Functional View

Stud#	Course#
25	3
25	7
28	3
32	7
32	9

argument		result
25	$----\!\!\!>$	{3,7}
28	$----\!\!\!>$	{3}
32	$----\!\!\!>$	{7,9}

10.1.3 Many–many relations

This causes problems of representation in most models. Consider the function Courses(Student), which is multi-valued. Its inverse function Students(Course) is also multi-valued. Thus one student may attend many courses and one course may be attended by many students. Suppose that, associated with the function Courses(Student), there is a value 'grade', for the marks obtained on the course. In Daplex one can represent this in two ways.

Two-argument function
We introduce the function Grade(Course,Student). On a diagram we would
have to represent it by an arrow with two tails – one for each entity. However,
this function is partial, since it is not defined for all combinations of course
and student. Shipman suggests one could avoid this by declaring a function
Grade(Courses(Student),Student), but this is not symmetric and looks peculiar.

Extra entity
Suppose we introduce a new entity type Enrolment, as in Fig. 10.2, with two
single-valued functions Course(Enrolment) and Student(Enrolment), and the
scalar-valued function Grade(Enrolment). Each instance of the Enrolment
entity corresponds to the successful enrolment of a student for a particular
course, culminating in the award of a grade. If we define the multi-valued
inverse of Student(Enrolment) as Enrolledfor(Student), then instead of the
function Courses(Student) we must now use the composed function Course
(Enrolledfor (Student)). This can be defined, as we shall see, even if Enrolledfor
(Student) is null, thus avoiding the problem of partial functions. It seems a
better representation of a many—many relationship if the relationship is information bearing; for example, if there is a value 'grade' associated with an instance
of the relationship rather than with the two entities separately. (In fact we shall
see that this is the only way to represent a many—many relationship in the
CODASYL model, described in Chapter 11).

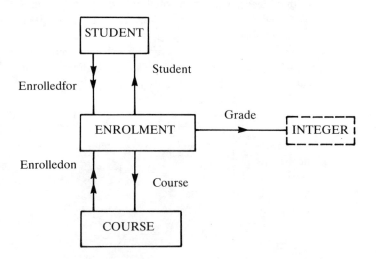

Fig. 10.2 – Enrolment entity for grade relationship.

10.1.4 One-to-one relations
Some functions on scalar values deliver a unique entity, and the inverse is also
single-valued. In this case the scalar value can act as a key to identify the instance
of the entity. Consider the function Identityno(Student) which delivers a unique
integer. The inverse of this, Studentwith(Id#), will deliver a unique student.

On a relational database it could be implemented by an index giving direct access to the Student record.

It is important to declare that such functions are one-to-one. In the later versions of Adaplex the clause e.g.:

> *unique*   identityno   *within*   student

would be used for this purpose. If several functions are involved the clause could be, e.g.

> *unique*   name, age, address,   *within*   student

i.e. the function Studentof(Name,Age,Address) is single-valued.

10.1.5 Sub-types
Both Daplex and Adaplex use the notion of sub-types introduced in Chapter 6. This depends on the idea that entities can play roles as other entities, in which case they have extra functions defined on them. For example, all persons have Names and Ages by virtue of being persons. Some persons play a role as instructor entities and have a Rank function by virtue of being instructors. Some persons, by virtue of being students, have Advisers and take Courses.

Since all instructors are persons, the set of all instructors is in one-to-one correspondence with a subset of the set of all persons, i.e. it is a sub-type of type Person. Similarly students are also a sub-type of person. The two sets (students and instructors) may overlap or be disjoint, depending on whether students of one subject are allowed to be instructors of another. In Adaplex the sub-type relationship is shown by use of the 'subtype' statement declaring the entity, and the overlap possibility is shown by use of the 'overlap' statement, as shown at the bottom left of Fig. 10.3.

10.1.6 Schema description
We can now look at the Adaplex schema (Fig. 10.3), which includes both the University database and the World Cup database. For each entity the names of the functions on it are defined. If they are scalar-valued, the usual Pascal type declaration is given. If they are single-valued, the entity name is given as the type of the function. If they are multi-valued, the type is 'set of ⟨entity name⟩'. Sometimes a function is shown with one entity, and the inverse function is also shown associated with the other entity (e.g. Vgames(venue) and Gstadium(game)). In Daplex the inverse function can be derived using INVERSE OF(F). In Adaplex the inverse function is only shown if it is supported directly by the database (using indexes or special pointers), since there is no INVERSE OF construct. Finally, the key functions are declared by the 'unique' clause, and subtypes by overlap clauses.

10.2 FUNCTION COMPOSITION IN THE FUNCTIONAL MODEL
In normal mathematical usage a function is single-valued, and thus, given two functions f(x) and g(x), it is straightforward to define the meaning of f(g(x)),

type person *is entity*

    name   : string[1. .30] ;
    age   : integer;
    phone   : *set of* string[1. .11];
end entity;

subtype instructor *is* person *entity*
    rank   : (asst, assoc, full);
    dept   : department;
    salary   : integer;
end entity;

subtype student *is* person *entity*
    identityno : integer;
    advisor   : instructor *partial;*
    courses   : *set of* course;
end entity;

type course *is entity*
    title   : string[1. .30] ;
    teacher   : instructor;
end entity;

type department *is entity*
    name   : string[1. .30] ;
    head   : instructor;
    students of : *set of* student;
end entity;

unique title *within* course
unique identityno *within* student

overlap student *with* instructor

type year *is entity*

    Year   : integer;
    Groups   : *set of* group
end entity;

type group *is entity*

    Group   : char;
    CompYear   : year;
    Ggames   : *set of* game;
    Gplaces   : *set of* place;
end entity;

type game *is entity*
    Game   : 1. .10;
    Date   : string[1. .6] ;
    CompGroup : group;
    Teama   : team;
    Scorea   : 0. .99;
    Teamb   : team;
    Scoreb   : 0. .99;
    Gstadium : venue;
end entity;

type venue *is entity*
    Stadium   : string[1. .10] ;
    Vgames   : *set of* game;

end entity;

type place *is entity;*
    Placing   : 1. .10;
    Pgroup   : group;
    Pteam   : team;
end entity;

type team *is entity*
    Team   : string[1. .10] ;
    Tplaces   : *set of* place;
end entity;

unique Stadium *within* venue
unique Year *within* year
unique Team *within* team

Fig. 10.3 – Adaplex schema example.

as in Chapter 3. However, if $g(x)$ produces a set of entities, how do we define the composition? There are two cases and the definitions below are as used in Adaplex (Smith, Fox and Landers 1981).

(a) F is single-valued or scalar-valued

$$f(g(x)) = \{y \mid y = f(z) \text{ and } z \text{ is in } g(x)\}$$

i.e. we form a set of the values of $f(z)$ for each z in the set produced by $g(x)$. In the case where $f(z)$ is undefined for one of the values of z then the function as a whole is considered to be undefined (i.e. partial).

(b) F is multi-valued

$$f(g(x)) = \{y \mid y \text{ is in } f(z) \text{ and } z \text{ is in } g(x)\}.$$

i.e. we take the union of the sets of values $f(z)$. Since f is always defined (even though it sometimes returns the null set), the composition is always defined.

10.2.1 Similarity to join of binary relations

The definition just given produces a result similar to the join operator in relational algebra. Let $F(z,y)$ and $G(x,z)$ be two binary relations, corresponding to functions f and g respectively. Then, if we form the join of F and G on the common attribute z, and then project this away, we get a new binary relation $COMP(x,y)$, equivalent to the composition of multi-valued functions just defined. An example is shown below.

Relational view

G			F			F joined-to G			COMP	
x	z		z	y		x	z	y	x	y
1	5		4	3		1	5	3	1	3
1	4		4	7		1	4	3	1	7
1	2		5	3		1	4	7	3	22
2	17		29	22		3	29	22		
3	29									

Functional view

$G(1) = \{5,4,2\}$	$F(4) = \{3,7\}$	$F(G(1)) = \{3,7\}$
$G(2) = \{17\}$	$F(5) = \{3\}$	$F(G(2)) = \{\}$
$G(3) = \{29\}$	$F(17) = \{\}$	$F(G(3)) = \{22\}$
	$F(29) = \{22\}$	

Thus we see that the process of taking the union of the sets in multi-valued function composition corresponds to the method used in Codd's natural join, and that just as the natural join is crucial to relational algebra, so function composition is crucial to the functional model.

FQL produces a different result, since it preserves the structure as a stream of streams rather than as a single flattened stream.

10.3 COMPARISONS OF SYNTAX FOR DATA MANIPULATION

Suppose we want to print the names of instructors of courses taken by students aged over 21, together with the ages of the students.

10.3.1 Adaplex

In Adaplex this is written as:

```
for each s in student
where age(s) >21
loop
        for each i in teacher(courses(s))
        loop
            print name(i),age(s)
        end loop
end loop
```

We have two nested 'for' loops, where the loop variable ranges over the members of a set, which may be a named entity type declared in the schema, or else an expression denoting a set produced by function application. The inner loop contains a print statement, which can print any scalar-valued functions of the entities referenced by the enclosing loop variables (i,s). In general, queries are formed by starting from a set, and then applying functions to derive a new set, and predicates to restrict it; a variable can then be used to range over this set, from which new sets can be derived, and so on. . . .

10.3.2 Daplex

The syntax of the Daplex implementation by Atkinson and Kulkarni is in Appendix V. In Daplex there is some overloading of names, so that the translator is supposed to work out where a name refers to a set or an instance and what its arguments are. Shipman argues that this is more user-friendly, but it is doubtful whether Daplex is really an end-user language. The Daplex version is:

```
FOR EACH student
SUCH THAT age(student) >21
        FOR EACH instructor (courses(student))
        PRINT name(instructor),age(student)
```

Both queries have a nested loop structure, and it is interesting to note that the print statement is not restricted to the innermost loop. This produces problems in translating to equivalent relational algebra or relational calculus expressions. For example, if we have a relational view of the database, using the relations:

```
Attends(Stud#, Course#)
Teaches(Inst#, Course#)
Students(Stud#, Name, Age, Sex)
Instructors(Inst#, Name, Age, Rank)
```

then we can write an equivalent query in relational algebra:

((Students selected_on [Age>21] projected_to Stud#,Age) joined_to
  Attends joined_to Teaches joined_to
  (Instructors projected_to Inst#,Name))
  projected_to Name,Age.

However, if the query is rewritten as:

FOR EACH student SUCH THAT age(student) >21
LOOP
    PRINT age(student)
    FOR EACH instructor(courses(student))
        PRINT name(instructor)
END LOOP

then the result is not a relation in normal form, but a sequence of ages each followed by a sequence of names.

10.3.3 Syntax for updates in Adaplex

It is possible in Adaplex to define updates on functions; that is, a new function is defined which produces the same results as the old function, everywhere except at specific points. If the function produces a set, then the update operators 'include' and 'exclude' define a new value for the set, with extra or fewer elements respectively. They could, for example, be implemented by applying 'Connect' or 'Disconnect' operations to a particular instance of a CODASYL set, as explained in the next chapter. Newer versions of Daplex (Appendix V; Fox *et al.* (1984)) also provide very similar update operations.

    The following example shows that a complicated selection expression, involving the existential quantifier 'for some', can be used to select particular student entities, which can then be used to update the function 'instructorsof', over departments in which these students major.

    for each s *in*
        studentsof(*the* d *in* department where name(d) = "Maths")
        where (for some c *in* courses(s) title(c) ="Algebra")
    loop
        for each d *in* dept(s)
        loop
            include s *in set* instructorsof(d)
        endloop
    endloop

A simple assignment statement can be used to update a scalar or single-valued function, e.g.

    age(*the* s *in* student *where* name(s) ="A.Smith") := 22

Note that we cannot just say age ("A.Smith") :=22. The 'the' operation is used to extract the single entity in a singleton which is the value of a Daplex set expression. This rather convoluted syntax emphasises that we are not identifying a tuple in a relation, but an instance of an entity by the value of one of its functions.

In Daplex this can be done more easily, since we can use the DEFINE statement to introduce a new function defined in terms of existing functions.

(i)   If 'name' is a key then we can define its inverse by

DEFINE snamed(n) → INVERSE OF name(student)

and use this in, e.g., age(snamed("A.Smith")) :=22

(ii)   In general we can define a suitable function, e.g.

DEFINE snamed(n) → THE student
            SUCH THAT name(student) = n

10.4 REPRESENTING A FUNCTIONAL SCHEMA BY RELATIONS

We can represent a functional schema by using objects and concepts from the relational model, which enables us to compare their capabilities.

Entities are represented by tuples in an 'Entity Relation', if we follow Chen's Entity-Relationship model as described in Chapter 6. Such a relation has one tuple for each occurrence of an entity of the given type. The tuples must be unique, which is usually arranged by including a field which identifies the entity (e.g. Identityno or Name for Person).

The set of all entities of a given type is found by scanning every tuple in the appropriate Entity Relation.

Scalar functions are represented by attributes of tuples in the Entity Relation (e.g. Rank and Salary in Fig. 10.4). If a Binary Relation model is used, then there is a separate relation pairing each attribute with the Identifier for the Entity.

Scalar multi-valued functions are represented by a separate binary relation, because of the need to use a normal form. Thus, for example, in Fig. 10.4, where an instructor has several phone numbers, a separate tuple is used to store each phone number for an instructor entity, paired with a common value for the entity identifier.

PERSON

Name	Phone
A.Smith	3241
A.Smith	2063
A.Smith	2195
F.Stone	3241

Name	Age
A.Smith	21
F.Stone	23
J.Tall	16
R.Todd	17

INSTRUCTOR/STUDENT

Name	Rank	Salary
A.Smith	asst	5000
F.Stone	assoc	9000

Name	Advisor
J.Tall	A.Smith
R.Todd	A.Smith

Fig. 10.4 – Relations for sub-types.

Single-valued functions are represented by storing the Identifier for another entity in a tuple of an Entity Relation. This is sometimes called a 'Foreign Key'. It is assumed that this key is stored in another Entity Relation (or the same relation − references can be cyclic) and the join operation is used to match the tuples. The big difference between the relational model and the functional model is that a relation contains only scalar values, although some of these are put in one-to-one correspondence with entity occurrences. Thus a *function* delivers a reference to an entity, but a *relation* delivers a value for an entity identifier, which must be matched with a value in another relation. In consequence, where relations are meant to represent relationships between real world objects, we have to use a number of integrity constraints to ensure, for example, that a value for a Foreign Key will be present in its Entity Relation and so on. These constraints are implicit in the functional model.

Multi-valued functions are represented by 'Relationship Relations' in Chen's model, which are often Binary Relations corresponding to multi-valued functions, as discussed earlier. They usually link pairs of Entity identifiers (e.g. Stud#, Course#). It is essential to use a separate relation where the function has a multi-valued inverse. If the inverse is single-valued, however, it can instead be represented as a Foreign Key in an Entity Relation, as described above.

Sub-types can be represented by using a common entity identifier for the Base Type and its sub-types, as in Fig. 10.4 where Name is the common identifier. One Entity Relation is used for the properties of the Base Type, whilst other Entity Relations each contain a subset of these identifiers, which are paired with attributes appropriate to the particular Sub-Type. Thus there is an Entity Relation for each Sub-Type. If the Sub-Types are not subject to an 'overlap' clause, then the subsets of identifiers must be non-overlapping.

10.5 REPRESENTING RELATIONS BY A DAPLEX SCHEMA

We have seen how a relational schema can be designed to represent a functional model schema. Let us now consider the reverse process. In the case of the CODASYL model, as we shall see, functions from records or entities onto sets are represented directly. In the case of a relational view, however, it is not quite so easy, because links are implicitly made by matching values from different relations, and we need to express this as a functional relationship. Shipman's paper shows a very nice way of doing this. We declare Student and Enrolment entities but the single-valued functions on them deliver not entities but integers, i.e. they are treated as scalar values. The relevant parts of the declarations are:

```
DECLARE  Student() —>> ENTITY
DECLARE  Stud# (Student) —> INTEGER

DECLARE  Enrolment() —>> ENTITY
DECLARE  Stud# (Enrolment) —> INTEGER
DECLARE  Course# (Enrolment) —> INTEGER

DECLARE  Course() —>> ENTITY
DECLARE  Course# (Course) —> INTEGER
```

Using these declarations we can express the multi-valued function Courses from a student to the set of courses he takes as:

DEFINE Courses(Student) —>> C IN Course
SUCH THAT SOME E in Enrolment HAS
Stud#(Student) = Stud#(E) and
Course#(E) = Course#(C)

The interesting thing is that the body of the function contains the 'join predicates', matching the Stud# attributes of relations Student and Enrolment, that occur in a relational calculus language like QUEL. Shipman actually shows the stages in rewriting a Daplex query on this schema into QUEL.

10.6 RELATIONSHIP TO ABSTRACT DATA TYPES

The notion of Abstract Data Types is that a type is defined implicitly by the operations on it; only these operations are allowed to be applied to instances of that type, and only these operations have access to its inner structure and know the details of its representation, as defined in CLU (Liskov *et al.* 1977) and RIGEL (Rowe and Shoens 1979). For example, the type 'Boolean', instead of being primitive, might be defined by the six functions (and, or, not, equal, true, false), and implemented in terms of two integer values 0 and −1, or else as the null list and non-null objects, and so on. Only the operations need to know which representation is used; this gives valuable modularity, and also security.

The functional data model uses this approach to define an entity. Instead of saying that it is represented by a record with certain contents, or by a tuple in a B-tree, it says what functions (or operations) are defined on it. The representation is left to the implementor and is defined at a lower level of abstraction. (The same principle governs the ANSI/SPARC proposals for separating details of CODASYL storage schemas from the conceptual schema, discussed in Chapter 11.)

Once the abstract types have been defined, it is possible to generate new types and arrange them in various hierarchies, as shown by Smith and Smith (1977), and described in Chapter 6. In general there are three methods of arranging the hierarchy: by generalisation, aggregation or association. The functional model supports the operation of generalisation, which gives a hierarchy of sub-types (a Person is a generalisation of Instructors and Students who in turn are generalisations of Science Students and Medical Students and so on). It also supports aggregation, in that an entity may have 'components' given by single-valued functions delivering entities which themselves have components, and so on until the components are scalar valued (e.g. an Enrolment has Course and Student components, and these have Name and Age components, and so on).

10.7 SUMMARY – KEY IDEAS

10.7.1 An abstract basis for CODASYL

The CODASYL model has long suffered from being looked on as an ad hoc collection of data storage techniques and has lacked the underlying soundness of the relational model. Daplex shows how to provide a functional language based on the use of functions that deliver sets as results, and which corresponds closely to the basic owner—member relationship in CODASYL, as we shall see in the next chapter.

10.7.2 Use of references not values
Daplex delivers a reference to an entity in some operations, and thus two entities with identical component values can still be distinguished by having distinct references. The notion that an expression can denote a unique unnamed object which exists separately from its components, and can be told apart from other objects, is important. Because the relational model lacks this, efforts have been made to introduce 'Surrogates' or unique identifiers for tuples in newer relational models such as RM/T (Codd 1979). These have the same utility as references but give the lie to the surface simplicity of the relational model.

10.7.3 Multi-valued function composition and join
These two operations are almost equivalent, as has been shown earlier, especially if Binary Relations are employed. However, there is a subtle difference in query formulation if n-ary relations are used. Most example queries in Daplex return a set of values of a single atomic type, e.g. a set of names or of ages, since this is a convenient result of composed functions. Most relational queries produce sets of tuples, with many components derived from different relations, since this is easily produced by joins of n-ary relations. Often these can be obtained in Daplex by applying functions to variables at different levels of nested loops. However, it may sometimes be necessary to use the 'Compound Of' operation, rather like '[,]' in FQL, which has the same effect as constructing a tuple in relational algebra.

10.7.4 Databases are for stored functions
The functional model removes the sharp distinction between data and program and especially between objects on secondary storage and objects created in memory during the running of a program. We have just two kinds of functions: computable functions, like sine and max etc., which are better not tabulated, and stored functions like Name(Employee), which are not easily calculated. However, any function may be composed with any other of conformable type, using the same syntax, and all functions have equal rights in this regard. Database query languages have suffered from an over-rigid division in this respect.

10.7.5 Making schemas extensible
The functional model is closely related to the binary relational model, and this allows one to add extra binary relations, representing new entities or relationships, *after* the database has been in use for some time. The binary relational database NDB (Winterbottom & Sharman 1979) has been constructed on these principles, and users regularly extend their database schemas. Similarly, in the Daplex implementation of Atkinson & Kulkarni, function declarations and entity declarations can be added or dropped. Surprisingly, such features are

rare in conventional DBMS, although there is clearly a need for it. Currently this is met by ad hoc restructuring tools or else by populating a new database. In order to do it cleanly the schema needs to be updatable and itself stored in the database. In a Daplex implementation the schema is represented as a collection of instances of special entities, whose attributes give the names of database entities etc. . . Similarly, in NDB, the schema is held in meta-relations; thus the schema can itself be updated as new entities and relationships are added or old ones deleted.

11

The CODASYL DBTG
database

11.1 INTRODUCTION

The CODASYL Database Task Group (DBTG) was set up in the 1960s to make proposals for extending the COBOL language to reference linked lists of records held on secondary storage. It was strongly influenced by the work of Charles Bachman who developed an early implementation of his ideas as Integrated Date Store (IDS). Bachman's ideas on the use of linked database records were presented as an ACM Turing Award Lecture (1973) 'The Programmer as Navigator'; it opened up a wonderful new world for the programmer, as he explored the many paths linking records on secondary storage.

The DBTG codified these ideas as a proposal for a standard, which was published in 1971. Following this there have been many implementations (IDS–II, IDMS, DMS 1100). Most of these are based on the 1971 report, or the slightly modified report of 1973. A further report was produced by the Data Description Language Committee (DDLC) in 1978, and revised slightly in 1981. The American Standards organisation ANSI is also working on a standard. Because all of these differ, and no manufacturer implements any report exactly, it is necessary to look at the manufacturer's manuals for precise information. The description below is based mainly on the IDS–II system, with notes about significant alterations, where these arise. The IDMS system is very similar to IDS–II, with minor variations in syntax, and a few unimplemented facilities.

Most of the very large databases which contain a variety of record types use the CODASYL system, or a simpler system such as TOTAL(®). By contrast relational databases such as INGRES and SYSTEM R started as research prototypes and only became available as commercial systems in the early 1980s. In general they do not use links between records and they rely instead on the construction of indexes in order to find related records, and thus speed up the join operation. However, for the largest databases the **CODASYL** method seems likely to remain the most popular until new hardware appears which makes possible a different method of doing joins. Interestingly, the **CODASYL** method directly supports the multi-valued functions of the Functional Data Model; we shall explore an interface to the FDM which uses this in Chapter 12.

In this chapter we first introduce the notion of a **CODASYL** 'set' relationship, and show how it is used to describe the abstract structure of the database by the device of a 'Bachman diagram'. This structure is described formally by a *schema* and we study how to write it down using the Data Description Language (DDL). This corresponds roughly to the global record type declarations that one finds at the start of a Cobol or Pascal program. We shall then look at the retrieval and update operations available on the records, using the **CODASYL** Data Manipulation Language (DML). This is effectively a set of special-purpose function calls available inside a Cobol, Fortran or PL/I program. An important consideration is how parameters are passed to these special-purpose routines through a **COMMON** area and certain special registers. In general all these operations are rather low level, and in the next chapter we will consider how to interface a **CODASYL** database to the various query languages that we have studied.

11.2 REPRESENTING SETS BY CHAINS AND POINTERS

The basic idea in **CODASYL** implementations is that of using linked lists to provide a representation of the function from an 'owner' record to a set of 'member' records, together with the inverse function from member to owner.

Suppose we want to associate an owner record of type stadium with a set of game records for games played in that stadium; two possible representations which are allowed in a **CODASYL** database are shown in Fig. 11.1.

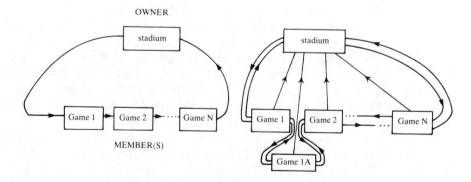

Fig. 11.1 – Codasyl set implementations.

The first representation is the simplest. If we know the location of the owner record, then to find the associated games records we just follow the trail of pointers from record to record until we return to our starting place. However the inverse process is slower. If we know the location of a member record, then we have to follow the pointers round until we get to the owner (which is specially marked). An improved representation, obtained at the cost of two extra pointers per record, is to let each record contain a pointer direct to the owner and also to the preceding record. In this way the owner is found immediately from the member.

The pointer to the prior record helps when it comes to inserting a new record in sequence. If we want to insert it before say, the second record, as in Fig. 11.1, then we find the preceding record and alter its pointer to point to the inserted record, which is then made to point to the original second record. Deletion is possible by reversing this process. In this way we get efficient updating of large data structures without a lot of copying and updating of indexes. We also get fast access to the owner. Finally if we wish to join, say, a Stadium relation to a Game relation, then to find the Game tuples matching each Stadium tuple we just follow the links round the chain.

11.2.1 CODASYL sets

This method of linking the owner to members is known, unfortunately, as a *CODASYL set,* and the pointers are known as *set pointers.* What in fact it represents is a function from the owner onto a set, i.e. a many-valued function, just as used in the Functional Data Model. Unfortunately the nomenclature has stuck! The set may, of course, have zero, one or more members; in other words it can be empty, or contain a singleton.

Access by hashing

The owner record can be accessed in various ways. It may have been found by navigating through some other set. However, it may also be found by address calculation (sometimes called *Hashing*), which calculates the approximate position of the record on disk from the value of its key. If the hashing rule is well chosen, then the record can be found with only one disk access. If the rule is poor then many records will hash to the same disk address, which usually identifies a *page* with space for a few tens of records. In bad cases the page will overflow to other pages which will slow the access. Most CODASYL record searches start by hashing and then follow set pointers.

Access by singular set

The snag with hashing is that it usually scatters the records all over the database in random order (in order to distribute them evenly over pages), but we may wish to examine them all in turn in key order. However, there is another possibility, which is to start from a unique database record. This record acts as owner for a number of different sets; for example, it may act as owner to all stadium records, where the links are threaded through the records in alphabetical order of stadium. By following through this set we shall visit all the records in order, although it will probably involve many page changes if the records are placed by hashing. A set such as this is known as a *Singular Set,* since there can only be one instance of any given set type which has a fixed record instance as owner.

Since it is obviously desirable to reduce page changes (and hence disk accesses), it is possible to request that member records are stored near their owners, instead of storing them by hashing. All these possibilities of storage placement give great potential for efficient access, but they make the database a lot harder for the casual user to set up. We shall deal with this now, but only briefly; full details on placement strategies and how to decide on them are given in (Wiederhold 1977; Date 1981).

11.2.2 Placement modes

Each different record type must be placed according to one of the following modes. All instances of a particular record type are placed in the same way.

CALC   Placement by calculating the disc address from the key (by hashing). It is usually randomised. It gives fast retrieval by primary key (the key most commonly chosen).

VIA   Placement close to owner. This reduces the page changes needed to follow through a set. However, the owners must themselves be well separated to leave space for the members (they are usually placed by hashing).

KEY   Placement in sequence, with space for insertions; rather as in an index sequential file, or a B-tree. The records are placed in order by key.

DIRECT   Placement by user algorithm. It may be used to place a unique record owning Singular Sets. However, the 1978 DDLC report recommends that such a record be found by record key access.

We shall study the access modes more closely when we look at the DML operations. For the moment we note that access passes through a sequence of records. We start either at the owner of a singular set, or by hashing; we continue by navigating along member records, or else up to the owner in another set, and then up to its owner, or down to its members, and so on.

11.3 A CODASYL SCHEMA AND ITS BACHMAN DIAGRAM

The abstract relationship between the owner and its set of members is called a 'set' relationship in CODASYL. All such relationships have to be declared in a *schema* which describes the types of records in the database and the types of set which are represented. The language used to write the schema is a *data description language (DDL)*. Thanks to the work of the DBTG (1971), the DDL is largely standardised. It contains a lot of details that do not concern us (Access, Privacy locks, etc., etc). More recent proposals by the DBTG (1978) suggest that it should be split into three parts:

the external schema should describe permitted user views;
the storage schema should describe record placement and implementation details;
the conceptual schema should describe the records, their attributes, and the set relationships between them.

We are mainly concerned with the conceptual schema although we will say a little about the other two below.

11.3.1 The conceptual schema

For each *Record Type* we declare its type name and its fields. The fields can be any of the basic types in Cobol or Fortran (integer, fixed or floating, real, fixed length string) together with arrays of fields (see Chapter 6). In fact they look exactly like Cobol records except that we cannot use the REDEFINES clause to declare variant records.

The difference from Cobol comes in the declaration of 'set relationships'. Instead of putting all the instances of a given record type in a file, each record type can appear either as Owner or as Member in one or more set type declarations. Let us now see some examples of this and how to construct a CODASYL schema for our World Cup database.

11.3.2 Declaring a hierarchical (one-to-many) relationship

Consider the relationship between Year records, Group records and Game records. In each Year of the competition there are many Groups, and in each Group there are many Games. We declare three set types: a 'Groups' set, a 'Ggames' set and a 'Years' set, which is a singular set, as shown in Fig. 11.2. The declarations are as shown in Fig. 11.2.

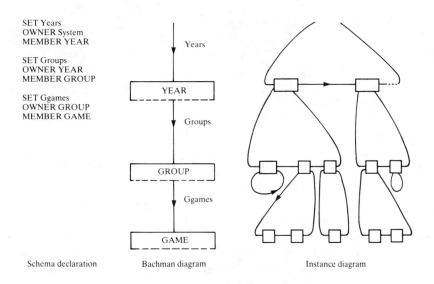

Fig. 11.2 – Set hierarchy.

For each set type we declare the owner and member record types. Fig. 11.2 also shows a *Bachman diagram* which represents the set declarations in a concise graphical form. There is a box for each record type. Each owner type is linked by an arrow to its member type in a given set, so that there is one arrow for

each set type. We write the set type name beside the arrow. Note that these are
set types and not set instances. The Instance diagram in Fig. 11.2 shows two
instances of a Groups set; one with three members and one with two. There are
three instances of Ggames sets, each owned by a unique Group record. Note
that these Group owner records do not all belong to the same instance of the
Groups set. Also two Group records own empty set instances. The crucial
thing is that each Ggame record has a unique Group record owner and thus can
belong to only *one* instance of a Ggames set. Similarly, each Group record
belongs to a unique instance of a Groups set with a unique Year record as
owner. Thus the records in the instance diagram form a hierarchy. In the instance
diagram the record instances form a kind of a tree, which we commonly use to
depict a hierarchy, with each record type appearing on a different level and
many records on one level being linked to only one record on the level above.

11.3.3 Declaring a net (many–many) relation

The hierarchy shows a 'one-to-many' relationship. Let us now look at how two
sets form a 'many–many' relationship. We take the example of Group, Link,
and Team records. A group contains many teams, and each team has a certain
placing in the final results for the group. However, the same team may also play in
many groups. Thus it is a 'many–many' relationship. We see this in Fig. 11.3.

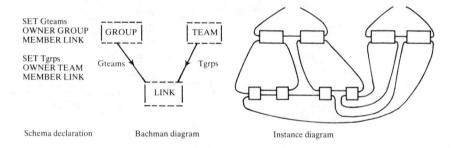

Fig. 11.3 – Many-to-many set relationship.

As we see, there are two instances of the Tgrps set; one owns two records
from one Gteams set instance and one record from another instance, the other
owns the remaining record. Note that although *different* Link records in the
same Gteams set instance may belong to different instances of *another* set type,
no one Link record can belong to two different instances of the *same* set type,
since it must have a unique owner.

As an abstraction, it is harder to grasp a many–many relationship than a
hierarchy. This is partly because the instance diagram is so much more complicated; the paths form a *net*, not a tree. Records are allowed to have more than
one owner, but only through different sets. Conceived of as a table (the GROUP_
PLAC relation), we find the many–many relation easier to cope with. The thing
to note is that we can sort the table in order of teams within each group or else

arranged by group for each team but we cannot arrange the table in both sequences at once. With a hierarchy there is no such difficulty: we can arrange the
GAMES table in order by games within group and by group within year.
This is why hierarchical relationships can easily be represented on sequential
tape files but net relationships cannot be represented so easily. The CODASYL
schema looks complicated, but it allows us to find all the results for a given
group or for a given team just by following the set pointers. However, the catch
is that we cannot cluster the Link record VIA both owners. Whichever set type
we choose as the owner for VIA placement, it will be slower to follow through
the other set type.

11.3.4 Declaring a generalised hierarchy

The record types we have looked at so far also provide an example of a more
general hierarchy (see Fig. 11.4).

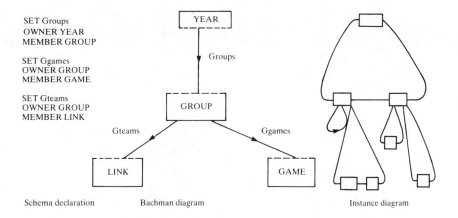

SET Groups
OWNER YEAR
MEMBER GROUP

SET Ggames
OWNER GROUP
MEMBER GAME

SET Gteams
OWNER GROUP
MEMBER LINK

Schema declaration   Bachman diagram   Instance diagram

Fig. 11.4 – Generalised hierarchy.

We still have a hierarchy, in that each record on a given level still has a
unique owner on the next level. However, it is now possible for one record to be
owner of two different set instances, but only if these are the instances of
different set types.

We have not done it in this case, but it is possible to use this to represent
a sub-type relationship, as explained later.

11.3.5 A cyclic hierarchy

The final possibility in a Bachman diagram is to have two sets which relate the
same owner record type to the same member record type (Fig. 11.5). Note that
it is not possible in DBTG CODASYL (1971) for the owner and member record
types in one set to be the same – the owner must always be a different type of
record from its members, although later proposals (DBTG 1978) have relaxed
this restriction. This abstract structure has a deceptively simple Bachman diagram

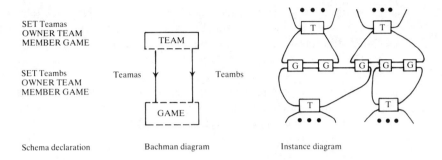

Schema declaration   Bachman diagram   Instance diagram

Fig. 11.5 – Cyclic hierarchy.

but it can be hard to grasp. It behaves like a degenerate case of the many–many relationship, where the two owner record types are the same. However, the consequence is that one can, for example, go down from a Team record to the Game records which it owns through one set and then back up to an owner Team record through the other set, from whence one can go down to the games of that team, and so on, recursively cycling through Game and Team records, as indicated in the instance diagram.

The classic relationship which can be represented in this way is the Part–Assembly relationship as in Fig. 11.6.

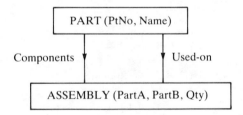

Fig. 11.6 – Part–Assembly relationship.

A 'Part' record describes a particular part used in assemblies, and gives its description and other details. An 'Assembly' record contains the names of two parts and details of how many of Part A are used in the manufacture of Part B. Each 'Part' record appears as owner of all Assembly records in which it is PartA, through a 'Components' set, i.e. it owns the set of all its immediate components. Each Part record also appears as owner of all Assembly records in which it is PartB, through a 'Used-On' set, i.e. it is related to the set of all assemblies in which it is used directly. By repeatedly going down the Components set and back up via the Used-on set we can traverse the tree of components of a particular part at all levels, i.e. its 'Explosion'. This is useful when working out the total stock of parts required to manufacture a big assembly. Alternatively, by repeatedly going down the Used-on set and back up via the Components set we can traverse the ancestor tree of all parts which contain a given part, directly or indirectly, (sometimes called its 'Implosion'). This is useful, for example, in determining those parts whose costs have to be changed, because a component has increased in price.

If we view this in terms of the Entity–Relationship Model, then the Part records form an Entity relation, and the Assembly records form a Relationship relation. To answer a query about the sub-components of a Part several levels down, we select this Part from the PART Relation and repeatedly join the ASSEMBLY Relation to the result.

11.4 OTHER DETAILS IN THE SET DESCRIPTION

11.4.1 Automatic and manual insertion

Until now we have made the implicit assumption that every member record instance has an owner, if it appears in a set declaration. This need not be so. However, if we wish to enforce it, then we must put the keyword 'AUTOMATIC' after the appropriate MEMBER clause in the set declaration in the schema. Then, whenever a new record of the given type is stored in the database, it will automatically be inserted into the appropriate set instance.

The method for selecting the set instance with the right owner is given in the schema in a *set selection* clause, associated with the set. The two common methods are:

SET SELECTION THRU APPLICATION This just means that the application programmer will leave a reference to the owner record in a given location (a so-called 'currency pointer') before executing the STORE instruction. This is the default case.

SET SELECTION THRU KEY ⟨field⟩ The ⟨field⟩ given must be a key for the owner record and the applications program must place a value in the location reserved for this field in working storage, before executing STORE.

If we do not wish the insertion into a set to be automatic, then we must use the keyword MANUAL in place of AUTOMATIC. There are two common reasons for this.

(i) The set in question may, for example, contain a restricted selection of records with a special property (e.g. all teams which are European). It may not be appropriate to all record instances, which thus must not be inserted automatically.

(ii) It may be inconvient for the logic of the application program to arrange that all the owner records are in place before storing the members. The program can carry out the process of linking owners to members, after storing both of them, by using the CONNECT verb.

11.4.2 Insertion and retention class

The keywords AUTOMATIC and MANUAL define the *insertion class* of a record type in given set type. We can also define the *retention class* using the keywords MANDATORY, OPTIONAL and FIXED to define the allowable methods of removing a record instance from an occurrence of a given set type. If the keyword is MANDATORY, then the record must always belong to some set occurrence; consequently we may not delete the owner of such a set until we have deleted all of its members, or else connected them to other owners. Thus it is common to use the keyword combination MANDATORY AUTO-MATIC to cause the system to enforce the constraint that every record of the given type always has an owner in the given set.

If the keyword used is FIXED then we can neither Disconnect the record from its owner nor reconnect it to a different owner, which is thus even more constraining than MANDATORY, which does allow us to reconnect the record to another owner. If instead the keyword used is OPTIONAL then there are no constraints.

The main significance of MANDATORY AUTOMATIC is that it provides a valuable integrity constraint, since it ensures that the FIND OWNER operation on a given record type will always return a reference to the owner and never an empty result. In the functional data model this is equivalent to saying that the corresponding function is total and not partial. It also allows us to use LOCATION mode VIA, because the member will always have an owner record and hence its position is always known.

11.4.3 Ordering within sets

The Relational Model does not define the ordering of tuples within a relation. However, the DBTG model does allow the schema to define the order of records within a set. This is desirable from the point of efficiency but it does not affect the logical view of the schema.

If, in a set declaration, we say that 'ORDER IS SORTED BY DEFINED KEYS', then we insist that, whenever records are inserted into a set occurrence, they must be inserted in the right place in sequence.

The KEY in question is given by a KEY clause following the entry for MEMBER   (see Fig. 11.8). It comprises one or more fields of the member record each qualified by ASCENDING or DESCENDING. Note that the key only has to be unique within a set occurrence; it does not have to be unique across all occurrences of the record type. For example another record of this type might happen to have the same values for its data fields but be distinguished by having a different owner. This organisation can be used in three ways.

(i) It can be used in conjunction with a check that there are no duplicates in the set (i.e. other records having the same KEY value). If we wish to enforce this, then we put DUPLICATES NOT ALLOWED at the end of the ORDER IS clause.

(ii) It can be used by particular application programs to save sorting results before printing. It can also be used to speed up searches for a whole list of members arranged in the right order, just as in the 'merge-join' technique explained in Chapter 8.

(iii) It can be used with very large set occurrences containing many members to provide a *search key or range key* to help locate a particular member. Instead of just chaining member records in sequence, we use a *pointer array* (see next section) combined with the key values to provide an index in sorted order to each set occurrence.

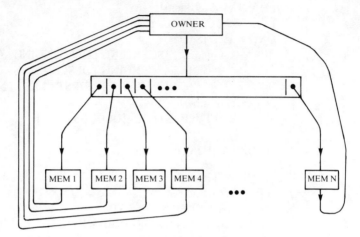

Fig. 11.7 – Pointer array representation of set.

11.4.4 Pointer array mode

In this mode we use a contiguous representation of a sequence instead of a chained representation. Instead of keeping a pointer to the next record with each record we keep an array of pointers to all the member records with the owner, as in Fig. 11.7. The space taken depends on the number of pointers; if there are many of them then they are organised as a B-tree, rather than as a single ordered vector (as explained by Knuth 1973, and Date 1981). However, we are saving the space for two pointers (next and prior) with each member, and only using one extra pointer with the owner. We can make space in this array to hold the search key value alongside each pointer, and thus we can hope to search an array of 'n' items in time proportional to 'log n' and not just proportional to 'n', as it would be for searching along a chained sequence in a fixed order. The price for this speed increase of course comes with the increased cost of insertion or deletion of records, since we may then have to expand or shrink the array; this is the reason for using a B-tree instead of a single array, when there are many pointers.

11.4.5 Summary of set entry

Examples of record entries and set entries for the World Cup database, together with a complete Bachman diagram, are given in Appendix III. The full syntax is given in the DBTG report and usually varies slightly from manufacturer to manufacturer. A basic skeleton syntax appears in Fig. 11.8. Note that provision is made for a set to contain more than one type of member record, thus forming a 'multi-member' set, as discussed in the next chapter.

The use of curly and square brackets in this grammar is as follows. Square brackets enclose phrases that may occur once or not at all; or if followed by '. . .', then the phrase may occur several times. Curly brackets enclose several alternatives, separated by vertical bars, one of which must be present.

```
SCHEMA NAME IS ⟨ident⟩.
    [ACCESS CONTROL etc. .]
RECORD NAME IS ⟨ident⟩;
        [KEY ⟨key-name⟩ {ASCENDING | DESCENDING} ⟨item-name⟩
                  [, {ASCENDING | DESCENDING} ⟨item-name⟩ ]...
                  DUPLICATES {FIRST | LAST | NOT ALLOWED} ]
    [ ⟨Cobol-level-number⟩
        ⟨item-name⟩ TYPE IS etc. .   [OCCURS etc. . ].
    ] ...
[RECORD NAME IS etc. .    ]...

SET NAME IS ⟨ident⟩;
OWNER IS ⟨rec-name⟩;
ORDER IS {NEXT | FIRST | LAST
            | SORTED BY DEFINED KEYS
                [ DUPLICATES {FIRST | LAST | NOT ALLOWED} ] }
MEMBER IS ⟨rec-name⟩;
    INSERTION IS {AUTOMATIC | MANUAL}
    RETENTION IS {FIXED | MANDATORY | OPTIONAL}
    [KEY IS ⟨key-field-list⟩] ;
    SET SELECTION THRU {APPLICATION | KEY ⟨keyname⟩}
[MEMBER IS etc]...
```

Fig. 11.8 – Basic skeleton of schema entries.

11.5 THE ANSI/SPARC PROPOSALS: EXTERNAL VIEWS AND STORAGE SCHEMAS

11.5.1 The sub-schema

The 1971 DBTG proposals introduced the concept of a *sub-schema*. The idea was that each user should use a particular subset of the schema, with his own synonyms for set names and field names and record type names. He could also specify procedures for converting data item values from their record values into the values retrieved via the sub-schema.

The idea is basically similar to that of providing External Views of a Relational Database, but it is not so general. The subset feature means that the user is only able to see those data fields, records and set names which are in the sub-schema; this helps to preserve privacy and stop unauthorised updating. The conversion procedures can be useful, e.g. for changes in units of measurement, or else for accommodating different storage conventions used in different host languages, e.g. storage of reals in Cobol and Fortran. The changes of name are also useful for accommodating different rules for variable names in different languages.

11.5.2 The storage schema

The ANSI-SPARC standards working party (ANSI 1975) proposed that the schema should be at two levels: the *conceptual schema* would describe the logical relationship between data items, together with integrity constraints, whilst at a lower level the *internal schema* or *storage schema* would contain details of allocation of records to storage areas, placement-strategy (CALC, VIA or SEQUENTIAL as mentioned earlier), use of indexes, set ordering, chain or pointer array mode etc., which impact on efficiency and implementation details. The method of writing the storage schema varies between manufacturers. Specific proposals were made in an Annexe to the DDLC JOD (1978) and are discussed by Knowles and Bell (1984).

11.5.3 The three-level schema

The working party also proposed multiple sub-schemas, with enhanced facilities, and called them *external schemas*. This organisation has been called the 'three-level schema'. If we think in terms of the functional data model (FDM), then the external schema features are provided by derived functions, and the conceptual schema features are provided by entity declarations together with statements about keys and sub-types and integrity constraints. The internal schema is at a lower level and may be hidden in the implementation of the FDM; alternatively if we choose to implement an FDM conceptual schema in terms of an actual relational database system, say using QUEL, then the details of how we do this becomes the internal schema. The main idea is that the many external views map onto one unique conceptual schema, which provides consistency, whilst at the same time isolating users from details of the implementation; these may be changed to give improved efficiency.

We may draw a diagram to illustrate the ANSI/SPARC approach (Fig. 11.9). The conceptual schema is related to the internal schema through a *conceptual/internal mapping.* This enables us to find the actual record or records in physical

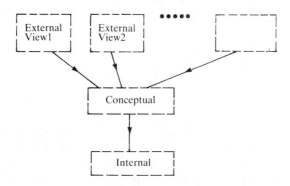

Fig. 11.9 – ANSI-SPARC schema architecture.

storage that constitute a record in the conceptual schema, together with any constraints to be enforced on operations on that record.

Each external schema is related to the conceptual by an *external/conceptual mapping*. This enables us to map names and values in the user's view onto the specified part of the conceptual schema description.

11.6 CODASYL DML OPERATIONS

11.6.1 Use of variables in work areas and registers

We are now in a position to list the different operations in the *data manipulation language* or DML. Commands in this language are embedded in a Fortran, Cobol or PL/I program. They refer to record type names, and to set type names, and also to the current instances of records and sets under consideration, which are held in global storage locations known as the *user work area (UWA)*. In a Fortran implementation such an area would be declared as though by a COMMON declaration. Each field in each record type would have its value stored in a COMMON variable of the appropriate type. Thus it is usual for field names in different records to be distinct.

The user interacts with the database by placing values in the UWA variables before executing DML operations, and by retrieving values from these locations afterwards, by using the usual assignment statements of the host language. If he wants to extract records repeatedly (e.g. to traverse a set) then he must write a loop in the normal way in the applications program, as in Fig. 11.10. In general, a DML command will only operate on one record instance at a time (an exception is the ERASE ALL command described later).

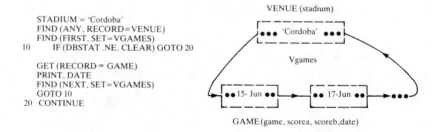

```
        STADIUM = 'Cordoba'
        FIND (ANY, RECORD=VENUE)
        FIND (FIRST, SET=VGAMES)
   10      IF (DBSTAT .NE. CLEAR) GOTO 20

        GET (RECORD = GAME)
        PRINT, DATE
        FIND (NEXT, SET=VGAMES)
        GOTO 10
   20  CONTINUE
```

Fig. 11.10 – CODASYL DML embedded in Fortran.

In Fig. 11.10 the DML commands used are FIND and GET. The program starts by locating a record for Cordoba stadium, by hashing the key. It then finds the first game record in the set, prints the date from it, and loops round finding the next game record in the set and so on until there are none left. The GET command copies a game record from disk into the UWA, where the PRINT statement can access the 'date' field, as though it were a Fortran variable.

Besides the UWA, the application program can inspect various registers which contain information on the state of the database. The status register (DB-STATUS or DBSTAT) contains information on any error condition following a failed DML operation. Some dialects of DML contain 'ERROR=' clauses which allow one to trap to a labelled instruction in the program when any error is detected, where the applications program must deal with it (or else by default the operating system will abort the run). If this is not so then it is necessary to test the status by means of an IF statement after each command. Similarly the test for whether there are any more records to visit in a set can be made on DBSTAT (as in Fig. 11.10), or else by using an 'END=' clause in the FIND command, rather as in a Fortran or Cobol READ statement.

The other registers giving information on the state of the database are the infamous *currency registers*. These each contain a *data base key (DBKEY)*, which references the position on disk of a record recently referenced by a DML command; this includes all records currently in the UWA. Most DML commands start by referencing these registers. The commands which find a record, or store a new record, return the position of this record by updating the currency registers. The registers thus act like global variables.

The actual form of the disk references used as DBKEYs may be relative to the start of a numbered disk page, and are of no concern to the programmer. They should enable the data base management system to locate the appropriate disk page immediately. The page may actually be in a buffer in store, if it has been fetched in by some prior command, and this buffer will act as a kind of cache memory to reduce disk transfers.

There is one currency register for every record type and set type in the database. The 'current of record type' register holds the DBKEY for the corresponding record instance most recently found or stored. The 'current of set type' register holds the DBKEY for the last record (either owner or member) that was accessed from the given set type. One record instance may of course be current for more than one set type, and it may even be different from the current of record type!

There is also a 'current of run unit' register, for the record accessed most recently by any command, and a 'current of realm' register for each separate realm (physical or logical disk unit) on which records are held, and which has been opened.

The bad thing about currency registers is that they are updated by side effects of DML operations which are not visible to the programmer. This is the worst kind of assignment programming and it is notoriously easy for faults to occur with it. When we come to consider the interface to a functional language (FQL), and to ASTRID, we shall see that it is necessary to sidestep this mechanism. The problem arises when a program is executing a loop over records in a set, and from within that loop accesses other records of that type, thereby accidentally altering the set currency registers. It does not arise when descending a simple or generalised hierarchy of sets and accessing other owner record types through net relationships, because the owner–member pointers do not cycle through more than one instance of any record type.

11.7 THE FORMS OF THE FIND COMMAND

The crucial DML operation is the FIND command, for locating a record by navigating or hashing. There are seven forms of the command, which we will categorise, following Olle (1978), either as 'out of the blue' commands, to locate a starting place for a search, or as 'navigation' commands to continue the search. We have not space here to explore all of the subtle nuances in syntax and usage of these commands, and the reader is referred to Olle for a fuller discussion. We give the commands in their form as used in Cobol; the Fortran versions, as for example in Fig. 11.10, use a syntax with the same keywords, but enclosed in brackets and separated by commas.

Out of the blue

(A) FIND ANY ⟨rec-name⟩ [USING ⟨keyname⟩] In current implementations (IDMS, IDSII), the USING clause is not specified and it finds an occurrence of a record which was placed by hashing (CALC mode). The key values (for the fields used in hashing) must be placed in the UWA beforehand. The newer specifications suggest that it should also be used to find a record instance by searching for the given key value in an index covering all records of this type. They also suggest that the distinction between hash access and indexing should be known only to the storage schema. If the KEY clause for a record is ordered, then the method should find the record with the next highest key if one is not there. If the KEY is not ordered (as with hashing) then it is an error if the record is not found.

(B) FIND FIRST ⟨rec name⟩ WITHIN ⟨realm name⟩ This finds the first record of a given type within a given *realm* or *area* which has been opened for searching. This can be used to find a special record owning all singular sets, which is usually placed near the start of the area. A database may have several areas, usually corresponding to separate random access files known to the operating system. The original DBTG report spoke of AREAs, and these are still used by current versions of IDMS and IDS-II. The sub-schema uses the term REALM to define a subset of the available areas. However, the DDLC report (1981) recommends removing all knowledge of areas down to the storage schema, so that the DML commands see only a single logical area.

(C) FIND DB-KEY ⟨dbkey⟩ This merely resets the currency registers to a state where the 'current of run-unit' and other appropriate registers point to a record which has been found some time earlier or whose database key is known to the program. If the desired database key is already in one of the other registers, then it is better to use the command 'FIND CURRENT ⟨record name⟩[WITHIN ⟨set name⟩|⟨realm name⟩]' which takes the DBKEY from current of record type, set type, or realm type as appropriate, and makes it current of run unit.

(D) FIND FIRST ⟨rec-name⟩ USING ⟨key-name⟩ This is used where a KEY clause is declared in the RECORD entry (see Fig. 11.8); thus every record occurrence of this type can be located by its key, regardless of set membership. The named key may contain one or more data items declared in the **KEY** clause. Usually this method is supported by some kind of index or B-tree which associates key values with **DBKEYs**. The method finds the record of this type with the lowest key value.

Navigation

(E) FIND FIRST|LAST ⟨rec name⟩ WITHIN ⟨set name⟩ This finds the first (or last) member record for a given set type. The owner record for the set (which establishes the set instance) must be current of the set type. It may have been found by an 'out of the blue' method or by previous navigation. The command gives an error if the set is empty.

(F) FIND NEXT|PRIOR ⟨rec name⟩ WITHIN ⟨set name⟩ This is used to navigate along a chain or pointer array finding the next member from the member which is current of set. It is usually repeated within a loop. If the current record is the last member then the command gives an error. If the keyword **PRIOR** is used instead of **NEXT** then it accesses the preceding member (usually using a backward pointer).

(G) FIND ⟨rec name⟩ WITHIN ⟨set name⟩ CURRENT USING ⟨search key⟩ This is used to find the member in a large set occurrence which has a given value for the search key field(s). The applications program places the desired key values in these fields in the **UWA** before executing the command. As remarked earlier it is unlikely to be efficient unless a pointer array implementation is used. It does, however, have the effect of scanning more than one record.

(H) FIND OWNER WITHIN ⟨set name⟩ This finds the owner record for the record that is current of run unit. If there is no owner for the given record an error results. It is better to use the special predicate 'IF MEMBER (⟨set name⟩)' to test beforehand if the current record does have an owner in the given set, where membership is not **AUTOMATIC MANDATORY**.

(I) FIND DUPLICATE ⟨rec name⟩ This is used following method **A** in the case where **CALC** mode is not used on an identifier for the record but instead on a secondary key which has multiple occurrences. This is rather unusual, but repeated application of this command allows one to retrieve all the occurrences.

(J) FIND DUPLICATE WITHIN ⟨set name⟩ USING ⟨search key⟩ This is used following method (G) if there are multiple records in a set with the same search key value, or else we are not using a search key but just some numerical field such as 'score' and looking for more games with the same score.

(K) FIND NEXT|PRIOR ⟨rec name⟩ WITHIN ⟨realm name⟩ This is used following method (B) and makes it possible to scan every record of a given type in the entire database, or in a given realm of it. It might be thought of as an act of desperation, but if one is examining a large part of the database through a hierarchy of sets it may be quicker to use this method instead, since it involves the minimum number of page changes — no page is ever revisited once it has been left, as it might be in the other method.

(L) FIND NEXT ⟨recname⟩ USING ⟨keyname⟩ This is used following method (D) to access all records of a given type in key order. It is only possible if an ordering is defined for the key, as when a B-tree index is used, and not when randomised hashing is applied. It can also be used following method A, which has located a record in the middle of a sequence.

The sheer range of FIND commands and their almost Byzantine intricacy is one of the reasons why DBTG databases are programmed only by experts. In later sections we shall be discussing how to provide interfaces to high-level query languages and thus avoid direct use of low level DML commands.

11.8 OTHER DML COMMANDS

We list below the other commands usually provided in DML, with a brief description of their usage. Fuller details are given by Olle (1978), Date (1981), and the manufacturer's reference manual.

READY {⟨realm name⟩|ALL} MODE IS {RETRIEVAL|UPDATE}
      [PROTECTED|EXCLUSIVE]
This opens one or more realms for access or update. It also says whether other users are allowed concurrent access or update.

FINISH ALL|⟨realm name⟩
This closes the database and flushes the buffers or else just closes off a particular realm.

GET ⟨record name⟩
This actually copies the current of run unit into the UWA. Almost all FIND commands need to be followed by a GET, otherwise one cannot inspect individual fields in the record. Some DMLs combine FIND and GET using the keyword FETCH.

ACCEPT ⟨dbkey⟩ FROM [⟨record name⟩|⟨set-name⟩|⟨realm-name⟩]
       CURRENCY
This provides a means to store away a currency indicator for subsequent use by a FIND DBKEY statement (option (C)). It is essential if the user wants to bypass the currency mechanism and take control, as in Buneman's scheme, which is described in Chapter 12.

STORE ⟨record name⟩
This copies the contents of the UWA to disk (via the buffers) and allocates it a DBKEY. If the record is an AUTOMATIC member of any sets then it is inserted into them, provided integrity checks are satisfied.

MODIFY ⟨record name⟩ [INCLUDING ⟨set-name-list⟩]
This writes back from the UWA a record, previously retrieved from the database, whose fields have been updated. If a list of set names is given, then it is assumed that the owner of the record in these sets is no longer

correct, or is inconsistent with the modified values of record fields; the record is connected into new set occurrences according to the set selection criteria given in the schema.

CONNECT ⟨rec name⟩ TO ⟨set name⟩
This inserts a record (current of run unit) into the set instance which is current of set type. Usually these currencies have been set by preceding FIND commands.

DISCONNECT ⟨rec name⟩ FROM ⟨set name⟩
This removes a record (current of run unit) from a set. It is only allowed if the membership is declared OPTIONAL in the schema.

ERASE [ALL] ⟨rec name⟩
This removes a record (the current of run-unit) from the database (it is the converse of STORE). If the keyword ALL is used it also removes all it descendants in any sets for which it is owner. This is useful if the record owns non-empty sets with MANDATORY or FIXED membership, which extend through many levels in a hierarchy.

DB ⟨subschema-name⟩ WITHIN ⟨schema-name⟩
This is a directive to the compiler for the host language, causing it to reserve space for the UWA in the program, and to check all names used in DML commands against the given sub-schema. The keyword INVOKE is used in Fortran, followed by '(SUBSCHEMA= ⟨name⟩, SCHEMA= ⟨name⟩)'.

11.9 SUMMARY

Systems based on the CODASYL proposals are in widespread use. Currently the ANSI committee are working on a simplified standardised version which will presumably increase its popularity even more. The use of the Bachman diagram to describe relationships between data types has become important as an aid to designing information systems, and it provides a valuable alternative to the relational method. The idea that abstract data relationships can be described in a conceptual schema and kept logically separate from the implementation details of the storage schema is an important one. Likewise the idea of providing multiple external views for different users, whilst keeping the whole collection of data integrated and consistent with the conceptual schema is very attractive.

Undoubtedly the efficiency of CODASYL implementations for performing access and update on very large databases has been an important factor in their widespread use. This efficiency has been purchased at the cost of using a baffling variety of storage strategies and DML commands. The complex side effects of these commands on the currency registers provide traps for the unwary. This has undoubtedly restricted the use of CODASYL databases, which is why it is important to provide access to them through higher level languages, as in relational systems. This is the topic of our final chapter.

12

Functional query languages for CODASYL databases

In general the advantage of the CODASYL method is that it allows efficient updating of collections of records and fast access to certain specified record types, which is useful for short transactions, combined with reasonable performance on joins, which can involve scanning large numbers of records. Its main disadvantages are the lack of a completely general high level query language and also of the kind of firm mathematical basis that underlies the relational model.

Recent developments are producing improvements in this area. Buneman has developed a very simple and elegant interface to the SEED CODASYL Database via FQL. The ASTRID system (Gray and Bell 1979) allows one to answer complex queries in an extended relational algebra, making efficient use of CODASYL's intrarecord links. Zaniolo (1979) has shown how to represent a CODASYL schema as a number of 'perceived records', corresponding to relations, and thus how to use the methods adopted for answering relational queries in a language such as SQL. Finally the Functional Data Model (FDM) provides a theoretical basis for the CODASYL model. Further, since the FDM can also map down to QUEL, it provides a possible common language for asking queries of a distributed database made up of individual CODASYL and relational databases.

In this chapter we start by looking at an FQL interface to a CODASYL database and at how it is implemented very simply by routines in Pascal which avoid currency registers. We then look at how DML operations in Daplex can be implemented using a similar technique. Next we discuss how to map schemas firstly from CODASYL to a Daplex equivalent, and secondly from CODASYL to a relational equivalent. Several ways of doing the relational mapping are described, followed by a description of how to translate the join operation (in combination with other relational algebra operations) into efficient code for accessing a CODASYL database. The last part of the chapter discusses problems not dealt with so far. It looks at the problems of update operations and of maintaining integrity constraints, and it concludes by looking at directions of current research into unresolved problems.

12.1 IMPLEMENTING THE FQL LANGUAGE ON A CODASYL DATABASE

The functions of FQL described in Chapter 5 return streams of tuples by lazy evaluation, or else return singleton tuples. Buneman, Menten and Root (1981) describe an implementation of these functions which uses CODASYL records to represent the tuples, identified by the DBKEY of the record. Instead of a stream of tuples we have a stream of references to records. When we apply a record selector function to a reference, we first have to bring the record into storage (by GET), and then return the value from the appropriate field of the record, held in the UWA.

Thus each operation on a tuple in FQL becomes an operation on a corresponding reference identifying a record in the database. The operation to get the next tuple from a stream often corresponds to finding the next record in the set or realm. The operation of applying an inverse function (e.g. ↑EMPLOYEE in Chapter 5) often corresponds to finding the owner record.

12.1.1 An alternative to currency registers

In order to write the run-time routines that implement the FQL operations it is necessary to by-pass the currency mechanism and the UWA and to implement all the DML commands as functions that take references to records as parameters, and which return them as results. The run-time routines (or the applications program) must provide storage for the DBKEYs (instead of using currency registers) and also provide storage for the records (instead of using the UWA). In consequence this storage can be allocated on a Pascal stack, so that one can write recursive programs without having to preserve and restore currency registers. Furthermore the functions do not have side effects on DBKEYs stored elsewhere.

Consider, for example, a fragment of Pascal, as in Buneman's implementation. This corresponds to Fig. 11.10 discussed earlier. It accesses all the Game records for games played in Cordoba, via the set VGames, and prints out the match dates.

```
type   StadName = packed array[1..16] of char;

       GameRec =     record
                         date : integer;
                         gameno : integer;
                     end;

       StadiumRec =  record
                         stadium : StadName;
                     end;
```

```
var    S : ↑StadiumRec; G : ↑GameRec;

     S := FFC_Stadium('Cordoba');
     G := FFS_VGames(S);
     while G ⟨⟩ nil do
     began
          writeln(G↑.date);
          G:=FNS_VGames(G)
     end;
```

Here the variables G and S hold references to Pascal records containing information about a game and a stadium respectively. Corresponding to each reference to a record in store there is a **DBKEY** referencing the corresponding record on disk. The corresponding **DBKEY** values are remembered by the run-time routines, so that the programmer cannot see them or corrupt them. The function FFC_ Stadium takes a name as parameter and returns a reference to a record of type StadiumRec, having found the **DBKEY** of the corresponding record on disk by hashing. In this example it finds the record for Cordoba stadium. FFS_VGames finds the first member in the VGames set owned by Cordoba, and takes a reference to the owner as parameter. It constructs a reference for a GameRec record to hold the result. FNS_VGames finds the next in set following the reference given as a parameter, and the loop continues placing new references in G repeatedly, until the set is empty. This is signalled by a null value in G, instead of requiring an error exit or a test of the database **DBSTAT** register. Game records are retrieved into memory as ordinary Pascal records, and their components (e.g. date) are accessed in the normal Pascal fashion.

It is important to note that the declarations for records such as GameRec do not include fields that contain references to other records, even though such fields are present in the records on disk. The idea is to apply functions such as FFS_VGames to these records, and to use the functions to follow the disk references, which are thus hidden from the Pascal user. The same idea is, of course, used in the FDM, but the Adaplex Schema in Fig. 10.3 makes functions that follow references to other records look just like record attribute selectors, and they are all listed together, instead of being declared separately.

The system automatically generates type declarations and external routines for FFC_Stadium, FFS_VGames, FNS_VGames etc., from the **CODASYL** schema declaration. The first three letters identify the version of the Find command or other command that is being used, and the main letters identify the **CODASYL** set type or record type. Each such function takes a particular Pascal type as input and has a Pascal type for its result. Thus the Pascal type-checking mechanism can be used to ensure that, for example, FNS_VGames is not applied to the variable S, which is of the wrong type.

Updating and storage of records is more complicated because of the need for automatic insertion into sets. However, this need not concern us here, because FQL is a language for queries only.

12.1.2 Use of DML operations by an FQL interpreter

An FQL interpreter can be written in Pascal using the above techniques as described in Buneman *et al.* (1982). An FQL function such as !Venues would return the sequence of references to stadium records, by first using FFS_Venues on the Venues singular set, and then using FNS_Venues, whenever the lazy evaluation mechanism decided it was time to do so. Eventually FNS_Venues would return nil, and !Venues would return a terminator.

An FQL inverse function such as ↑Stadium would use FFC_Stadium, taking advantage of the hash key for fast access. However, a multi-valued inverse function such as ↑Date would have to access all the stadium records in the realm (using FIND modes (B) and (K)), and select those records with the specified Date value.

A single-valued function such as 'Venue' applied to a Game would use FOS_VGames (find owner in set) to return the reference to the Venue record. If a stream of Games is supplied, and 'Venue' is applied to all of them by using the '*' operation, then FOS_VGames will be called for each one in turn by the lazy evaluation mechanism (Chapter 5).

The restriction operation '|' in FQL is implemented by accessing the components for each referenced record in turn; the data values are tested and only those references to records which satisfy the test are passed on.

The 'tupling operator' ([. .]) creates data structures in main storage whose components may be data values or references. Their contents are accessed by the selector functions #1, #2 etc., as explained in Chapter 5. Clearly some type checking of the contents is desirable, and this is carried out by FQL.

12.1.3 Summary

We see that an FQL interpreter is remarkably simple and elegant and provides an attractive high level alternative to CODASYL DML, whilst making good use of most of the CODASYL facilities. It is restricted, however, to querying and not updating.

12.2 IMPLEMENTING DAPLEX FUNCTIONS ON CODASYL

Daplex is rather different from FQL in that it works with sets instead of streams; consequently it cannot always make use of lazy evaluation. Clearly we can represent entity occurrences in Daplex by the DBKEYs of the corresponding entity records, much as for FQL. A single Daplex 'for' loop iterating over all instances of a given entity record will either access them through a singular set (e.g. by using FFS–X and FNS–X) or else by searching through a realm. The precise control structure which calls these DML commands depends on how Daplex is implemented. If it is embedded in a procedural language like ADA, then it will probably just be a 'while loop', inside which ADA variables can be altered and printed etc.; if it is interpreted directly (Atkinson and Kulkarni 1984) then there is scope for lazy evaluation and other techniques for query optimisation.

Consider the case shown in Fig. 12.1, which writes the date and stadium for each game, in stadium order, using the functions defined by the Adaplex schema of Fig. 10.3. Here Daplex uses nested loops iterating over the Daplex equivalent of a CODASYL set, with the owner established by the outer loop variable and the member being scanned by the inner loop variable. We write a corresponding inner looper in Pascal; we use FFS_VGames to initialise it, and inside the loop we use FNS_VGames to get the new value for the loop variable G. This correspondence is shown in Fig. 12.1.

```
for each s in venue                 S:=FFS_Venues(SYSREC);
   for each g in Vgames(s)          while S ⟨⟩ nil do
      print Date(g), Stadium(s)     begin
                                       G:=FFS_VGames(S);
                                       while G⟨⟩ nil do
                                       begin
                                          writeln(G↑.Date, S↑.Stadium)
                                          G:=FNS_VGames(G)
                                       end;
                                       S:=FNS_Venues(S);
                                    end
```

Fig. 12.1 – Daplex and Pascal DML equivalents.

We can easily extend the example in Fig. 12.1 to illustrate the single-valued functions. Suppose we want a single-valued function of game, such as Group. We can embed, for example, 'for the r in CompGroup(g)' in the inner loop of the Daplex version and correspondingly put R:=FOS_GGames(G) in the inner loop of the Pascal version.

12.2.1 Daplex composed functions
The implementation of a composition of multivalued functions, as in 'for each x in f(g(z))', can be difficult, because Daplex requires that f(g(z)) denote a set with no duplicate members. In this way it is different from the nested loop form 'for each y in g(z) do for each x in f(y) do . . .'. This is because when f is applied to two different values of y (or g(z)) it may produce the same value of x. In the nested loop case the outer loop variable has a different value in the two cases. However, in the case of composition all the values of f(g(z)) form one set and any given value will only be presented once in the for loop over the composed function.

If the multi-valued functions correspond exactly to CODASYL sets then there is no difficulty in composing two such functions, because each member must have a unique owner at each level, and so conversely two different owners cannot reference the same member. Thus there can be no duplicates to eliminate. However, if we compose a multi-valued function with a single-valued function, as in 'CompGroup(Vgames(venue))', then it will be necessary to remove duplicates.

12.3 REPRESENTING A DAPLEX SCHEMA BY CODASYL SETS

We have seen some examples of how we can use DML operations on CODASYL sets to represent Daplex functions. Let us now summarise a correspondence between Daplex objects and CODASYL ones, much as we did for the Daplex to relational mapping in Chapter 10, with reference to the example schema in Fig. 10.3.

— *Entities* such as 'game' are represented by instances of game 'records'; thus entity types correspond to record types.

— *The set of all entities* of a given type is represented either by a singular set with a system owner or else by a scan of all records of that type in realms of the database.

— *Scalar functions,* e.g. Date(game), Scorea(game), are represented by storing their values in fields in the record representing the entity.

— *Scalar multi-valued functions* are represented by storing an array of values in the record. We have not used this in the World Cup schema, but we could for example have an array giving the number of minutes from the start at which each goal was scored held in the Game record, and a corresponding Daplex function 'GoalTimes'.

— *Single-valued functions* such as Gstadium(game) are represented by storing an owner pointer in the record, to represent the member to owner relationship. Since a set must have a unique owner this satisfies the 'single-valued' requirement.

— *Multi-valued functions* such as Vgames(venue) are represented by CODASYL set pointers linking on owner to its member (or by a pointer array). On current hardware this is the most efficient way known of implementing this function with very large databases. It saves using indexes, such as those used in relational implementations, but it makes it harder to add extra functions later, because there is usually no space left in the records for the extra set pointers.

If the multi-valued function has a multi-valued inverse, e.g. Teams(group) and Groups(team), then it is necessary to introduce an extra record type linking the two owners, (such as Placing in the World Cup Schema). This is, in any case, necessary if the many—many relationship has its own attribute which depends on both entities, and needs to be stored in the link record, such as the final place of the team in the group.

— *Scalar functions with unique inverse.* The inverse function to identify the entity instance from a scalar key is usually implemented by using a hashing function from the key value, where the entity record has been stored in CALC mode. Otherwise it is necessary to search all instances of that entity type until one finds the one with the right key. The CODASYL schema has facilities (duplicates not allowed) for enforcing the uniqueness of a given key, as discussed in Chapter 11.

12.3.1 Sub-types

The CODASYL model does not provide any special way of representing subtypes.

It is possible to do it by using sets with multi-member record types. For example, as in Fig. 12.2, a Team record might own a set of team members, with different record types for some of the members, thus forming a *multi-member* set. There might be special records for 'captain' and 'goalkeeper', with extra information particular to these positions. The multi-member set is shown on the Bachman diagram by joining the different member record types in any particular set by a horizontal line.

Bachman and Daya (1977) have suggested replacing these by sets with a single-member type, containing instances of the various record types which are allowed to play the 'role' of member in that set. Thus for example both 'captain' and 'goalkeeper' could play the role of 'team member'. Both 'team member' and 'referee' could play the role of 'person'. Bachman's scheme is not currently (1984) available but it is possible to implement it by keeping to conventions on how multi-members sets are used.

An alternative representation of sub-types is to use sets which have only zero or one members in each instance. For example, as in Fig. 12.2, a person who is a referee would own a referee record through a 'referees' set, which gave extra details of their qualifications. Persons who were not referees would own empty sets. This can be extended to several levels, for example, a person record could own a team-member record which owned a goalkeeper record.

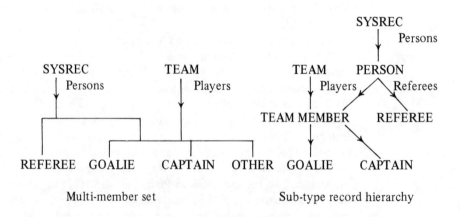

Fig. 12.2 – Sub-types in CODASYL.

12.4 FORMING A RELATIONAL VIEW OF A BASIC CODASYL SCHEMA

In order to use one of the relational query languages on a CODASYL database it is necessary to form a relational view of it. Various methods have been suggested by Kay (1975), Zaniolo (1979), Bell (1980), Rosenthal and Reiner (1982), which we shall now discuss. In general it is difficult to generate a relational view automatically from a given schema, for reasons given later, but the principles are fairly well established.

12.4.1 The anchor record approach

Kay (1975) implemented a database system written in BCPL which allowed both CODASYL and relational operations on the same data. He introduced the concept of an *anchor record* whose instances are (usually) in one-to-one correspondence with tuples in the corresponding relation. Thus for every tuple there is a matching record instance. Attributes of the tuple could be obtained from its anchor record in various ways:

(i) From fields stored in the anchor record (the most usual way).

(ii) From fields in owner(s) of the anchor record, and from their owners recursively. This is in general necessary to provide key fields for the relational tuple, though in some cases the CODASYL system may arrange to store the same value in both owner and member records, in order to save time accessing the owner.

(iii) From fields stored in an array in the anchor record. In this case we generate one tuple for each array element and thus there are many tuples for each anchor record.

(iv) From a derived field whose value depends on whether the anchor record is a member of a given (manual) set. For example, there might be a set of all games involving European teams. Again, the colour of a car might be given by set membership. This method is often used to represent sub-type information, as discussed above.

(v) From a derived value representing the ordinal position of the anchor record in a set. If we wish to represent such information in a relation then we have to put it in explicitly as an extra attribute, since we cannot rely on the order of the tuples!

(vi) From the results of a procedure, calculating information which is functionally dependent on the values in the anchor record (or its owners).

The idea of an anchor record is useful for establishing a correspondence between CODASYL and relational schemas at the conceptual schema level. However, at the external schema level it is often desirable for the user to see a more general 'Perceived record' which is constructed essentially from the 'join' of tuples derived from various anchor records. Thus it may contain non-key information derived from other records, usually the owners of the anchor record. The BCS working group DBAWG has made proposals along these lines (Tagg 1981) for a generalised subschema facility for CODASYL which would make it easier to build relational interfaces.

12.4.2 Zaniolo's method

Zaniolo (1979) devised an algorithm for generating a relational view automatically from a certain class of CODASYL schemas. Essentially his method depends on defining a relation corresponding to each record type. Each relation needs a unique key which is provided by migrating key information down from the owner records as in Kay's method. One big advantage of the method is that it preserves referential integrity for those relations derived from records with automatic mandatory set membership; this is because the migrated key values can come only from the relational tuple which is derived from the owner record instance, and thus a join on the migrated values is bound to find a matching tuple. The algorithm depends on having keys declared for records in the schema by 'duplicates not allowed' clauses, and it shows how to derive such a key for each relation.

The algorithm proceeds in two stages. In the first stage we endeavour to find a *proper synonym* for the DBKEY of every record; this is a combination of data item values from the record, possibly including values migrated from its owner records and higher owners, which uniquely identifies the record, and thus takes the place of a DBKEY. We start with any record types which have either

(i) a key declared as duplicate not allowed (DNA) in the record declaration, and which must not include null values; or

(ii) a key declared DNA in the set declaration for a singular set, of which the record is an automatic mandatory member.

Either of these keys is a proper synonym, and we have seen how they can be used to find a record by 'out of the blue' methods (A) and (C) in Chapter 11. The non-null DNA condition means that they must find a unique record.

We can then define the proper synonym for the DBKEY of any member record which has a proper synonym X for its owner in some set S, of which it is an automatic mandatory member; if the fields(s) Y are declared to be a non-null DNA key in the set S, then the proper synonym is the concatenation of X and Y. This is unique because X uniquely defines the set instance and Y identifies the member of the instance. The process is repeated for the next level member records, but does not continue past any member record type which has been assigned a proper synonym, so as to avoid an infinite cycle. Note that some record types may have more than one proper synonym.

In the second stage we define a separate relation for each and every record type in the schema. This relation includes:

(i) an attribute for every field in the record;

(ii) migrated fields giving the proper synonym (where available) for every owner of the record.

If every record type has a proper synonym then the fields and migrated fields forming these proper synonyms will constitute the primary keys of the corresponding relations. If any owner type does not have a proper synonym then we have to allow for null values in some of the migrated fields in the member. If any member record type does not have a proper synonym then there is the possibility that two such record instances with the same owner may have all fields the same and thus be indistinguishable. It would then be necessary to add an extra field, for example representing the position of the record in the set, as in Kay's method.

In some cases there may actually be a DNA set key which is not shown in the schema, so the synonym is not found. For example the proper synonym of the Link record in the World Cup schema (Appendix III) is (Year, Group, Team), using (Year, Group) as the migrated proper synonym of one owner and (Team) as the undeclared DNA key of the Gteams set, since we know that any given team cannot appear twice in the placings for the same group. The reason why we cannot usually declare this DNA key is that Team is not actually a field in the Link record; however, in some CODASYL systems we can overcome this problem by declaring such a field as a VIRTUAL field in the Link record, whose actual SOURCE is the Team record.

12.4.3 Reiner and Rosenthal's method

Rosenthal and Reiner (1982) have suggested an alternative technique whereby the relations contain items like DBKEYs, which are used in place of migrated data item values to identify tuples. We represent records and sets as relations by the following mapping.

(i)   We define a relation for each record type, containing a column for each field and an extra column for the DBKEY of the record (such an attribute is sometimes called a *surrogate*). In fact we do not have to use an actual DBKEY, only some unique value which is in one-to-one correspondence with it.

(ii) We represent each set by a relation which has one tuple for each member record and contains the DBKEYs of both the owner and member records.

(iii) We represent actual relations seen in the user view (which may be chosen for example using Zaniolo's algorithm) by joins and projections of relations from (i) and (ii), such that the user does not see any DBKEY.

It is suggested that operations on the relations in the view can be expanded by substitution into a form containing only operations on the basic relations. The costing mechanism described below for the System R relational database can then be applied to choose a method of matching the DBKEYs for a 'set' relation and 'record' relations so as to join them. In fact, the idea is to treat a CODASYL set as though it were a particular kind of index, which makes it look just like a relational implementation.

12.4.4 The ASTRID mapping

Bell and Gray (1980) have developed a mapping for CODASYL databases which allows any query formulated in ASTRID relational algebra to be answered against a CODASYL database.

The mapping makes use of the anchor record idea of Kay to define relations from record types with migrated keys. It allows the possibility of extra attributes corresponding to optional set membership and position in set (Kay's methods (iv) and (v) as well as Kay's basic methods (i) and (ii).

Consider the case of the Bachman diagram shown below with five record types and five set types.

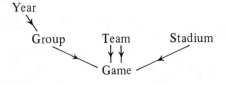

For Zaniolo's method we need five relations; however there is an interesting question regarding the number of relations derivable from Game as an anchor record.

(a) With Zaniolo's method, we would just derive one relation by migrating the keys of the Year, Group, Team and Stadium records (all owners of Game) down into the Games relation.

(b) Since we only need year, group and game information to identify the relational tuple then we could instead make up three relations based on Game as anchor — one entity relation and two relationship relations thus:

GEN(year,group,game,date)   {Entity}
GRL(year,group,game,stadium)   {Relationship}
GAMES(year,group,game,teama,scorea,teamb,scoreb)   {Relationship}

(c) Since there is not much entity information associated with GEN, and since every Game record has a Stadium owner, it is possible to join GEN and GRL into one STAD_ALLOC relation as used in the World Cup schema (Appendix I).

(d) Alternatively, suppose an anchor record such as Game already contains a primary key attribute, e.g. ISGN, the (imaginary) International Standard Game Number, which uniquely identifies a football game. Then we could develop a binary relational view with nine relations each pairing a different attribute of GAMES or STAD_ALLOC with the ISGN attribute. However, in order to use this information we would have to keep joining on ISGN values and, since it turns out that the ASTRID system would generate the same code whichever way we did it, it is better to use fewer relations (GAMES and STAD_ALLOC) which saves in translation time and produces a more intelligible user view.

If we apply the same method to the Placing and Team records we find that the relation for the Placing record requires keys from both Group and Team owners, so that we do not have a separate Placing 'Entity' relation, like GEN in the case of Game. This is only to be expected because, although the Bachman diagram is similar in the two cases, the Placing record is really there only to represent a relationship and not an entity with its own key attribute, as we know from analysis of the relational case.

Further, it should be noted that in certain cases we do not need to define a relation for a particular record type. Consider the case where the record contains only key information, which is migrated down to provide a key for a member record which is an automatic mandatory member, and where every owner has at least one member. Then we can obtain the relation for the owner record by simply projecting the relation for the member record onto the migrated key attributes. This is why, for example, there is no separate relation for Groups or Year records in the World Cup schema.

Thus the ASTRID method has one relation per record type formed by migrating enough values for a proper synonym, as in Zaniolo's method. These constitute the 'Entity' relations, and we can eliminate those which are obtainable as projections of other Entity relations, for which they provide migrated keys. We also need one extra 'Relationshop' relation for each of those set-types such as VGAMES, which do not provide migrated owner synonyms for the 'Entity' relations. Thus instead of migrating all the owner information into a single relational tuple as in Zaniolo's method, we form a number of separate relations, which are effectively projections of this; this makes it less likely that they contain null values and it also makes it easier to consider alternative access paths which do not access unwanted owner information.

12.4.5 Mapping features in existing CODASYL databases

The relations may have extra attributes derived from their anchor record via Kay's methods (iv) and (v). These could in principle be defined in a CODASYL subschema entry for the record if the 'perceived record' facility was provided. In the current ASTRID implementation a suitable subroutine is generated which, whenever it is called to access the anchor record of the given type computes the extra attribute values and places them in COMMON storage, which is treated as though it were part of the UWA.

Arrays or *repeating groups* inside records are dealt with by treating them as pseudo-sets with each pseudo-member containing a different array element, as in Kay's method (iii). When the pseudo-set is accessed a piece of code just returns the next item from the array, together with key information from the fixed part of the record, and without invoking any extra DML statements. Thus it costs very little in time or extra space.

A *multi-member set* type can be treated as though it were a number of separate set types with a common owner record type. In fact the multi-member feature is often used to reduce the number of actual different set types which are needed in the implementation, so as to reduce the space taken by the pointers for each set type in the owner and member records. The only inefficiency involved in access is the time taken in skipping instances of unwanted record types.

If the set members represent variant records then it is possible through a generalised subschema facility to return them as instances of a single record type containing all possible attributes, together with a tag field to indicate which fields are relevant. The corresponding relation would have null values for many of its attributes in each tuple. However, this is not easy to deal with in relational algebra.

Thus the ASTRID mapping is actually defined as a sequence of record accesses interleaved with *instructions* to compute attributes from the fields and in other ways (see Fig. 12.3). In fact more than one sequence of accesses can be given for the same relation which will compute the same fields in a different sequence and possibly by a different method. For example if a key field in the owner is also stored in the member record (e.g. 'dstad' in Fig. 12.3), then one method would start from the owner and use its key field, while another would start by taking the value from the member record instead of the owner, which may save a record access. Again, if the ordinal number of a record in a set is needed, then only that sequence of accesses which started from the owner and

traversal **STAD_ALLOC** 1
{Starts from Singular Set access
to **YEAR** record, keys come in
ascending order }

order   asc year, asc group,
          asc game

singgen of **YEARR** via **YEARS**
realising
          year from year
downgen to **GROUPR** via **GROUPS**
realising
          group from group
downgen to **GAMER** via **GGAMES**
realising
          game from game,
          date from date,
          stadium from dstad

{Assumes extra field dstad
in **GAME** is duplicate of
venue field in owner}
(* end SA1 *)

traversal **STAD_ALLOC** 2
{Starts from hash access to
VENUE record; key values come
in any order }

order   noord year,
          noord group, noord game

vbgen of **VENUER** using venue
realising
          stadium from venue
downgen to **GAMER** via **VGAMES**
realising
          game from game,
          date from date
upgen to **GROUPR** via **GGAMES**
realising
          group from group
upgen from **GROUPR** to **YEARR**
          via **GROUPS**
realising
          year from year
(* end SA2 *)

Fig. 12.3 – Alternative traversals for STAD_ALLOC relation.

visited each member in sequence would be used, since it makes it easy to call a routine to generate the ordinal value.

Essentially the mapping is given as a number of alternative functions, or pieces of code, which makes it easy to deal with existing databases which use conventions for representing implicit information that are not given in the schema. Since it is oriented towards arbitrary databases the relational schema cannot be generated automatically. A template schema can however be generated, which covers all the standard cases. It is then edited to allow for individual peculiarities of CODASYL implementations.

12.5 IMPLEMENTING RELATIONAL ALGEBRA OPERATIONS ON CODASYL

In this section we shall look at one method of implementing the operations of relational algebra on a CODASYL database: the 'perceived record routine' method. This uses many of the techniques developed by IBM's System R for implementing joins, selections and projections on streams of tuples retrieved from stored relations. Its mapping method is based on Zaniolo's and it views the database as one or more perceived record types. All instances of such a record can be found by calling a particular *generator routine* (which may also be parametrised to select particular records).

In the next section we shall consider another method (**ASTRID**) which, instead of performing the operations on streams of data values, attempts to *modify the code* of the generator routine, so as to produce a more efficient routine which makes good use of CODASYL set links. It appears that the code modification to give the effect of a join usually works well because the CODASYL sets have been designed to give quick answers to frequently-asked queries; it is as though the information regarding which tuples match which other tuples in certain frequently-used joins has been precomputed and stored as CODASYL chain links! When the method fails, it falls back on generating code for a 'co-routine' (see below), which will operate on streams of tuples much as in the other method. Another advantage of code modification is that it allows one to use the very general **ASTRID** mapping method described earlier, which represents relations as pieces of code which generate them.

12.5.1 Join methods for routines for perceived records

In the perceived record routine method the CODASYL database is seen as a number of perceived record types, for each of which there is a separate generator routine which can be used in one of two ways. If used for *sequential access,* it returns the next tuple in the relation each time it is called. If used for *direct access* it takes extra selection information as a parameter and returns one or more matching records as a result; this is done by hashing or using an index. The representation of relations by such routines was pioneered by Lorie *et al.* (1979) and used in the research storage system (**RSS**) of System R (Chamberlin *et al.* 1981). Following a theoretical study of Blasgen and Eswaran (1976), they decided to concentrate on two main methods for joining relations: the *nested loop (value based) join* and the *sort merge join.*

The *nested loop* (value based) join relies on using a repeat loop to call the generator for the first relation and fetch every tuple in turn; each time round it calls the generator for the second relation with the key value required to match this tuple. The tuples are retrieved and concatenated in the usual fashion. If however the generator routine cannot carry out the selection required to find the matching tuples then the *sort merge* method is used instead. The tuples generated by one routine are stored and sorted in a temporary storage and then retrieved in the order required to match the tuples generated from the second relation. The logic is similar to that used to merge two magnetic tapes, as explained in Chapter 8.

If multiple joins are needed then it may be possible to put one nested loop inside another, otherwise the stream of tuples resulting from a merge can be fed into another merge. It is possible to build a 'coroutine' which generates the tuples resulting from the join, one by one, each time it is called. A coroutine is just a subroutine that arranges to resume its activity from the point where it last exited, whenever it is called again. The output from a coroutine may pass through a 'filter' which selects particular tuples or projects them, or else along a 'pipe' to be merged with output from another coroutine. The 'pipes' act as buffers holding the next tuple or group of tuples until required. This architecture saves storing intermediate results on disk as large 'temporary relations'. It was used by Kay (1975) and in PRTV (Todd 1976) and also to some extent in System R. The same principle is used in Buneman's FQL interpreter, discussed at the start of the chapter, where the lazy evaluator decides when to suck the next tuple from a pipe.

Because of the many different ways of doing combinations of joins by the above techniques, Selinger *et al.* (1979) developed a method for translating an SQL query into code which makes good use of the various access paths available in System R. Selinger's method essentially grows a tree of alternative combinations of joins. The path from the root to each represents an alternative access path to the relations through different routines (direct or sequential access through a generator or a coroutine) and has an associated cost. Costs are estimated based on: (i) number of page changes to scan a relation or an index; (ii) whether a selection test can be executed directly via an index (corresponding roughly to access via a record or set key in CODASYL); (iii) the time taken to sort a relation prior to projection or a merge join. Some pruning is done by keeping only the best of alternative costed paths. Finally the path with the lowest cost is chosen.

12.6 THE ASTRID SYSTEM OF CODE MODIFICATION

The ASTRID system implements the relational algebra operations by a technique of code generation and modification. Every relation is represented by one or more *traversals* which act as generators for it. Basically these traversals consist of a number of loops which access fields from the anchor record and related records. For each relation in the schema, there is one traversal starting from the anchor record and an alternative one starting from each owner. Traversals can be combined and modified to give derived traversals which implement the effect of relational operations as explained below.

12.6.1 Traversals

We can now define a *traversal* of a relation more precisely. It is a description of a piece of code which realises the tuples of the relation one at a time by accessing the records in some sequence, following the set pointers and computing the values as necessary. Thus it is a *generator* for a relation. Corresponding to each relation stored in the database (e.g. GAMES) we hold on file one or more *base traversals*. Each one is essentially a description of a piece of code with a number of nested loops.

We have a notation for traversals as follows. Internally it is represented by a Prolog list structure. There are three obvious base traversals of STAD_ALLOC.

$$S(YEAR) \rightarrow D(GROUP) \rightarrow D(GAME) \rightarrow U(VENUE) \qquad \{SA1\}$$
$$V(VENUE) \rightarrow D(GAME) \rightarrow U(GROUP) \rightarrow U(YEAR) \qquad \{SA2\}$$
$$B(GROUP) \rightarrow U(YEAR) \rightarrow D(GAME) \rightarrow U(VENUE) \qquad \{SA3\}$$

Here S means a *singular set* access to visit all records of a given type (there is only one set owning all year records), D means go down to visit all member records belonging to the given owner using the appropriate set type (if this is ambiguous it is specified) and U means go up to visit the owner of a given record. V means direct access to the record containing a value (usually given by selection). B means visit every record of that type in the database.

Thus the traversal SA1 visits all year records known to the system, for each year record it visits the group records and for each group record it visits the game records and their venue owners. In an Algol-like syntax we can represent the corresponding code as:

for each **YEAR** record do
  for each **GROUP** record owner by **YEAR** do
    for each **GAME** record owned by **GROUP** do
      for the **VENUE** owner of **GAME** do
        print YEAR.year, GROUP.group, GAME.game,
          VENUE.stadium, GAME.date.

Thus each arrow in a traversal represents an inner level of nested code. Note that the record generations such as D(GAME) in SA3 must follow those such as B(GROUP), which generates the owner for GAME, but they need not be consecutive.

12.6.2 Combination and modification of traversals
Corresponding to every algebraic operation on a given relation there is a modification to its traversal which produces a derived traversal, generating the new relation. This derived traversal can then be modified by the next operation and so on. The resulting traversal depends somewhat on the order of application of operations specified by the user. However, many of these are commutative and the order of others can be improved by top level rewriting, using the methods of Chapter 9.

12.6.3 Modification by selection
Consider a query in **ASTRID** relational algebra requesting information on games in Cordoba stadium before 1982:

STAD_ALLOC selected-on [stadium="Cordoba" and (year<1982)]

We can modify the base traversal SA1 by incorporating 'select' nodes:

S(YEAR) → select(year) → D(GROUP) → D(GAME) → U(VENUE)
                                 → select(stadium) {SA1A}

Here the 'select' element in the traversal means that an explicit test is made inside the loop after generating the year value, to see if it satisfies the condition. If not, the innermost loops are not performed and the test is retried on the next year value. Thus for SA1A the modified code would be:

    for each **YEAR** record do
     if **YEAR**.year < 1982 then
      for each **GROUP** owned by this **YEAR** do
       for each **GAME** owned by this **GROUP** do
        for the **VENUE** owner of this **GAME DO**
         if **VENUE**.stadium = "Cordoba" then
          print **YEAR**.year, **GROUP**.group, **GAME**.game,
           VENUE.stadium, **GAME**.date

Similarly we can modify the alternative traversal SA2 to give:

$$V(VENUE) \rightarrow select(stadium) \rightarrow D(GAME) \rightarrow U(GROUP) \rightarrow U(YEAR)$$
$$\rightarrow select(year) \ \{SA2A\}$$

In this case the select clause on stadium can be implemented directly as part of the 'for the **VENUE**' statement. This visits far fewer records and will be best. In general we incorporate select nodes as early as possible in order to avoid doing unnecessary inner loops.

12.6.4 Modification by extension
These modifications incorporate 'extend' nodes and are very similar to selections except that the performance of the rest of the traversal is not conditional on them. The generated code will initialise local variables in which the derived values are stored. This saves writing the relation to disk with extra fields. Subsequent selections can make use of these values.

12.6.5 Modification by projection
This modification can often be done either (a) by not printing so many columns from a given record or (b) by truncating the traversal and not visiting certain record types.
  For example, the query

    STAD_ALLOC projected_to year, group, game

can be done using the truncated traversal:

$$S(YEAR) \rightarrow D(GROUP) \rightarrow D(GAME)$$

since we know that every **GAME** record must have a **VENUE** owner, and we are not interested in the fields of that owner.
  However, the query

    STAD_ALLOC selected_on [stadium="Cordoba"]
      projected_to year, group

requires the traversal:

$$S(YEAR) \rightarrow D(GROUP) \rightarrow D(GAME) \rightarrow project$$
           |
           | $\rightarrow U(VENUE) \rightarrow select(stadium)$

The part of the traversal beyond the project operation is called the 'lost traversal'. It still appears as an inner nested loop but it no longer generates any column values for printing. However, this part of the traversal must be executed until at least one tuple is found that satisfies the selection. (The game might not be played in Cordoba.). If the lost traversal contains no selections, and consists solely of 'U' operations finding the owner in AUTOMATIC MANDATORY sets, then we can excise it. If, in addition, it includes 'D' operations, and we know that the sets concerned are guaranteed not to be null, then it can still be excised.

In general the truncation method can be used only if the list of columns for projection is naturally generated without duplication. That is, we could put a print statement somewhere in the nested loops which would never print the same combination of values out twice for the given columns. If this fails the system falls back on sorting a batch of tuples in memory and removing duplicates. This is represented by putting the project operation first on a line by itself, as would happen if we used SA2 thus:

project

$\rightarrow$ V(VENUE) $\rightarrow$ select(Stadium) $\rightarrow$ D(GAME) $\rightarrow$ U(GROUP) $\rightarrow$ U(YEAR)

The group_by operation acts very like projection and is discussed in Gray (1981). The main difference is that it arranges to compute derived fields from fields found by executing the 'lost traversal'. In the case where a sort is necessary, and the group-by operation appears at the front of the traversal, it is possible to combine the sorting and grouping operations as shown by Esslemont and Gray (1982).

12.6.6 Combination by JOIN

Since join is based on a cartesian product, it can be formed by a nested for loop with one iteration for each record type involved. This is very similar to a traversal structure, and it turns out that the traversal representing the join can often be formed simply by concatenating parts of the separate traversals (Bell 1980, Gray 1984). The selections for matching are then performed automatically by the fact that a CODASYL owner record will in many cases be linked to just those records whose values would have been selected by the join operator! Let us consider examples of this using

RES:= STAD_ALLOC joined_to GROUP_PLAC

We use traversal SA1 with GP1 for GROUP_PLAC:

S(YEAR) $\rightarrow$ D(GROUP) $\rightarrow$ D(LINK) $\rightarrow$ U(TEAM)   {GP1}

These both have a 'common start' section.

S(YEAR) $\rightarrow$ D(GROUP)

which generates the common attributes in the two cases. If we concatenate the traversals keeping one copy of the common start we get

$$S(YEAR) \to D(GROUP) \to D(GAME) \to U(VENUE) \to D(LINK)$$
$$\to U(TEAM)$$

we can also get in the other order;

$$S(YEAR) \to D(GROUP) \to D(LINK) \to U(TEAM) \to D(GAME)$$
$$\to U(VENUE)$$

Both traversals correspond to nested loop code which will produce the desired tuples though in a different sequence. Which is best depends on subsequent selections. If a selection on 'placing = 1' is made after 'D(LINK)' then the second method is best as it visits fewer records.

One can also join traversals where the start of one traversal matches the end or middle of the second. We can do this with the alternative traversals:

$$V(VENUE) \to D(GAME) \to U(GROUP) \to U(YEAR) \quad \{SA2\} \text{ and}$$
$$B(GROUP) \to U(YEAR) \to D(LINK) \to U(TEAM) \quad \{GP2\}$$

to give

$$V(VENUE) \to D(GAME) \to U(GROUP) \to U(YEAR) \to D(LINK)$$
$$\to U(TEAM)$$

We notice here that a B(GROUP) since it visits all records can match a U(GROUP) which visits only certain records because join has the properties of an intersection.

The second traversal (using SA2,GP2) would be preferred if a subsequent selection were made on stadium as it could use V(VENUE) efficiently. General conditions for choosing an optimum are discussed in (Esslemont and Gray 1982). Basically these are: (i) choose the traversal accessing the fewest records, estimated roughly from the average number of members per owner, and the selectivity of the predicates; (ii) for two such traversals choose the one accessing the fewest pages, estimated from the average page changes per set traversal; (iii) if such a traversal sorts over 1000 records, reconsider.

12.6.7 General conditions for join by overlap
We call this method of doing a join by matching common segments of a traversal a 'join by overlap'. The general conditions for it are given in (Bell 1980).

We define the 'common column generation part' or CCG part as the section of traversal that produces the common attribute values in the two cases (e.g. S(YEAR) → D(GROUP) or B(GROUP) → U(YEAR)). The conditions are:

(i)   The CCG part on both sides must be derived from the same access method to the same instances of the same record types through the same set types in the same sequence. (However, an initial B can match an S, U or D, as explained earlier). If any other columns are realised in the CCG part they must be functionally dependent on the common attribute values (for example, be in the same records).

(ii) Selection and extension elements are allowed in the CCG part, since they can be combined into the final traversal. Projections are allowed if no common columns are generated by the part beyond the 'project' node.

(iii) The CCG part must be the leading part of one traversal.

(iv) The common attributes must be natually generated without duplication; this means that a print statement inserted in the nested loops just after the CCG part would not print out the same combination of values twice for the common columns. Given this, it follows that for each value of the common columns generated by one traversal, the modified code will automatically generate all those tuples with the same values for the common columns from the other traversal, since it is using the same instances of the same record types in both modified and unmodified versions.

12.6.8 Extensions to join algorithm

The method actually used is more complicated than that presented because:

(i) There are two other join methods: the value-based method and the sort merge method as described for System R. The value-based method joins a traversal starting with a V access element onto the end of a traversal which supplies values required for selection by this element. The 'sort merge' join is a fall-back case which always allows the join to be implemented.

(ii) It is possible to have a partial match and then complete the join by merging. This has the advantage of doing a number of small sorts in memory rather than one large sort.

12.7 PROBLEMS OF UPDATES AND THEIR MAPPING

We have seen how to map queries in various types of relational and functional query languages onto a CODASYL database. However, there are considerable problems when we come to consider updates, which we shall outline below.

The operations for performing updates in CODASYL are at a very low level and depend very heavily on assignment and side effects. This is very different from a functional language where we describe the new state of the database as a copy of the old state with some new values and items replacing old ones. The point is that although *logically* we may copy the entire database, we do not want to perform the *physical* equivalent of this, as done in a magnetic tape file update. In Adaplex, as we saw earlier, assignment statements have been introduced into a language which was originally functional, in order to gain efficiency.

12.7.1 Simple update by modify

The easiest update to map is the modification of attribute values for an existing entity, where we do not alter its identifier (primary key). In SQL we could say, for example:

```
UPDATE GAMES
SET Scorea = 5
    Scoreb = Scoreb + 1
WHERE Year = 1978 AND Group = 'A' and Game =1
```

This changes the scores for one particular game. If the selection condition were changed to 'Game > 1', then it would change the scores for several games.

We can also select records for update by use of a join as an intersection thus:

UPDATE GAMES
SET Scorea = 0
WHERE Year = 1978 AND Group = 2 AND
    Game = (Select Game
          FROM STAD_ALLOC
          WHERE Year = 1978 AND Group = 2
          AND Stadium = "Cordoba")

This query updates values in GAMES tuples in Group 2 in 1978 which were played in Cordoba. We can map both these examples fairly easily onto a CODASYL implementation by treating the update as a query, generating code which will FIND the record, and then insert code to assign the new field values followed by a MODIFY command.

12.7.2 Problems of combined deletion and insertion

The first problem comes when the user wishes to assign to a key field, e.g. Year = Year + 1. This is quite rightly disallowed in many systems. The proper procedure is to create a new tuple by copying values from the old one and then deleting the old tuple and inserting the new one. The syntax for deletion and insertion in SQL is shown by:

DELETE GAMES
WHERE Year = 1978 AND Group = 2 AND Game > 3
INSERT INTO GAMES :
    ⟨1978, 2, 4, "Scotland", 3, "England", 0⟩

The first example deletes all games in 1978 in Group 2 with game number above 3. This could be done in a CODASYL database by generating code to FIND each game and then inserting an ERASE command. The insertion command specifies a tuple with literal values for the attributes in the order of their declaration in the schema. This is more difficult to implement in CODASYL, since it implicitly requires one to FIND the owner records with Year = 1978 and Group = 2 before placing the remaining attributes in the UWA and issuing a STORE command.

Unfortunately in SQL we have to write the DELETE and INSERT commands as separate tasks which do not communicate or pass values to one another. Hence it is hard to insert a tuple, when some of its values are taken from a tuple. which has just been deleted. This problem can be overcome by embedding SQL in a host language, such as PL/I, and using the variables of the host language to store these values, but we have then lost much of the advantage of a high level query language.

12.7.3 Temporary inconsistency

The problem of deletion and insertion gets much worse in CODASYL when the record representing the entity is the MANDATORY owner of records in various sets. In theory we have to use ERASE ALL to remove all its descendants before removing it, only to have to insert them all back again once the record for the new entity is in place! In fact we should use a special variant of the MODIFY command, with the side effect of disconnecting a record from one set and connecting it into another when the key is changed, in order to overcome this problem.

Suppose that the GAMES record contains an explicit Year field which duplicates that of the owner. As an alternative to deletion and insertion, we could first MODIFY the Year field to contain the new value and then use DISCONNECT and CONNECT to give the record its new set ownership. However, after we have done the first operation and before we complete the second, the database is temporarily in an inconsistent state. It is necessary to lock out other users from doing retrievals and to ensure that if the CONNECT fails then we undo the MODIFY as well. This introduces the idea of a *transaction* which contains several commands which are to be treated as an indivisible whole. Various *'commitment protocols'* have been devised to enforce this, and the reader is referred to Ullman (1980) or Date (1983) for details.

Another example of this problem is where two or three records point to one another in a cycle, so that an alteration to or removal of any of them requires alteration or removal of the others.

12.7.4 Problems of updating views

Another problem concerns whether we can allow a user to update a view of the database. If the view is based on a simple subschema, like CODASYL, which just reduces the number of record types and fields that the user can see, then there is not much problem, as long as the users are only modifying the fields and not structures.

Null value on insertion

Problems arise if users insert records, because the actual stored records may contain extra fields which are not visible to the user through the view; these fields will have to be initialised to null. The records could be marked inaccessible to other users until the null values have been replaced; otherwise the query languages will have to be extended to cope with them. Default values could be used instead of nulls, as long as the user knows how to interpret their occurrence in answer to queries.

Loss of key information

A second problem obviously arises if the view is a projection of a stored relation involving the removal of duplicates. In this case, if the user attempts an insertion, then the full primary key value of the stored relational tuple will not be entered and thus the tuple cannot be inserted. Similar considerations apply to views derived from Group-by. In theory deletions are possible, in that deleting a tuple in the view should delete *all* tuples that project to that tuple, but it is not clear that this is desirable, since the user is unaware of which extra tuples are being deleted.

Multiple underlying tuples

A third class of problems arise with views based on joins of relations. If the view is a projection of this then we get the problems just discussed, of null values on insertion and of loss of key information. If the join preserves the prime keys of both relations then, for each tuple in the view, we can locate the underlying tuples in the stored relations from their keys and perform the appropriate actions on them. However, even in this case there are problems with insertions. Firstly the prime key of one of the tuples underlying the inserted tuple may already be in the database; it did not feature in the join, because there was no matching tuple from the other stored relation (intersection property). In this case the insertion must be inhibited for reasons not visible to the user. Secondly if the view is based on a 'cartesian product' then one must insert not single tuples, but a whole group of tuples, based on the product of the underlying tuples. Because of these problems the System R implementation of SQL does not allow updates based on joins. However, Dayal and Bernstein (1978) have made proposals which would allow it in certain cases. We should also note that Codd's initial idea of decomposing relations into normal forms was to avoid these so-called 'update anomalies', by ensuring that relations in this form could not themselves be constructed from joins of simpler relations.

12.8 INTEGRITY CONSTRAINTS

We expect the data in a database to be maintained by a variety of users, some of them not experts. Thus as far as possible we want to protect users from the consequences of their own mistakes. In particular we want to ensure that any changes to the database do not leave it containing inconsistent information or impossible values.

We ask the database management system to check for inconsistent information at update time. It does this on the basis of various rules and predicates, called *integrity constraints*, since these act as a constraint on allowable updates. They can come in various forms, some of which we have met.

Data validation

This concerns values to be stored in fields in a record. Various kinds of check can be made:

Type checks, e.g. as used in a program language to prohibit storing a string in an integer field;

Range checks, e.g. to check Year>0 and <2000, or that a character is $>$ 'A' and $<$ 'F';

Inter-field checks, which check the value of one field against values computed from others in the same record, e.g. Date of Marriage $>$ Date of Birth $+ 14$

New vs old, which constrains the new value of the field by comparison with the old.

Key integrity

This requires that the primary key field of a record or tuple should not contain null values. Date (1981) calls this 'entity integrity'. In the case of a relation, we also require that the primary key value is not duplicated in the relation. In CODASYL systems, one can use the 'DUPLICATES NOT ALLOWED' clause to enforce unique keys both for records and within sets.

Referential integrity

This requires that a foreign key stored in a record or tuple should always have a matching primary key value stored in another record or tuple, which belongs to a specified record type or relation.

This will be enforced in CODASYL systems where the primary key is stored in a record which is the MANDATORY AUTOMATIC owner of the given record through a specified set. In the case of the functional model it is implicit, because the function that returns the 'foreign key' actually returns a reference to the entity where the value is, and thus the entity occurrence must exist.

12.8.1 Constraints in Daplex and QBE

Integrity constraints may be written with various degrees of complexity depending on the language. An integrity constraint can be formulated as a special kind of query; it is the job of the system to ensure that the answer to the query always stays true, and updates which would make the answer false are rejected. The most general forms are those appearing in Adaplex and relational calculus, which allow the full generality of quantified predicate calculus statements, as shown in Chapters 7 and 10.

For example, in the EFDM (Appendix V) one can declare the following types of constraint:

Non-Null Values

>CONSTRAINT c1 ON age(person) → TOTAL

Null values are not allowed for the age function; it must be initialised when the entity instance is created.

Non-Updateable Values

>CONSTRAINT c2 ON sex(person) → FIXED

Once a person's sex has been entered it may not be changed, except by deleting and recreating the entity (like mode FIXED for a field in a CODASYL schema).

Key Constraint

>CONSTRAINT c3 ON name(person), age(person) → UNIQUE

This is just like a 'unique' declaration in Adaplex.

Non-Overlapping Subtypes

>CONSTRAINT c4 ON student, instructor → DISJOINT

This is the converse of the 'overlap' declaration in Adaplex.

General Constraint

> CONSTRAINT c5 ON courses(student) →
> ALL c in courses(student) HAS sex(student) = sex(teacher(c))

This constrains the set of courses taken by a student to those courses taken by an instructor of the same sex. The constraint can be used to constrain the allowable values of arguments to a function, or results of a function.

Zloof (1978) has suggested an extension to QBE for expressing constraints; these can be translated easily into calculus form and implemented in Prolog, as shown by Neves et $al.$ (1983).

12.8.2 Problems of implementation

The checks on data validation and key integrity can be made directly when the record is being stored. The check on referential integrity usually involves access to one other record whose key is known. However, constraints that involve universal quantifiers are more costly. For example the constraint

$$\text{Manages}(Y,X) \wedge \text{Salary}(Y,S1) \wedge \text{Salary}(X,S2) \rightarrow (S1 > S2)$$

expresses the requirement that managers earn more than any of their employees. Thus whenever the manager's salary is updated (strictly speaking decreased) it is necessary to check the records for all his subordinates.

The same constraint could be expressed in QBE (Neves et $al.$ 1983) as:

MANAGES	Boss#	Emp#
ic.	_Y	_X

EMPS	Emp#	Salary	Tax	Insurance
	_Y	_S1		
	_X	_S2		

CONDITIONS
_S1 > _S2

The command 'ic.' means 'insert constraint'. The constraint is in the form of a predicate in the condition box, whose variables are instantiated by a query on a tuple in the MANAGES relation. The predicate must be satisfied for every such tuple. The constraint will be checked against all existing data in the MANAGES relation at the time of declaration, and it will not be accepted until the existing data satisfies it. The constraint will be checked thereafter whenever the EMPS or

MANAGES relations are updated, and the update will be aborted unless the constraint is satisfied. It is possible to print existing constraints with the 'pc.' command, and to drop constraints by using 'dc.'. More complex constraints can be expressed by using the 'implies' operator in the condition box. For example if we wished the constraint to apply only to managers with salaries over 50,000 then we should use the predicate:

$$\_S1 > 50000 \text{ implies } \_S1 > \_S2$$

Frost and Whittaker (1983) have proposed an algorithm for checking a certain class of constraints expressed in terms of binary relations, where no term contains any function symbols, but it is not particularly fast.

Thus, although the functional languages and relational calculus provide a very nice way of expressing constraints, there are many open research problems on how to implement them efficiently.

12.9 FUTURE DEVELOPMENTS

We shall now briefly discuss some areas where research is in progress.

12.9.1 Distributed databases

A distributed database comprises a number of separate databases, usually held on different processors, often at separate geographic locations. One can treat it as one large database, so that the user is unaware that answers to his queries come from different places and have been joined and union-ed together into a single result. Alternatively one can view it as a *multi-database* as proposed by Litwin and Kabbaj (1982), where each database is independent, but agrees to provide schema information and answer queries, leaving the user to compose the results.

In the first case one can have a *homogeneous* system, where each site or *node* runs the same software. This was the case with the earliest system SDD-1 (Rothnie *et al.* 1980), and with the distributed version of System R, known as R* (Williams *et al.* 1982). In the case of R* all sites understand a variant of SQL and ship relations to other sites in response to queries. Another alternative is to have an *inhomogeneous* network where each node may use a different DBMS. This is the case with MULTIBASE (Smith *et al.* 1981) and PROTEUS (Stocker *et al.* 1984).

In the case of PROTEUS, the local query language at each node (ASTRID, SQL, QUEL etc.) must be translated into a standard DML used across the network and each node must provide a view through a universal DDL, so that schemas in this DDL can be sent across the network. For PROTEUS the DML is based on relational algebra and the DDL uses seventeen 'meta-relations' (Stocker and Cantie 1983) to describe the relations which the network perceives to be stored at each site. In the case of MULTIBASE the common DDL is expected to be based on Daplex, and the DML may be based on relational calculus such as QUEL. It is not clear precisely how these two rather different languages will fit.

12.9.2 Meta data

Another area of interest is the representation of schema information so that it can be transmitted and understood by remote users. The DDL used in CODASYL systems is not very suitable for this purpose and a relational view is proving most popular because it can itself be represented as 'meta-relations'. The proposals of Stocker and Cantie (1983) allow one to represent a CODASYL schema as relations through the ASTRID mapping; they can also represent an Adaplex schema as though it were stored as relations; in both cases details of the stored relations giving their names, attribute names, attribute types, keys and integrity constraints are held as meta-relations.

Another way of presenting meta-data is to use meta-relations in a binary relational model as proposed by, for example, Fahlman (1979), Lavington and Azmoodeh (1982). Among other things, this makes use of the meta-relations IS–A and IS–SUB meaning 'member-of' and 'subset-of' respectively. Using these we can make statements like

> JOCK IS–A TEACHER
> MARY IS–A TEACHER
> TEACHER IS–SUB PERSON

The IS–A meta-relation allows one to make statements about attribute types and the IS–SUB meta-relation allows one to make statements about sub-types.

12.9.3 Knowledge bases

The data models we have examined (relational, CODASYL, functional) are oriented towards fixed length records containing fields of fixed types. However, we need to be able to store and represent other kinds of data which does not fit so easily into this format. In particular the data structures used in artificial intelligence use list and tree structures consisting of variable length sequences of items of variant types. We have seen examples of this in Prolog, where unit clauses may contain terms which are lists. A great challenge is to extend database models so as to encompass the storage and description both of unit clauses and non-unit clauses used by Prolog, and of other such structures. In this connection the functional data model looks most promising, since it is closely related to the semantic net structures which are popular in artificial intelligence (Shipman 1979). However, it will be necessary to incorporate more type checking into the model, as for example in the Hope language discussed in Chapter 5.

12.9.4 Interpretations of logic

The discussion of Prolog in Chapter 4 may have seemed to imply that the only way to interpret Logic as programs is by using Horn clauses with depth-first left-to-right evaluation. This is the way that most current interpreters work, basically for efficiency on present hardware. However instead of evaluating clauses in a fixed order, it is possible to let the interpreter choose its own order of evaluation, as in ABSYS (Foster and Elcock 1968) and ABSET (Elcock *et al.* 1971); this uses more storage, but it is more general and relies less on the skill of the programmer. The methods used in ABSYS and ABSET are also adaptable for parallel computation, as in PARLOG (Clark and Gregory 1982) and Concurrent Prolog (Shapiro 1983). In these systems clauses are evaluated in parallel, both within a clause ('and-parallelism') and considering alternative clauses ('or-parallelism'). Such systems cannot use the 'cut' facility, and other control mechanisms are being devised.

Another interesting development is the work of logicians such as Reiter in formalising deduction with incomplete knowledge. Throughout this book, starting with our Set-interpretation of predicates in Chapter 2, we have made the *Closed World Assumption.* This assumes that the database is the universe, thus if a piece of data is not in the database, then the corresponding fact is not true. Hence we are able to treat Negation as Failure (Clark 1978), and use a simple implementation of the 'not' operation in Prolog, as given in Chapter 4. For example, if we fail to find any facts of the form 'brother(X,harry)' in the database then we assume that harry has no brothers. However, it may simply be that we don't know enough about harry to be able to record these facts. New methods of reasoning are being developed which take account of these limitations.

12.10 CONCLUSION

We have seen how the abstract ideas of the predicate calculus and the lambda calculus discussed in the early part of this book have found their expression in the query languages used on databases as described in the later part. These ideas have proved very useful in providing a high level interface for the user and in transforming queries for efficient optimisation on the various database implementations. In this chapter we have seen ways of accessing a CODASYL database through functional languages such as FQL, Daplex and relational algebra. We have considered the use of relational algebra in some detail, since it can also be transformed to and from calculus notation, as described in Chapter 9. These methods are now fairly well established.

The aim of this book has been to show that there is a kind of duality between functional and logic-based methods of expressing programs, which is fundamental to our understanding of programming. We have used the database query languages to illustrate the advantages and disadvantages of each method, and also to show the importance of being able to handle sets of items in both styles of programming. Another important topic has been the ability to formalise abstract descriptions of data and associated integrity constraints, as used in database schemas, and we have seen how to do this in a functional language (Daplex), which makes use of predicates and quantifiers. Kowalski (1982a) has stated that 'logic programming is an extension of functional programming'; even so, functional programming is such an important topic that it is worth study in its own right. It may be that, as with the 'wave–particle' duality in physics, neither approach is superior, and that we need both methods in building abstract models of the real world and in defining how to compute with these models.

Appendix I

Relations for the World Cup database

(**** Relational schema for the World Cup database ****)

relation GAMES

int	year	(* Competition Year *)
char*1	group	(* Group of teams *)
int	game	(* Game No. within Group *)
char*9	teamA	(* First team in game *)
int	scoreA	(* Goal Score of First Team *)
char*9	teamB	(* Second Team *)
int	scoreB	(* Goal Score of Second Team *)

key   year, group, game

(*————————————————————*)

relation STAD_ALLOC

int	year	(* Competition Year *)
char*1	group	(* Group of teams *)
int	game	(* Game No. within Group *)
char*13	stadium	(* Stadium used for Game *)
char*6	date	(* Date game was played *)

key   year, group, game

(*————————————————————*)

relation GROUP_PLAC

int	year	(* Competition Year *)
char*1	group	(* Group of teams *)
char*9	team	(* Team name *)
int	placing	(* Final placing within Group *)

key   year, group, placing
key   year, group, team

(*————————————————————*)

relation TEAMS

char*9	team	(* Team name *)

key   team

(*————————————————————*)

YEARS

Year
. . .
1966
1970
1974
1978

GROUPS

Year	Group
1978	1
1978	2
1978	3
1978	4
1978	A
1978	B
1978	F

TEAMS

Team
Argentina
Austria
Brazil
France
Holland
Hungary
Iran
Italy
Mexico
Peru
Poland
Scotland
Spain
Sweden
Tunisia
W.Germany

VENUES

Stadium
Buenos Aires
Cordoba
Mar Del Plata
Mendoza
Rosario
Velez

GROUP_PLAC

Year	Group	Team	Placing
1978	1	Italy	1
1978	1	Argentina	2
1978	1	France	3
1978	1	Hungary	4
1978	2	Poland	1
1978	2	W.Germany	2
1978	2	Tunisia	3
1978	2	Mexico	4
1978	3	Austria	1
1978	3	Brazil	2
1978	3	Spain	3
1978	3	Sweden	4
1978	4	Peru	1
1978	4	Holland	2
1978	4	Scotland	3
1978	4	Iran	4
1978	A	Holland	1
1978	A	Italy	2
1978	A	W.Germany	3
1978	A	Austria	4
1978	B	Argentina	1
1978	B	Brazil	2
1978	B	Poland	3
1978	B	Peru	4
1978	F	Argentina	1
1978	F	Holland	2
1978	F	Brazil	3
1978	F	Italy	4

STAD_ALLOC

Year	Group	Game	Stadium	Date
1978	1	1	Buenos Aires	2_Jun
1978	1	2	Mar Del Plata	2_Jun
1978	1	3	Mar Del Plata	6_Jun
1978	1	4	Buenos Aires	6_Jun
1978	1	5	Mar Del Plata	10_Jun
1978	1	6	Buenos Aires	10_Jun
1978	2	1	Buenos Aires	1_Jun
1978	2	2	Rosario	2_Jun
1978	2	3	Cordoba	6_Jun
1978	2	4	Rosario	6_Jun
1978	2	5	Cordoba	10_Jun
1978	2	6	Rosario	10_Jun
1978	3	1	Velez	3_Jun
1978	3	2	Mar Del Plata	3_Jun
1978	3	3	Velez	7_Jun
1978	3	4	Mar Del Plata	7_Jun
1978	3	5	Mar Del Plata	11_Jun
1978	3	6	Velez	11_Jun
1978	4	1	Cordoba	3_Jun
1978	4	2	Mendoza	3_Jun
1978	4	3	Cordoba	7_Jun
1978	4	4	Mendoza	7_Jun
1978	4	5	Mendoza	11_Jun
1978	4	6	Cordoba	11_Jun
1978	A	1	Cordoba	14_Jun
1978	A	2	Buenos Aires	14_Jun
1978	A	3	Buenos Aires	18_Jun
1978	A	4	Cordoba	18_Jun
1978	A	5	Cordoba	21_Jun
1978	A	6	Buenos Aires	21_Jun
1978	B	1	Rosario	14_Jun
1978	B	2	Mendoza	14_Jun
1978	B	3	Rosario	18_Jun
1978	B	4	Mendoza	18_Jun
1978	B	5	Mendoza	21_Jun
1978	B	6	Rosario	21_Jun
1978	F	1	Buenos Aires	24_Jun
1978	F	2	Buenos Aires	25_Jun

GAMES

Year	Group	Game	TeamA	ScoreA	TeamB	ScoreB
1978	1	1	Argentina	2	Hungary	1
1978	1	2	France	1	Italy	2
1978	1	3	Italy	3	Hungary	1
1978	1	4	Argentina	2	France	1
1978	1	5	France	3	Hungary	1
1978	1	6	Italy	1	Argentina	0
1978	2	1	W.Germany	0	Poland	0
1978	2	2	Tunisia	3	Mexico	1
1978	2	3	Mexico	0	W.Germany	6
1978	2	4	Poland	1	Tunisia	0
1978	2	5	Tunisia	0	W.Germany	0
1978	2	6	Mexico	1	Poland	3
1978	3	1	Spain	1	Austria	2
1978	3	2	Sweden	1	Brazil	1
1978	3	3	Austria	1	Sweden	0
1978	3	4	Brazil	0	Spain	0
1978	3	5	Brazil	1	Austria	0
1978	3	6	Sweden	0	Spain	1
1978	4	1	Peru	3	Scotland	1
1978	4	2	Holland	3	Iran	0
1978	4	3	Scotland	1	Iran	1
1978	4	4	Holland	0	Peru	0
1978	4	5	Scotland	3	Holland	2
1978	4	6	Peru	4	Iran	1
1978	A	1	Austria	1	Holland	5
1978	A	2	W.Germany	0	Italy	0
1978	A	3	Italy	1	Austria	0
1978	A	4	Holland	2	W.Germany	2
1978	A	5	Austria	3	W.Germany	2
1978	A	6	Holland	2	Italy	1
1978	B	1	Poland	0	Argentina	2
1978	B	2	Brazil	3	Peru	0
1978	B	3	Argentina	0	Brazil	0
1978	B	4	Peru	0	Poland	1
1978	B	5	Brazil	3	Poland	1
1978	B	6	Peru	0	Argentina	6
1978	F	1	Italy	1	Brazil	2
1978	F	2	Holland	1	Argentina	3

MATCHES

Year	Group	Game
1978	1	1
1978	1	2
1978	1	3
1978	1	4
1978	1	5
1978	1	6
1978	2	1
1978	2	2
1978	2	3
1978	2	4
1978	2	5
1978	2	6
1978	3	1
1978	3	2
1978	3	3
1978	3	4
1978	3	5
1978	3	6
1978	4	1
1978	4	2
1978	4	3
1978	4	4
1978	4	5
1978	4	6
1978	A	1
1978	A	2
1978	A	3
1978	A	4
1978	A	5
1978	A	6
1978	B	1
1978	B	2
1978	B	3
1978	B	4
1978	B	5
1978	B	6
1978	F	1
1978	F	2

Appendix II

ASTRID relational algebra syntax

Note that this grammar uses the original BNF notation, in which the only meta-symbols are '|', '::=' and '⟨. . .⟩'. The square bracket symbols actually appear in queries, and do not denote alternative options, as in some versions of BNF.

Reserved keywords are shown in upper case for clarity in the BNF although they must appear in lower case in a query. It is recommended that relation names be the only upper case symbols in a query.

⟨query definition⟩   ::= ⟨statement list⟩ ⟨newline⟩ ⟨output defn⟩
⟨statement list⟩   ::= ⟨statement list⟩ ⟨newline⟩ ⟨statement⟩ |
                         ⟨statement⟩
⟨output defn⟩   ::= OUTPUT ⟨ident⟩ ⟨order defn⟩ | OUTPUT ⟨ident⟩
⟨order defn⟩   ::= ⟨order list⟩ | ⟨order list⟩: |⟨order list⟩ ENDKEY
⟨order list⟩   ::= ⟨order list⟩,⟨order element⟩ | ⟨order element⟩
⟨order element⟩   ::= ASC | DESC

⟨statement⟩   ::= ⟨ident⟩ := ⟨cardinal exp⟩ |
                         ⟨ident⟩ BECOMES ⟨cardinal exp⟩
⟨cardinal exp⟩   ::= ⟨cardinal exp⟩ ⟨card op⟩ ⟨modifier exp⟩ | ⟨modifier exp⟩
⟨card op⟩   ::= + | UNION | . | INTERSECT_WITH | − | WITHOUT |
                         * | JOINED_TO | ** | PRODUCED_WITH | / | DIVIDED_BY
⟨modifier exp⟩   ::= ⟨modifier exp⟩ ;[⟨exp⟩] |
                         ⟨modifier exp⟩ SELECTED_ON[⟨exp⟩] |
                         ⟨modifier exp⟩ ;−[⟨exp⟩] |
                         ⟨modifier exp⟩ LIMITED_BY[⟨exp⟩] |

⟨modifier exp⟩ % ⟨ident list⟩ |
⟨modifier exp⟩ PROJECTED_TO ⟨ident list⟩ |
⟨modifier exp⟩ %. . ⟨rename list⟩ |
⟨modifier exp⟩ RENAMING ⟨rename list⟩ |
⟨modifier exp⟩ %– ⟨ident list⟩ |
⟨modifier exp⟩ DISCARDING ⟨ident list⟩ |
⟨modifier exp⟩ %+[⟨assign list⟩] |
⟨modifier exp⟩ EXTEND_BY[⟨assign list⟩] |
⟨modifier exp⟩ %[⟨ident list⟩ : ⟨assign list⟩] |
⟨modifier exp⟩ GROUP_BY[⟨ident list⟩ CREATING
⟨assign list⟩] |

⟨rel primary⟩

⟨rename list⟩	::=	⟨rename list⟩,⟨rename item⟩	⟨rename item⟩
⟨rename item⟩	::=	⟨ident⟩ → ⟨ident⟩	⟨ident⟩ AS ⟨ident⟩
⟨rel primary⟩	::=	⟨ident⟩	(⟨cardinal exp⟩)
⟨assign list⟩	::=	⟨assign list⟩,⟨ass item⟩	⟨ass item⟩
⟨ass item⟩	::=	⟨ident⟩ := ⟨exp⟩	⟨ident⟩ BECOMES ⟨exp⟩
⟨exp⟩	::=	⟨if exp⟩	⟨or **exp**⟩
⟨if exp⟩	::=	IF ⟨exp⟩ THEN ⟨exp⟩ ELSE ⟨exp⟩
⟨or exp⟩	::=	⟨or exp⟩ OR ⟨and exp⟩	⟨and exp⟩
⟨and exp⟩	::=	⟨and exp⟩ AND ⟨ineq exp⟩	⟨ineq exp⟩
⟨ineq exp⟩	::=	⟨add exp⟩ ⟨ineq op⟩ ⟨add exp⟩	⟨add exp⟩
⟨ineq op⟩	::=	<	≤	>	≥	=	<>
⟨add exp⟩	::=	⟨add exp⟩ ⟨add op⟩ ⟨mult exp⟩	⟨mult exp⟩
⟨add op⟩	::=	+	–
⟨mult exp⟩	::=	⟨mult exp⟩ ⟨mult op⟩ ⟨factor⟩	⟨factor⟩
⟨mult op⟩	::=	*	/	DIV	REM
⟨factor⟩	::=	⟨primary⟩	⟨sign⟩ ⟨primary⟩
⟨sign⟩	::=	+	–	NOT
⟨primary⟩	::=	⟨atomic⟩	(⟨exp⟩)
⟨atomic⟩	::=	⟨const⟩	⟨ident⟩	⟨function⟩
⟨function⟩	::=	⟨ident⟩	⟨ident⟩(⟨exp list⟩)
⟨exp list⟩	::=	⟨exp list⟩,⟨exp⟩	⟨exp⟩
⟨ident⟩	::=	⟨alphabetic char⟩⟨ident tail⟩	⟨alphabetic char⟩
⟨ident tail⟩	::=	⟨ident tail⟩ ⟨ident char⟩	⟨ident char⟩
⟨ident char⟩	::=	⟨alphabetic char⟩	⟨digit⟩	
⟨const⟩	::=	⟨arith const⟩	⟨boolean const⟩	⟨string const⟩
⟨arith const⟩	::=	⟨integer const⟩	⟨real const⟩
⟨integer const⟩	::=	⟨digit string⟩
⟨digit string⟩	::=	⟨digit string⟩ ⟨digit⟩	⟨digit⟩
⟨real const⟩	::=	⟨fractional part⟩ E ⟨exponent part⟩	⟨fractional part⟩
⟨fractional part⟩	::=	⟨digit string⟩ . ⟨digit string⟩
⟨exponent part⟩	::=	⟨integer const⟩	⟨sign⟩ ⟨integer const⟩
⟨boolean const⟩	::=	TRUE	FALSE

⟨string const⟩   ::= "⟨char string⟩"
⟨char string⟩   ::= ⟨char string⟩ ⟨char⟩ | ⟨char⟩ | ⟨empty⟩
⟨char⟩   ::= ⟨any character except special characters '"' or '*'⟩ |
                       *⟨any character⟩
(Values of characters which change when escaped within a string:
    *t = tab
    *n = newline
    *" = "as a non-special character
    ** = * as a non-special character
    *⟨newline⟩ − ⟨newline⟩ is ignored and next character (which may not be
    ⟨newline⟩) is considered to be escaped)

⟨alphabetic char⟩ ::= a b c d e f g h i j k
                         l m n o p q r s t u v
                         w x y z A B C D E F G
                         H I J K L M N O P Q R
                         S T U V W X Y Z
⟨digit⟩   ::= 0 1 2 3 4 5 6 7 8 9

⟨open comment⟩   ::= /* | (*
⟨close comment⟩   ::= */ | *) | ⟨newline⟩

Appendix III

Bachman diagram and IDS-II schema DDL for the World Cup database

1. BACHMAN DIAGRAM FOR THE WORLD CUP DATABASE

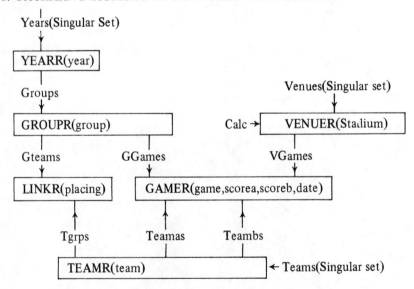

2. IDS-II SCHEMA DDL FOR WORLD CUP DATABASE

{This is an IDS-II schema for the World Cup database. Note that there are some extra clauses such as LINKED TO OWNER and SET IS PRIOR PROCESSABLE, which declare that owner and prior pointers are needed in members, which are not used in some manufacturer's DDL. Note also that the LOCATION MODE clauses and the WITHIN clauses are given in a separate storage schema in later versions of CODASYL standards. Finally, record names have an extra R on the end, to avoid confusion with field names (GAMER, GAME). }

SCHEMA NAME IS WCUP.

AREA NAME IS AREA1.

RECORD NAME IS STEAM;
      LOCATION MODE IS DIRECT ADC;
      WITHIN AREA1.
RECORD NAME IS YEARR;
      LOCATION MODE IS VIA YEARS SET;
      WITHIN AREA1.
      02 YEAR TYPE IS BINARY.
RECORD NAME IS GROUPR;
      LOCATION MODE IS VIA GROUPS SET;
      WITHIN AREA1.
      02 GROUP TYPE IS CHARACTER 1.
RECORD NAME IS GAMER;
      LOCATION MODE IS VIA GGAMES SET;
      WITHIN AREA1.
      02 GAME TYPE IS BINARY.
      02 SCOREA TYPE IS BINARY.
      02 SCOREB TYPE IS BINARY.
      02 DATE TYPE IS CHARACTER 6.
RECORD NAME IS VENUER;
      LOCATION MODE IS DIRECT ADC;
      KEY NAME IS VENUK
         ASCENDING VENUE
         DUPLICATES NOT ALLOWED;
      WITHIN AREA1.
      02 VENUE TYPE IS CHARACTER 13.
RECORD NAME IS TEAMR;
      LOCATION MODE IS CALC USING TEAM
         DUPLICATES NOT ALLOWED;
      WITHIN AREA1.
      02 TEAM TYPE IS CHARACTER 9.
RECORD NAME IS LINKR;
      LOCATION MODE IS VIA GTEAMS SET:
      WITHIN AREA1.
      02 PLACING TYPE IS BINARY.

SET   NAME IS YEARS;
      OWNER IS STEAM;

```
        SET IS PRIOR PROCESSABLE;
        ORDER IS SORTED BY DEFINED KEYS
               DUPLICATES NOT ALLOWED.
        MEMBER IS YEARR
               INSERTION IS AUTOMATIC RETENTION IS MANDATORY
               LINKED TO OWNER
               KEY IS ASCENDING YEAR;
               SET SELECTION FOR YEARS
                  THRU APPLICATION.

SET  NAME IS GROUPS;
        OWNER IS YEARR;
        SET IS PRIOR PROCESSABLE;
        ORDER IS SORTED BY DEFINED KEYS
               DUPLICATES NOT ALLOWED.
        MEMBER IS GROUPR
               INSERTION IS AUTOMATIC RETENTION IS MANDATORY
               LINKED TO OWNER
               KEY IS ASCENDING GROUP;
               SET SELECTION FOR GROUPS
                  THRU APPLICATION.

SET  NAME IS GGAMES;
        OWNER IS GROUPR;
        SET IS PRIOR PROCESSABLE;
        ORDER IS SORTED BY DEFINED KEYS
               DUPLICATES NOT ALLOWED.
        MEMBER IS GAMER
               INSERTION IS AUTOMATIC RETENTION IS MANDATORY
               LINKED TO OWNER
               KEY IS ASCENDING GAME;
               SET SELECTION FOR GGAMES
                  THRU APPLICATION.

SET  NAME IS VGAMES;
        OWNER IS VENUER;
        SET IS PRIOR PROCESSABLE;
        ORDER IS NEXT.
        MEMBER IS GAMER
               INSERTION IS MANUAL RETENTION IS OPTIONAL
               LINKED TO OWNER;
               SET SELECTION FOR VGAMES
                  THRU APPLICATION.

SET  NAME IS GTEAMS;
        OWNER IS GROUPR;
        SET IS PRIOR PROCESSABLE;
```

```
            ORDER IS SORTED BY DEFINED KEYS
                DUPLICATES NOT ALLOWED.
            MEMBER IS LINKR
                    INSERTION IS AUTOMATIC RETENTION IS MANDATORY
                    LINKED TO OWNER
                    KEY IS ASCENDING PLACING;
                    SET SELECTION FOR GTEAMS
                        THRU APPLICATION.

SET   NAME IS TGRPS;
        OWNER IS TEAMR;
        SET IS PRIOR PROCESSABLE;
        ORDER IS NEXT.
        MEMBER IS LINKR
                INSERTION IS AUTOMATIC RETENTION IS OPTIONAL
                LINKED TO OWNER;
                SET SELECTION FOR TGRPS
                    THRU APPLICATION.

SET   NAME IS TEAMAS;
        OWNER IS TEAMR;
        SET IS PRIOR PROCESSABLE;
        ORDER IS NEXT.
        MEMBER IS GAMER
                INSERTION IS MANUAL RETENTION IS OPTIONAL
                LINKED TO OWNER;
                SET SELECTION FOR TEAMAS
                    THRU APPLICATION.

SET   NAME IS TEAMBS;
        OWNER IS TEAMR;
        SET IS PRIOR PROCESSABLE;
        ORDER IS NEXT.
        MEMBER IS GAMER
                INSERTION IS MANUAL RETENTION IS OPTIONAL
                LINKED TO OWNER;
                SET SELECTION FOR TEAMBS
                    THRU APPLICATION.

SET   NAME IS TEAMS;
        OWNER IS STEAM;
        SET IS PRIOR PROCESSABLE:
        ORDER IS SORTED BY DEFINED KEYS
                DUPLICATES NOT ALLOWED.
        MEMBER IS TEAMR
                INSERTION IS AUTOMATIC RETENTION IS MANDATORY
                LINKED TO OWNER
```

```
                    KEY IS DESCENDING TEAM;
                    SET SELECTION FOR TEAMS
                    THRU APPLICATION.


END_SCHEMA.
```

Appendix IV

Syntax for SQL

This syntax covers the examples used in Date (1981), and also in RASQL (Knowles *et al.* 1984). Versions used by various manufacturers will probably provide a subset of that given here. Although the syntax as shown is recursive through ⟨sub-query⟩, actual systems are unlikely to allow much depth of nesting of queries. Also the HAVING clause following GROUP BY will probably be restricted to fairly simple classes of ⟨predicate⟩.

The meta-symbols used are '::=' and '|' and '[' and ']'. Square brackets are used to enclose optional items.

⟨query⟩	::=	⟨query-exp⟩| ⟨query-exp⟩ **ORDER BY** ⟨sort-list⟩
⟨sort-list⟩	::=	⟨order-item⟩ | ⟨order-item⟩ , ⟨sort-list⟩
⟨order-item⟩	::=	⟨col-spec⟩ **ASC** | ⟨col-spec⟩ **DESC** | ⟨col-spec⟩
⟨query-exp⟩	::=	⟨query-spec⟩ **UNION** ⟨query-spec⟩ | ⟨query-spec⟩
⟨query-spec⟩	::=	**SELECT [UNIQUE]** ⟨select-list⟩ **FROM** ⟨table-list⟩ **[WHERE** ⟨search-cond⟩**]** **[GROUP BY** ⟨col-list⟩ **[HAVING** ⟨search-cond⟩**]]**
⟨table-list⟩	::=	⟨table-spec⟩ | ⟨table-spec⟩ , ⟨table-list⟩
⟨table-spec⟩	::=	⟨relation-name⟩ | ⟨relation-name⟩ **[AS]** ⟨synonym⟩
⟨table-name⟩	::=	⟨relation-name⟩ | ⟨synonym⟩
⟨col-list⟩	::=	⟨col-spec⟩ | ⟨col-spec⟩ , ⟨col-list⟩
⟨select-list⟩	::=	* | **ALL** | ⟨val-list⟩
⟨val-list⟩	::=	⟨val-expr⟩ | ⟨val-expr⟩ , ⟨val-list⟩

⟨val-expr⟩   ::= ⟨val-expr⟩ + ⟨term⟩ | ⟨val-expr⟩ − ⟨term⟩ | ⟨term⟩
⟨term⟩   ::= ⟨term⟩ * ⟨factor⟩ | ⟨term⟩ / ⟨factor⟩ | ⟨factor⟩
⟨factor⟩   ::= ⟨primary⟩ | − ⟨primary⟩
⟨primary⟩   ::= ⟨constant⟩ | ⟨col-spec⟩ | ⟨fun-spec⟩ | (⟨val-expr⟩)
⟨fun-spec⟩   ::= ⟨agg-fun⟩ (⟨simp-exp⟩) |
                      COUNT (UNIQUE ⟨col-spec⟩)
⟨agg-fun⟩   ::= COUNT | MAX | MIN | SUM | AVG
⟨col-spec⟩   ::= ⟨column-name⟩ | ⟨table-name⟩ . ⟨column-name⟩
⟨simp-exp⟩   ::= ⟨simp-exp⟩ + ⟨sterm⟩ | ⟨simp-exp⟩ − ⟨sterm⟩ | ⟨sterm⟩
⟨sterm⟩   ::= ⟨sterm⟩ * ⟨sfactor⟩ | ⟨sterm⟩ | ⟨sfactor⟩ | ⟨sfactor⟩
⟨sfactor⟩   ::= ⟨sprimary⟩ | − ⟨sprimary⟩
⟨sprimary⟩   ::= ⟨constant⟩ | ⟨col-spec⟩ | (⟨simp-exp⟩)

⟨search-cond⟩   ::= ⟨bool-term⟩ | ⟨search-cond⟩ OR ⟨bool-term⟩
⟨bool-term⟩   ::= ⟨bool-fac⟩ | ⟨bool-term⟩ AND ⟨bool-fac⟩
⟨bool-fac⟩   ::= ⟨bool-primary⟩ | NOT ⟨bool-primary⟩
⟨bool-primary⟩ ::= ⟨predicate⟩ | (⟨search-cond⟩)

⟨predicate⟩   ::= ⟨comparison⟩ | ⟨quantified⟩ | EXISTS ⟨sub-query⟩
⟨sub-query⟩   ::= (⟨query-spec⟩)

⟨comparison⟩   ::= ⟨val-expr⟩ ⟨comp-op⟩ ⟨val-expr⟩ |
                      ⟨val-expr⟩ ⟨comp-op⟩ ⟨query-spec⟩
⟨comp-op⟩   ::= = | < | ≤ | ≥ | > | ¬=
⟨quantified⟩   ::= ⟨val-expr⟩ ⟨comp-op⟩ ALL ⟨sub-query⟩ |
                      ⟨val-expr⟩ ⟨comp-op⟩ ANY ⟨sub-query⟩ |
                      ⟨val-expr⟩ [NOT] IN ⟨sub-query⟩

RASQL has a more general form for ⟨quantified⟩, which allows boolean grouping functions ALL and ANY (as in ASTRID), together with set constants given as a list of explicit members, and tuples given as a list of explicit components.

⟨quantified⟩   ::= ⟨tuple⟩ IS [NOT] IN ⟨wset⟩ |
                      ⟨wset⟩ ⟨srelop⟩ ⟨wset⟩ |
                      ANY (⟨simp-exp⟩) | ALL (⟨simp-exp⟩)
⟨tuple⟩   ::= ⟨tuple-spec⟩ | ⟨simp-exp⟩
⟨tuple-spec⟩   ::= "⟨" ⟨simp-explist⟩ "⟩"
⟨simp-explist⟩   ::= ⟨simp-exp⟩ | ⟨simp-exp⟩, ⟨simp-explist⟩
⟨srelop⟩   ::= [NOT] EQUALS | CONTAINS | DOES NOT CONTAIN
⟨wset⟩   ::= ⟨query-spec⟩ | ⟨set-constant⟩
⟨set-constant⟩   ::= (⟨member⟩ [, ⟨member⟩])
⟨member⟩   ::= ⟨tuple-spec⟩ | ⟨constant⟩

Appendix V

Daplex syntax

Syntax for a dialect of **DAPLEX** called **EFDM** (Extended Functional Data Model) as given by Atkinson and Kulkarni (1984); (reproduced, by permission, from their *User Manual* (1983)).

⟨command⟩   ::= ⟨imperative⟩ |
               DECLARE ⟨funcspec⟩ ⟨arrow⟩ ENTITY |
               DECLARE ⟨funcspec⟩ ⟨arrow⟩ ⟨typeid⟩ |
               DEFINE ⟨funcspec⟩ ⟨arrow⟩ ⟨fundef⟩ |
               CONSTRAINT ⟨ident⟩ ON ⟨funlist⟩ "→" ⟨ctype⟩ |
               DROP ⟨funcspec⟩ | DROP ⟨viewid⟩ | DROP ⟨ident⟩ |
               VIEW ⟨viewid⟩ IS ⟨dedclauses⟩ END

⟨dedclauses⟩   ::= DEDUCE ⟨funcspec⟩ ⟨arrow⟩ ⟨typeid⟩ USING ⟨fundef⟩ |
               ⟨dedclauses⟩ ⟨dedclauses⟩

⟨arrow⟩   ::= "→" | "—>>"

⟨ctype⟩   ::= TOTAL | FIXED | UNIQUE | DISJOINT | ⟨pred⟩

⟨funlist⟩   ::= ⟨typeid⟩ [,⟨funlist⟩] |
               ⟨funcid⟩ "(" ⟨arglist⟩ ")" [,⟨funlist⟩]

⟨imperative⟩   ::= FOR EACH ⟨set⟩ ⟨imperative⟩ |
               FOR ⟨singlevar⟩ ⟨imperativelist⟩ |
               PRINT ⟨stuple⟩ |
               LET ⟨svfuncall⟩ "=" ⟨singleton⟩ |
               LET ⟨mvfuncall⟩ "=" ⟨expr⟩ |
               INCLUDE ⟨fcall⟩ "=" ⟨set⟩ |
               EXCLUDE ⟨fcall⟩ "=" ⟨set⟩ |
               DELETE ⟨singlevar⟩ | DELETE ⟨svfuncall⟩ | DELETE ⟨vblid⟩

⟨imperativelist⟩ ::= ⟨imperative⟩ ";" | ⟨imperative⟩ , ⟨imperativelist⟩
⟨fcall⟩   ::= ⟨svfuncall⟩ | ⟨mvfuncall⟩ | ⟨typeid⟩

⟨set⟩   ::= ⟨vblid⟩ IN ⟨set1⟩ [SUCH THAT ⟨pred⟩] [AS ⟨typeid⟩]
⟨set1⟩   ::= ⟨mvfuncall⟩ | ⟨typeid⟩ | " {" ⟨stuple⟩ " }" |
                      "(" ⟨set⟩ ⟨set-op⟩ ⟨set⟩ ")"
⟨set-op⟩   ::= UNION | INTERSECTION | DIFFERENCE

⟨expr⟩   ::= ⟨set⟩ | ⟨singleton⟩
⟨singleton⟩   ::= ⟨const⟩ | ⟨vblid⟩ | ⟨svfuncall⟩ | ⟨singlevar⟩ |
                      ⟨pred⟩ | ⟨aexp⟩ | ⟨aggcall⟩ | "(" ⟨singleton⟩ ")"
⟨singlevar⟩   ::= THE ⟨set⟩ | A NEW ⟨vblid⟩ IN ⟨typeid⟩
⟨pred⟩   ::= ⟨svfuncall⟩ | ⟨boolterm⟩ |
                      ⟨quant⟩ ⟨set⟩ HAS ⟨pred⟩
⟨quant⟩   ::= SOME | ALL | NO | EXACTLY ⟨integer⟩ |
                      AT LEAST ⟨integer⟩ | AT MOST ⟨integer⟩
⟨aggcall⟩   ::= COUNT "(" ⟨set⟩ ")" | MAX "(" ⟨set⟩ ")" | MIN "(" ⟨set⟩ ")" |
                      TOTAL "(" OVER ⟨mtuple⟩ ⟨singleton⟩ ")" |
                      AVERAGE "(" OVER ⟨mtuple⟩ ⟨singleton⟩ ")"

⟨boolterm⟩   ::= ⟨boolfac⟩ | ⟨boolterm⟩ OR ⟨boolfac⟩
⟨boolfac⟩   ::= ⟨boolv⟩ | ⟨boolfac⟩ AND ⟨boolv⟩
⟨boolv⟩   ::= ⟨bprim⟩ | NOT ⟨bprim⟩
⟨bprim⟩   ::= ⟨aexp⟩ ⟨comp-op⟩ ⟨aexp⟩ | ⟨vblid⟩ | ⟨bool⟩ |
                      "(" ⟨pred⟩ ")"
⟨aexp⟩   ::= [+|−] ⟨uns⟩
⟨uns⟩   ::= ⟨term⟩ | ⟨uns⟩ + ⟨term⟩ | ⟨uns⟩ − ⟨term⟩ | ⟨uns⟩ ++ ⟨term⟩
⟨term⟩   ::= ⟨fac⟩ | ⟨term⟩ * ⟨fac⟩ | ⟨term⟩ / ⟨fac⟩ | ⟨term⟩ REM ⟨fac⟩
⟨fac⟩   ::= ⟨singleton⟩ [AS ⟨typeid⟩]
⟨svfuncall⟩   ::= ⟨funcid⟩ "(" ⟨stuple⟩ ")"
⟨stuple⟩   ::= ⟨singleton⟩ | ⟨singleton⟩ , ⟨stuple⟩
⟨mvfuncall⟩   ::= ⟨funcid⟩ "(" ⟨mtuple⟩ ")"
⟨mtuple⟩   ::= ⟨expr⟩ | ⟨expr⟩ , ⟨mtuple⟩

⟨fundef⟩   ::= ⟨expr⟩ | TRANSITIVE OF ⟨expr⟩ |
                      INVERSE OF ⟨funcspec⟩ | COMPOUND OF ⟨mtuple⟩
⟨funcspec⟩   ::= ⟨funcid⟩ "(" [⟨arglist⟩] ")"
⟨arglist⟩   ::= ⟨typeid⟩ | ⟨typeid⟩ , ⟨arglist⟩

⟨comp-op⟩   ::= > | < | ⩾ | ⩽ | = | ~
⟨integer⟩   ::= ⟨singleton⟩
⟨const⟩   ::= ⟨int⟩ | ⟨bool⟩ | ⟨string⟩

⟨vblid⟩   ::= ⟨ident⟩
⟨typeid⟩   ::= ⟨ident⟩

USAGE OF COMMANDS

DECLARE to declare a new entity type and the functions on it.
DEFINE to define a derived function.
FOR EACH to retrieve and display data on each entity in a set.
FOR A NEW to create a new entity.
LET to assign a new single value for a function.
INCLUDE to define or increase a multiple value for a function.
EXCLUDE to exclude items from a multiple value.
DELETE to delete an existing entity.
PRINT to output results to the screen.
CONSTRAINT to specify a constraint.
VIEW to define a view.
DROP to drop an existing function, entity type, constraint or view defn.

DIFFERENCES FROM DAPLEX (FOX *et al.* 1984).

DAPLEX has more general facilities for update transactions, but no facilities for declaring views, and only UNIQUE and OVERLAP constraints. Apart from this the main difference is in the use of keywords in the syntax:

EFDM	DAPLEX
SUCH THAT	WHERE
SOME	FOR SOME
DELETE	DESTROY
ALL	FOR EVERY
FOR EACH ⟨set⟩	FOR EACH ⟨set⟩
⟨imperative⟩	LOOP ⟨imperativelist⟩ END LOOP
INCLUDE ⟨fcall⟩ = ⟨set⟩	INCLUDE ⟨set⟩ INTO ⟨fcall⟩
EXCLUDE ⟨fcall⟩ = ⟨set⟩	EXCLUDE ⟨set⟩ FROM ⟨fcall⟩
FOR A NEW ⟨vblid⟩ IN	CREATE NEW
⟨typeid⟩	⟨typeid⟩
LET ⟨fun⟩ = ⟨exp⟩	"(" ⟨fun⟩ "⇒" ⟨exp⟩ , . . . ")"

References

ANSI (1975), 'Interim Report of the ANSI/X3/SPARC Study Group on Data Base Management Systems', *ACM SIGFIDET*, 7, 2, 3–139.

Atkinson, K. G., & Kulkarni, K. G. (1984), 'Experimenting with the Functional Data Model', in *Databases: Role and Structure*, P. M. Stocker (ed.), Cambridge University Press.

Bachman, C. W. (1973), 'The Programmer as Navigator', *Comm ACM*, **16**, 653–658.

Bachman, C. W., & Daya, M. (1977), 'The Role Concept in Data Models', *Proc. 3rd VLDB Conf.* (Tokyo), pp. 464–477.

Backus, J. (1978), 'Can programming be liberated from the von Neumann style? A functional style and its algebra of programs', *Comm ACM*, **21**, 613–641.

Bell, R. (1980), 'Automatic Generation of Programs for Retrieving Information from CODASYL Data Bases', Ph.D. Thesis, University of Aberdeen, Scotland.

Bell, R., & Gray, P. M. D. (1980), 'Description of Access Paths for Realising Relations from a CODASYL Database', Report AUCS/TR8001, Computing Science Dept., Aberdeen University.

Blasgen, M. W., & Eswaran, K. P. (1976), 'On the Evaluation of Queries in a Relational Data Base System', IBM Research Report RJ1745.

Bundy, A., Byrd, L., Luger, G., Mellish, C., & Palmer, M. (1979), 'Solving Mechanics Problems using Meta-Level Inference', in *Expert Systems in the Micro-Electronic Age*, D. Michie (ed.), Edinburgh University Press, pp. 50–64.

Bundy, A. (1983), *Computer Modelling of Mathematical Reasoning*, Academic Press.

Buneman, P., & Frankel, R. E. (1979), 'FQL – A Functional Query Language', *Proc. SIGMOD79 Conf.* (Boston), P. A. Bernstein (ed.), pp. 52–59.

Buneman, P., Frankel, R. E., & Nikhil, R. (1982), 'An Implementation Technique for Database Query Languages', *ACM TODS*, **7**, 164–186.

Buneman, O. P., Menten, L., & Root, D. (1981), 'A Codasyl Interface for Pascal and Ada', Research report, Dept. of Computer Science, University of Pennsylvania.

Burstall, R. M., & Darlington, J. (1977), 'A Transformation System for Developing Recursive Programs', *J. ACM*, **24**, 44–67.

Burstall, R. M., Collins, J. S., & Popplestone, R. J. (1971), *Programming in POP–2*, Edinburgh University Press.

Burstall, R. M., MacQueen, D. B., & Sannella, D. T. (1981), 'HOPE: an Experimental Applicative Language', Edinburgh University Computer Science Report CSR–62–80 (updated 1981).

Chamberlin, D. D. *et al.* (1976), 'SEQUEL2: A Unified Approach to Data Definition, Manipulation, and Control', *IBM Journal of R&D*, **20**, 560–575.

Chamberlin, D. D. *et al.* (1981), 'A History and Evaluation of System R', *Comm ACM*, **24**, 632–646.

Chang, C., & Lee, R. C. (1973), *Symbolic Logic and Mechanical Theorem Proving*, Academic Press.

Chen, P. S. (1976), 'The Entity–Relationship Model – towards a unified view of data', *ACM TODS*, **1**, 9–36.

Clark, K. L. (1978), 'Negation as Failure', in *Logic and Databases*, H. Gallaire & J. Minker (eds.), Plenum Press, pp. 293–324.

Clocksin, W. F., & Mellish, C. S. (1981), *Programming in Prolog*, Springer-Verlag.

CODASYL Data Description Language Committee (1978), 'DDL Journal of Development.

CODASYL COBOL Committee (1978), 'COBOL Journal of Development'.

CODASYL Data Description Language Committee (1981), 'DDL Journal of Development'.

Codd, E. F. (1970), 'A relational model of data for large shared data banks', *Comm ACM*, **13**, 377–387.

Codd, E. F. (1972), 'Relational completeness of data base sublanguages', in *Data Base Systems*, R. Rustin (ed.), Prentice-Hall, New York, pp. 65–98.

Codd, E. F. (1979), 'Extending the database relational model to capture more meaning', *ACM TODS*, **4**, 397–434.

Colmerauer, A. *et al.* (1973), 'Etude et Realisation d'un système PROLOG', Convention de Research IRIA-Sesori No 77030.

Colmerauer, A. (1983), 'Prolog in 10 Figures', *Proc. IJCAI-83* (Karlsruhe), A. Bundy (ed.), pp. 487–499.

Curry, H. B., & Feys, R. (1958), *Combinatory Logic*, Princeton University Press.

DBTG (Data Base Task Group) of CODASYL Programming Language Committee (1971), 'Report', ACM.

Date, C. J. (1981), *An Introduction to Database Systems*, 3rd edn, Addison-Wesley.

Date, C. J. (1983), *An Introduction to Database Systems*, Vol. 2, Addison-Wesley.

Dayal, U., & Bernstein, P. A. (1978), 'On the Updatability of Relational Views', *Proc. 4th VLDB Conf.* (Berlin), pp. 368–377.

Elcock, E. W., Foster, J. M., Gray, P. M. D., McGregor, J. J., & Murray, A. M. (1971), 'Abset, a Programming Language Based on Sets: Motivation and Examples', in *Machine Intelligence 6*, B. Meltzer & D. Michie (eds.), Edinburgh University Press, pp. 467–492.

Esslemont, P. E., & Gray, P. M. D. (1982), 'The Performance of a relational Interface to a Codasyl Database', in *Proc. 2nd British National Conf. on Databases* (Bristol), S. M. Deen & P. H. Hammersley (eds.).

Fahlman, S. E. (1979), *NETL: A system for representation and using real-world knowledge*, MIT Press.

Foster, J. M., & Elcock, E. W. (1969), 'ABSYS 1: an incremental compiler for assertions: an introduction', in *Machine Intelligence 4*, B. Meltzer & D. Michie (eds.), Edinburgh University Press, pp. 423–429.

Fox, S., Landers, T., Ries, D. R., & Rosenberg, R. L. (1984), 'Daplex Users Manual', Report CCA–84–01, Computer Corporation of America, Cambridge, Mass.

Friedman, D. P., & Wise, D. S. (1976), 'CONS should not evaluate its arguments', in *Automata, Languages and Programming*, S. Michaelson & R. Milner (eds.), Edinburgh University Press.

Frost, R. A., & Whittaker, S. (1983), 'A Step towards the Automatic Maintenance of the Semantic Integrity of Databases', *Comp. J.*, **26**, pp. 124–133.

Gerritsen, R. (1978), *Seed Reference Manual*, International Database Systems, Philadelphia, Pa.

Gray, P. M. D. (1981), 'The GROUP_BY Operation in Relational Algebra', *Proc. BNCOD–1 Conf.*, S. M. Deen & P. H. Hammersley (eds.), Pentech Press, pp. 84–98.

Gray, P. M. D. (1984), 'Implementing the Join Operation on Codasyl DBMS', in *Databases: Role and Structure*, P. M. Stocker (ed.), Cambridge University Press.

Gray, P. M. D., & Bell, R. (1979), 'Use of simulators to help the inexpert in automatic program generation', *Proc. Euro-IFIP79 Conf.*, P. A. Samet (ed.), North-Holland, pp. 613–620.

Gray, P. M. D., & Moffat, D. S. (1983), 'Manipulating Descriptions of Programs for Database Access', *Proc. Eighth International Joint Conference on Artificial Intelligence, IJCAI-83* (Karlsruhe), A. Bundy (ed.), pp. 21–24.

Green, C. C. (1969), 'The Application of Theorem Proving to Question-Answering Systems', Ph.D. Thesis, Report CS138, Computing Science, Stanford University.

Grogono, P. (1980), *Programming in Pascal*, Addison-Wesley.

Hall, P. A. V., Hitchcock, P., & Todd, S. J. P. (1975), 'An algebra of relations for machine computation', *Proc. 23rd ACM Symposium on Principles of Programming Languages*, pp. 225–232.

Henderson, P., & Morris, J. H. (1976), 'A lazy evaluator', *Proc. 3rd ACM Symposium on Principles of Programming Languages*, pp. 95–103.

Henderson, P. (1980), *Functional Programming: Application and Implementation*, Prentice-Hall.

Hewitt, C. (1972), 'Description and theoretical analysis (using schemata) of PLANNER: a language for proving theorems and manipulating models in a Robot', Ph.D. Thesis, M.I.T. AI Laboratory Report AI–TR–258.

Hoare, C. A. R. (1972), 'Notes on Data Structuring', in *Structured Programming*, O.-J. Dahl, E.W. Dijkstra, & C.A.R. Hoare (eds.), Academic Press.

IBM Corporation (1979), 'Query-by-Example: Terminal User's Guide', IBM Form No. SH20-2078.

Katz, R. H., & Goodman, N. (1981), 'View Processing in MULTIBASE, A Heterogeneous Database System', in *Entity-Relationship Approach to Information Modelling and Analysis'*, P.P. Chen (ed.), ER Institute, New York.

Kay, M. H. (1975), 'An Assessment of the CODASYL DDL for Use with a Relational Subschema', in *Data Base Description*, Douque & Nijssen (eds.), North-Holland, pp. 199–214.

Knowles, J. S., & Bell, D. M. R. (1984), 'The CODASYL Model', in *Databases: Role and Structure*, P.M. Stocker (ed.), Cambridge University Press.

Knowles, J. S., & Hendry, D. C. (1984), 'A tutorial introduction to an SQL-type language' in *Databases: Role and Structure*, P.M. Stocker (ed.), Cambridge University Press.

Knuth, D. E. (1973), *The Art of Computer Programming*, Vol. 3: *Sorting and Searching*, Addison-Wesley.

Kowalski, R. A. (1974), 'Logic for Problem Solving', Memo 75, Dept. of Computational Logic, Edinburgh University.

Kowalski, R. A. (1979), 'Algorithm = Logic + Control', *Comm. ACM*, **22**, 424–436.

Kowalski, R. A. (1982), 'Prolog as a Logic Programming Language', in *B.C.S. Expert Systems Newsletter*, 5 (April 1982), 10–16.

Kowalski, R. A. (1982a), 'Logic Programming for the Fifth Generation', in *Proc. International Conf. on Fifth Generation Systems: Dawn to the Second Computer Age*, SPL International, UK.

Landin, P. J. (1964), 'The Mechanical Evaluation of Expressions', *Computer Journal*, **6**, 308–320.

Landin, P. J. (1965), 'A correspondence between ALGOL 60 and Church's lambda notation: Part 1', *Comm. ACM*, **8**, 89–101, 158–165.

Landin, P. J. (1966), 'A Lambda Calculus Approach', in *Advances in Programming and Non-Numerical Computation*, L. Fox (ed.), Pergamon Press.

Lavington, S. H., & Azmoodeh, M. (1982), 'IFS – a Proposal for a Database Machine', *Proc. 2nd British National Conf. on Databases* (Bristol).

Lindsey, D. C. (1983), 'RaSQL: An SQL-like interface to databases on Honeywell GCOS', *Proc. HLSUA Forum*, Honeywell.

Liskov, B. *et al.* (1977), 'Abstraction Mechanisms in CLU', *Comm. ACM*, **20**, 564–576.

Litwin, W., & Kabbaj, K. (1982), 'Manipulation of relational multidatabases', Research Report INRIA, Le Chesnay, France.

Lloyd, J. W. (1981), 'Implementing clause indexing in Deductive Database Systems', Research Report 81/4, Computer Science Dept., Melbourne University, Australia.

Lorie, R. A., & Nilsson, J. F. (1979), 'An access specification language for a relational database system', *IBM J. R&D,* **23,** 286–298.

McCarthy, J. (1960), 'Recursive Functions of Symbolic Expressions and their Computation by Machine', *Comm. ACM,* **3,** 184–195.

McLeod, D., & Heimbigner, D. (1980), 'A Federated Architecture for Database Systems', *Proc. AFIPS Conf.,* USA.

Merrett, T. H. (1984), *Relational Information Systems,* Prentice-Hall.

Milner, R. (1978), 'A theory of type polymorphism in programming', *J. Comput. Syst. Sci.,* **17,** 348–375.

Moore, L. (1980), *Foundations of Programming with Pascal,* Ellis Horwood, Chichester.

Mylopoulos, J., & Levesque, H. J. (1984), 'An Overview of Knowledge Representation' in *On Conceptual Modelling,* M. L. Brodie, J. Mylopoulos & J. W. Schmidt (eds.), Springer-Verlag, 3–17.

Neves, J. C., Anderson, S. O., & Williams, M. H. (1983), 'A Prolog implementation of Query-by-Example', *Proc. 7th International Computing Symposium* (Nurnberg).

Nilsson, N. J. (1980), *Principles of Artificial Intelligence,* Springer-Verlag.

Olle, T. W. (1978), *The CODASYL Approach to Data Base Management,* John Wiley.

Pecherer, R. M. (1975), 'Efficient Evaluation of Expressions in a Relational Algebra', *Proc. ACM Pacific Conf.* (San Francisco), ACM.

Pereira, F. C. N., & Warren, D. H. D. (1980), 'Definite Clause Grammers for Language Analysis – A Survey of the Formalism and a Comparison with Augmented Transition Networks', *Artificial Intelligence,* **13,** 231–278.

Pirotte, A. (1978), 'High Level Data Base Query Languages', in *Logic and Data Bases',* H. Gallaire & J. Minker (eds.), Plenum Press, pp. 409–433.

Robinson, J. A. (1979), *Logic: Form and Function. The Mechanisation of Deductive Reasoning,* Edinburgh University Press.

Rosenthal, A., & Reiner, D. (1982), 'Querying Relational Views of Networks', *Proc. IEEE COMP SAC'82* (Chicago).

Rothnie, J. B., Jr., Bernstein, P. A., Fox, S., Goodman, N., Hammer, M., Landers, T. A., Reeve, C., Shipman, D,. & Wong, E. (1980), 'Introduction to System for Distributed Databases (SDD–1)', *ACM TODS,* **5.**

Rowe, L., & Shoens, K. (1979), 'Data Abstraction, Views and Updates in RIGEL', in *Proc. ACM SIGMOD 79 Conf.* (Boston), P. A. Bernstein (ed.).

Selinger, P. G., Astrahan, M. M., Chamberlin, D. D., Lorie, R. A., & Price, T. G. (1979), 'Access Path Selection in a Relational Database Management System', *Proc. ACM SIGMOD 79 Conf.* (Boston), P. A. Bernstein (ed), pp. 23–34.

Shipman, D. (1979), 'The Functional Data Model and the Data Language DAPLEX', *Proc. ACM SIGMOD 79 Conf.* (Boston); revised and printed in *ACM TODS,* **6,** 140–173.

Shortliffe, E. H. (1976), *Computer-Based Medical Consultations: MYCIN,* Elsevier.

Smith, J. M., & Smith, D. C. P. (1977), 'Database Abstractions: Aggregation and generalization', *ACM TODS,* **2**, 105–133.

Smith, J. M., & Chang, P. Y. T. (1975), 'Optimising the performance of a relational algebra database interface', *Comm. ACM,* **18**, 568–579.

Smith, J. M., Bernstein, P. A., Dayal, U., Goodman, N., Landers, T., Lin, K. W. T., & Wong, E. (1981), 'Multibase – integrating heterogeneous distributed database systems', *Proc. AFIPS Conf.* **50**, pp. 487–499.

Smith, J. M., Fox, S., & Landers, T. A. (1981), *Reference Manual for ADAPLEX,* Computer Corporation of America, Cambridge, Mass.

Stefik, M., Aikins, J., Balzer, R., Benoit, J., Birnbaum, L., Hayes-Roth, F., & Sacerdoti, E. (1982), 'The Orginisation of Expert Systems, A. Tutorial', *Artificial Intelligence,* **18**, 135–173.

Stocker, P. M., & Cantie, R. (1983), 'A Target Locical Schema: The ACS', *Proc. 9th VLDB Conference* (Florence).

Stocker, P. M., Atkinson, M. P., Gray, P. M. D., Gray, W. A., Johnson, R. G., Shave, M. R., & Oxborrow, E. A. (1984), 'PROTEUS: A Search for Standard Components in an Inhomogeneous Distributed Database System', in *Databases: Role and Structure,* P. M. Stocker (ed.), Cambridge University Press.

Stoll, R. R. (1961), *Sets, Logic and Axiomatic Theories,* W. H. Freeman.

Stonebraker, M. R., Wong, E., & Kreps, P. (1976), 'The Design and Implementation of INGRES', *ACM TODS,* **1**, 189–222.

Tagg, R. M. (1981), 'Query Languages for some Current DBMS', *Proc. BNCOD–1* (Cambridge), S. M. Deen & P. H. Hammersley (eds.), Pentech Press, pp. 99–117.

Todd, S. J. P. (1976), 'The Peterlee Relational Test Vehicle – a system overview', *IBM Syst. J.,* **15**, 285–308.

Todd, S. J. P., & Verhofstad, J. S. M. (1978), 'An Optimiser for a Relational Database System', IBM UK Scientific Centre, Peterlee.

Townsend, H. R. (1982), 'Determinism Rules OK: Another Notation for Prolog!', *A.I.S.B. Newsletter,* **44**, 12–14.

Turner, D. A. (1976), 'SASL Language Manual', Dept. of Computational Science, University of St. Andrews.

Turner, D. A. (1979), 'A New Implementation Technique for Applicative Languages', *Software Practice and Experience,* **9**, 31–49.

Turner, D. A. (1981), 'The Semantic Elegance of Applicative Languages', *Proc. ACM Conf. on Functional Programming Languages and Computer Architecture* (Portsmouth, New Hampshire), pp. 85–92.

Turner, D. A. (1982), 'Recursion Equations as a Programming Language', in *Functional Programming and its Applications,* J. Darlington, P. Henderson, & D. Turner (eds.), Cambridge University Press.

Ullman, J. D. (1980), *Principles of Database Systems,* Pitman Publishing.

Warren, D. H. D. (1981a), 'Higher-order extensions to Prolog – are they needed?', in *Machine Intelligence 10*, D. Michie, J. Hayes, & Y. H. Pao (eds.), Ellis Horwood, Chichester.

Warren, D. H. D. (1981b), 'Efficient Processing of Interactive Relational Database Queries expressed in Logic', *Proc. 7th VLDB conference* (Cannes), pp. 272–281.

Wiederhold, G. (1977), *Database Design*, McGraw-Hill.

Williams, R. *et al.* (1982), 'R*: An Overview of the Architecture', in *Improving Database Usability and Responsiveness*, P. Schauermann (ed.), Academic Press, pp. 1–27.

Winterbottom, N. & Sharman, G. C. H. (1979), 'NDB: Non-Programmer Data Base Facility', *Report TR. 12.179*, IBM (UK) Laboratories, Winchester.

Wirth, N. (1971), 'Program Development by Stepwise Refinement', *Comm. ACM*, **14**, 221–227.

Zaniolo, C. (1979), 'Design of Relational Views over Network Schemas', *Proc. ACM SIGMOD79 Conf.* (Boston), P. A. Bernstein (ed.), pp. 179–190.

Zloof, M. M. (1977), 'Query-by-Example: A Data Base Language', *IBM Sys J.*, **16**, 324–343.

Zloof, M. M. (1978), 'Security and Integrity within the Query-by-Example Database Management Language', IBM Research Report RC6982, Yorktown Heights.

Zloof, M. M., & de Jong, S. P. (1977), 'The System for Business Automation (SBA): Programming Language', *Comm. ACM*, **20**, 385–395.

Index